LT. T. G. SHANAHAN, U. S. N. Ret.
7448 Sommers Rd.   Tel. WAVerly 6046

HAJJI BABA

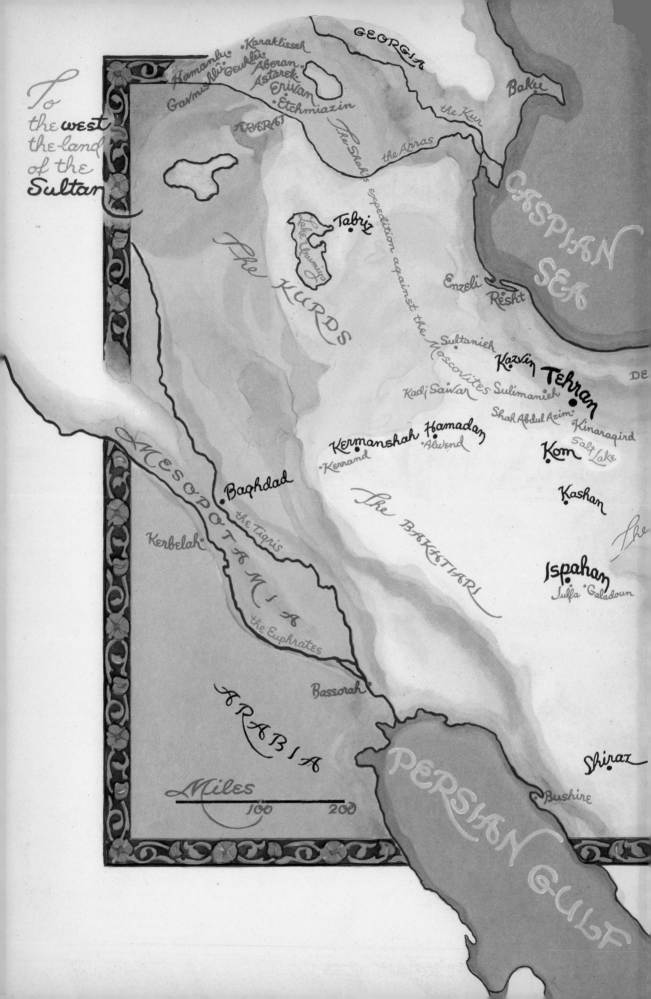

The Imperial Domain of
His Majesty, The Shah
of

PERSIA

TURKESTAN

GUKLAN

Turcoman predatory excursions from the plains of Kipchâk

Asterabad

ÉND

Semnan

Meshed

To
the east
the land of
The Emirs
of

KHORASSAN

AFGHANISTAN

GREAT SALT DESERT

LUT DESERT

For the reader's easier
understanding & memory
these are the towns visited
by HAJJI BABA
son of Kerbelai Hassan
the celebrated barber
of Ispahan

Baldridge

With a Profusion of Pictures

by

Cyrus LeRoy Baldridge

THE ADVENTURES OF
HAJJI BABA
OF ISPAHAN

by JAMES MORIER

Illustrated by Cyrus LeRoy Baldridge

Random House inc.~New York
MCMXXXVII

Persicos Amo

FOREWORD BY CHRISTOPHER MORLEY

THE only word that occurs to me to describe this famous old book is one that is distinctly unfashionable; it is long since I have seen the adjective in current print. The word is *droll*; not droll in the Balzacian sense, but in the suggestion of odd humor, unexpected and kindly, covertly facetious, mischievously wise. You will find yourself, after reading, unconsciously echoing or imitating the Persian manner of florid imagery. Let us say, then, that the reader's path will be strewn with sugar candy. And I could wish for everyone (*Mashallah!*) the same way of reading it that fell to me. For this, until lately, was one of those innumerable classics which one has heard praised since boyhood, but never read. I knew by hearsay that it was inspired by the even more famous *Gil Blas*; but except for some long-ago textbook extracts I hadn't read that either.

. It was my good fortune, in the summer just past, to spend two months in a bungalow above Lake Champlain. During that time I was devoted, with as nearly complete concentration as this world allows its bedevilled citizens, to finishing a job of work. The whole situation was as unlikely as possible: to begin with, no matter how absurd it may sound, my conscious thought was actually engrossed upon the Siege of Troy, which happened about 3,000 years ago; and in my imagination the dulcet waters of that narrow lake became the fretted Hellespont; the fields of rocks and berries and the pineglade behind us were the slopes of Mount Ida. For the first time in many years I was living in a house where there was no telephone; this in itself an adventure incomparable, though sometimes, walking in the field to forecast or reconsider, one would take a sharp trill of cricket or low ringing note of insect for the instrument of Jehannum and would start like a frightened horse. Then one returned to the vision by which those outcrops of pink-and-lichen porphyry had become the ramparts of Troy. These and contingent meditations were my pleasure, and my only anxiety the ungracious one of approaching the cheery sociability of a summer colony by asymptote rather than head-on. All this I admit irrelevant, but I mention it to emphasize the fact that my mind had a previous engagement. As has everyone's. And one phase of literary criticism rarely mentioned is, what was the critic's frame of mind or prepossession when reading the book. It is the most important calculable coefficient in the scandalously emotional algebra of book reviewing.

On this excursion from routine I had taken *Hajjî Baba* with me as laxative, and with that Adirondack cabin I shall always associate Morier's book. All day, and until toward midnight, whether swimming, idling in a rowboat, driving through hills, crossing the little Essex-Charlotte ferry to Vermont or enjoying the humors of a summer theatre, my inward absolute attention was upon the private concern. But I knew gratefully that on the bedside stand lay a copy of *Hajjî* (in the minuscule World's Classics edition edited by Mr. C. W. Stewart). I knew that late in the evening *Hajjî* would be available for reading in bed. To resume Morier's pseudo-Persian metaphors, no matter how much abomination I must eat in my own task, no matter how cruelly fortune might pluck my beard (such is the fascination of the Persian beards in this book, I thought seriously of growing one) the young barber of Ispahan was waiting with his rich merriment. There was never a pleasanter book for *lectio in lectulo*. Next morning I would retrieve the copy where it had fallen under the couch, and lay it prospectively ready for the night. As it is a tale of generous proportions, and I read only a few pages at a time, it lasted me all that mountain interlude, and indeed a good deal longer still. Autumn fires were burning on the hearth before I finished it, still horizontal. It seemed that (like the poet in Chapter 7) I had contrived a wheel for perpetual motion ("which only wants one little addition to go round for ever"). But it does not require many pages for the reader to observe that Morier is truly a great sheikh or effendi in the matter of story-telling. He knows the art which (see Chapter 45) is to make his tale interminable and still interest his audience. May his house prosper! I kiss his knee!

I had got as far as Chapter 29, the dinner given to the Shah, when a memorable heat wave smote our wooden one-story camp and the tar paper began to bubble on the roof. Such weather, everyone said, was unheard of in that region; but none the less the local dog show had been arranged in a blazing field, and I had promised to serve as one of the judges. The result was a heat prostration which incapacitated the deponent in several days of fever and lassitude. This was interesting and even valuable: I had never before realized how continued high fever burns dull actuality from the mind, purifies and transmutes, accosts the most ordinary objects with a glittering grin of fantasy. I remember for instance poring fascinated upon a bottle of witch hazel which bore the label of S. Bogan, a drug jobber in Brooklyn; finding delicious mysteries in the word *hamamelis* and seeing curious suggestions of prose style in Mr. Bogan's rather casual text; and wondering also why an intellectual instrument of such splendor (prose I mean) could beget the painful appositive *prosaic*. This too links with *Hajji*, who was abed with me. I attribute to the dinner in Chapter 29 a pleasing hallucination. On the table there stood a small green glass candle-stick, guttered over with wax; and gazing on this in supine swoon, I suddenly believed it a Persian sherbet or at least a crème de menthe frappé. Just what I wanted, I exclaimed, and tottered from bed to enjoy it.

I spare you further interweavings of *Hajji Baba* and his persisting reader. The point is, in some such way as that this book is best read: as pure enjoyment, little by little, and over an extended period. In fact, as that psychologically fashionable tonic, An Escape. Unless one is an eastern expert and knows the local color—as Mr. Baldridge does, who has made this edition a delight—the only comment that one feels competent to make is just that, the book's high enjoyability. How marvellously Morier has counterfeited the particular oriental genius of ironic narration; how much good humored satire he insinuates—not only at the expense of Mussulmen, but also upon the Franks and the Ingliz and all other infidels. Perhaps the comedy of his description of the European nations, toward the end, is a little too overt; that depends upon one's taste in comedy. And even the Persians themselves, I believe, have sometimes been fooled by this savory and subtle burlesque, and have thought it a genuine document. And of course while we suppose ourselves smiling at the humor of Persian warfare, plunder, political corruption or lovemaking, we may find that the smile is tweaking inward a little.

It would be impertinent to point out how many vivid yarns are woven into the fabric and pattern of this broad Persian rug, on which one may comfortably sit or sprawl for a long time. One of the favorites will surely be the Adventure in the Bath, but all Hajji's ups and downs are delightful. As "itinerant vendor of smoke," dervish, poet's secretary, physician, lover, executioner, matrimonial agent, or ambassador he remains the same ingenious rogue. He lives as the dervish advised, on men's weakness and credulity; but they also on his, for the tables turn constantly. Undoubtedly there is a moral to be found but few will pause to labor it. When a book keeps itself alive, as this has, for considerably over a century (it was first published in 1824) it must have above all the high quality of readability. It is leisurely, abundant, and worldly-wise. And how Morier (himself a skilful artist) would have been pleased by this colorful edition!

CHRISTOPHER MORLEY

September, 1937

CONCERNING THE ORIGINS OF THIS BOOK

IT was logical that James Morier, son of a British Consul in Constantinople, should have become a diplomat and that his career should have been in the Middle East. The period of his life—the first half of the Nineteenth Century—was crowded with colorful incident and great adventure. Europe had discovered the "glamorous East." Religious missions and "factories" of traders were following the flag into "darkest Africa." Empire-Building had begun. Napoleon was seeking to ingratiate himself with the Shah of Persia, ruler of the "highway to India," where England and Russia were already in sharp competition for his royal favor.

It was in 1807 that the young Morier, keen of eye and quick of imagination, was appointed to the British Embassy in Persia, and set out upon his first tour of duty. This British Mission continued for two years. In 1810, Morier again returned to Persia, where he remained as his country's representative until 1815, during the last year acting as Chief of the Embassy in Teheran, the Persian capital. It was not, however, until several years later that, when he retired from official life, he began to devote himself to literary work, which occupied him until he died in 1849.

The flower of his unique experiences and sensitive observations, *Hajjî Baba*, was first published in 1824. It immediately became popular in England. In its first year, two editions were published. For public interest in Persia, romantic as well as political, was then recently awakened and still at its keenest. The book at once received high praise from literary men of the time: among them Sir Walter Scott, who declared that Morier "described the manners and vices of the Eastern nations not only with fidelity but with the humor of Le Sage and the ludicrous power of Fielding himself." In 1835 *Hajjî Baba* was again reprinted, and since that time there have been numerous editions.

Statesman and author, James Morier was also an artist of considerable ability. During his sojourn in the East he had made hundreds of drawings as well as sketches in color. These he supplemented with copious marginal notes which, explaining the colors and fabrics of costumes, must have often served to keep his memory alive when he wrote those scenes of graphic description that have the unmistakable ring of authenticity. For many the 1896 edition of *Hajjî Baba* is most interesting because it contains a number of these sketches by Morier. His drawings had also appeared with his other books, the *First Journey* (1812) and the *Second Journey* (1818).

Three years after the publication of *Hajjî Baba*, Morier wrote a sequel, *Adventures of Hajjî Baba in England*, based upon the experiences of Mirza Abul Hussan, the Persian Ambassador whom he had accompanied to England in 1809. In this, forsaking the East for the West, Morier portrays British manners and customs as they appear to the visiting Persian, who is amazed and distracted by the uncouthness prevailing in England.

The text of this latest reprint of *Hajjî Baba* follows that of the second edition of 1824 as revised by Morier. The opening "Letter of Peregrine Persic" follows the more complete text of the first edition but makes use also of minor alterations made subsequently by Morier. The footnotes are from the editions of 1824 and of 1835.

NOTE BY THE ILLUSTRATOR AFTER HIS YEAR IN PERSIA

A CENTURY has passed since Morier's time. And Iran of today is not the Persia of Hajjî Baba. Rickety postchaises are gone; upon ancient routes—now modern motor-roads—lorries displace camel caravans. Yet journeying is not without adventure. During winter the motor-traveller is menaced by ten-foot snow-drifts in sierras; during summer he crosses blistering salt deserts, still traversed by Hajjî's Turkomen. Hotels are few and of a frontier type. Travellers sleep, therefore, in tea-houses, pioneer garages or crumbling caravanserais. And he fares best who carries a cooking-kit, with alcohol stove to be fuelled with "Russian spirits."

"Oriental" is synonymous with "glamour." Persia is an oriental land, long symbolized by flower-strewn rugs, lyrical descriptions of Persian gardens, gay miniatures, and old tales of people whose garb was lovely and fantastic. In reality, the flowery fields of rug and miniature memorialize the wondrous—but brief—miracle of Spring in a half-empty land whose starkness often beats harshly upon the eye. And, in the name of modernism, the old costumes have been abolished by government decree.

Hajjî, the barber's apprentice, would not, however, be a spiritual stranger in Iran, where his "life," translated into Persian and once believed to be the work of a native author, delights literate Iranis—though they deem it unsuitable for the young! For more than a century is required for any great alteration in a people's character. The provincial suspiciousness survives. Sketching in Holy Meshed, near the Afghan border—where Hajjî became a water-carrier—I was surrounded by a street crowd. In the Far East I had always found crowds friendly and diverting. In the African "bush" whole tribes had assembled to watch the sketching of their chiefs. But this Meshed crowd, composed of muttering and unsmiling men, was different. How different I discovered when, prior to my discreet but speedy flight, my interpreter translated the speech of a pink-bearded elder who said, "The last man who made pictures here was stoned to death."

Under a dictatorship, provincial suspiciousness is exaggerated by wide-spread espionage, always necessary to a suppression of civil liberties. And to move about at all I was obliged to procure, in addition to other passes, a special permit from the Shah's own Commissioner of Police. "The American, Baldridge," was officially granted permission to "be in all parts of the Imperial Domain to paint; all facilities to be given him." But, during the ensuing year, this handsome document proved worthless. Repeatedly I was driven out of cities by gum-shoe activities which, bordering upon persecution, were engaged in by my official protectors—the police! I fled Ispahan to preserve my pictures from a Police Superintendent, bent upon "confiscating those disapproved; especially all sketches of women."

I did, however, succeed in making hundreds of sketches. And while men in costumes are subject to fines in cities, remote villages abound in people unaware of the decree or too poverty-stricken to conform. Licensed mullahs and dervishes are exempt from the law. A helpful model was "Darvish Sefer," found singing the couplets of Omar to Ispahan's craftsmen beneath the vaulted ceilings of the mediaeval bazaar. And a professional dancing-girl in Teheran posed for the pictures of Zeenab.

Much that is picturesque is being razed to make way for "foreign style" buildings and motor-traffic. But that which remains is kindly preserved by the dry air. In Kum, where Hajjî sought sanctuary, the golden dome gleams upon the mosque, beside which corpses and clothes are still washed in a murky stream—whose water the townspeople drink. Upon the Maidan of Ispahan—a painting of which serves as cover for this book— two marble goal-posts remain at one end of the polo-field of Shah Abbas, the Great. And neither modernism nor time nor weather can ever dim the drama of Persian vistas, the hard clear colours, the mountains of Colah Cazi, or the snowy peak of Demawend which continues to inspire the emotions that humbled the ebullient barber.

The Persia of Hajjî Baba is doomed. Nevertheless, with its shrewd delineation of character, Morier's *Hajjî Baba* is destined to remain invaluable. It is unthinkable that, having survived centuries of despotism, the Persian character should soon alter greatly.

Given a picaresque tale of by-gone Persia, an artist is at once tempted to borrow from the Persian miniatures, those formalized pictures which reveal a delicately whimsical world. But the Persia of Hajjî was not, by many centuries, the Persia of the miniature painters. And the tale of Hajjî is rife with pungent realism. In the illustrations I have, therefore, attempted to provide a corresponding realism, based upon an intimate knowledge of Persia and the Persians.   *C. L. B.*

THUS ARE THE ADVENTURES OF HAJJI BABA OF ISPAHAN
SET FORTH IN EIGHTY CHAPTERS

OF HAJJI BABA'S BIRTH AND EDUCATION   5

HAJJI COMMENCES HIS TRAVELS; AND HIS CAPTIVITY   8

INTO WHAT HANDS HAJJI FALLS. HIS LUCKY RAZORS   13

OF HIS INGENUITY IN RESCUING HIS MASTER'S MONEY   16

HAJJI BABA BECOMES A ROBBER IN HIS OWN DEFENCE   20

CONCERNING THE THREE PRISONERS TAKEN BY THE TURCOMANS   27

HAJJI BABA EVINCES A FEELING DISPOSITION. THE POET ASKER   30

HAJJI BABA ESCAPES FROM THE TURCOMANS   35

HAJJI BABA, IN HIS DISTRESS, BECOMES A WATER-CARRIER   41

HE MAKES A SOLILOQUY, AND BECOMES A VENDER OF SMOKE   44

HISTORY OF DERVISH SEFER, AND OF TWO OTHER DERVISHES   48

HAJJI FINDS THAT FRAUD DOES NOT REMAIN UNPUNISHED   59

HE LEAVES MESHED, IS CURED, AND RELATES A STORY   63

OF THE MAN HE MEETS, AND OF THE CONSEQUENCES   68

HAJJI REACHES TEHRAN, AND GOES TO THE POET'S HOUSE   72

HE PLANS FOR THE FUTURE, AND IS INVOLVED IN A QUARREL   74

WITH NEW CLOTHES HE APPEARS IN A NEW CHARACTER   78

THE POET RETURNS FROM CAPTIVITY AND THE CONSEQUENCES   81

HAJJI GETS INTO THE SERVICE OF THE KING'S PHYSICIAN   84

HE SUCCEEDS IN DECEIVING TWO OF THE FACULTY   88

THE MANNER IN WHICH THE SHAH TAKES MEDICINE   93

HAJJI BABA ASKS THE DOCTOR FOR A SALARY   97

HE BECOMES DISSATISFIED, AND FALLS IN LOVE   99

HE HAS AN INTERVIEW WITH THE FAIR ZEENAB   102

THE LOVERS MEET AGAIN, AND ARE VERY HAPPY   107

THE HISTORY OF ZEENAB, THE CURDISH SLAVE   113

THE CHIEF PHYSICIAN RECEIVES THE SHAH AS HIS GUEST   129

CONCERNING THE PRESENT MADE THE SHAH OF PERSIA   133

AN EVENT DESTRUCTIVE TO HAJJI BABA'S HAPPINESS   140

HAJJI LOSES THE FAIR OBJECT OF HIS AFFECTIONS   144

HE IS CALLED UPON TO EXERT HIS SKILL AS A DOCTOR   147

HAJJI BECOMES AN EXECUTIONER   150

HE ACCOMPANIES THE SHAH TO HIS CAMP   156

HAJJI BABA GIVES A SPECIMEN OF PERSIAN DESPOTISM   161

FORTUNE SMILES UPON HAJJI AND PROMOTES HIM   169

HE MEETS WITH A YOUNG MAN AND WOMAN IN DISTRESS   172

THE HISTORY OF YUSUF, THE ARMENIAN, AND HIS WIFE   177

THE RESOLUTION WHICH HAJJI TAKES IN CONSEQUENCE   201

THE ARMENIAN PROVES HIMSELF WORTHY OF CONFIDENCE   204

HAJJI SHOWS HIMSELF A FRIEND TO THE DISTRESSED   207

HE DESCRIBES AN EXPEDITION AGAINST THE RUSSIANS   215

HE GIVES A SPECIMEN OF LYING ON A GRAND SCALE   220

HE RELATES A HORRID TALE AND THE CONSEQUENCES   222

HE MEETS WITH A FRIEND, WHO SECURES HIM FROM DANGER   230

A CURIOUS STORY DIVERTS HIS MELANCHOLY THOUGHTS   237

HE ASSOCIATES WITH THE MOST CELEBRATED DIVINE IN PERSIA   241

HAJJI IS ROBBED BY HIS FRIEND, AND LEFT DESTITUTE   247

HAJJI BABA CLOSES THE EYES OF HIS DYING FATHER   253

HE BECOMES HEIR TO PROPERTY WHICH IS NOT TO BE FOUND   262

SHOWING THE STEPS HE TAKES TO DISCOVER HIS PROPERTY   267

OF THE DIVINER'S SUCCESS IN MAKING DISCOVERIES   272

HAJJI BABA QUITS HIS MOTHER, AND BECOMES A SCRIBE   276

THE MOLLAH NADAN GIVES AN ACCOUNT OF HIS NEW SCHEME   281

HAJJI BABA BECOMES A PROMOTER OF MATRIMONY   285

OF THE MAN HE MEETS; AND OF A MARRIAGE   289

THE AMBITION OF THE MOLLAH RUINS HIS DISCIPLES   294

HAJJI MEETS AN EXTRAORDINARY ADVENTURE IN THE BATH   299

THE CONSEQUENCES END IN APPARENT GOOD FORTUNE   303

HAJJI BABA DOES NOT SHINE IN HONESTY   307

SHOWING THAT NO CONFIDENCE CAN EXIST BETWEEN ROGUES   318

THE PUNISHMENT DUE TO HAJJI FALLS UPON NADAN   322

HAJJI BABA FEELS ALL THE ALARMS OF GUILT   325

HIS GOOD STARS AGAIN BEFRIEND AND SET HIM FREE   331

HE REACHES BAGDAD AND TURNS HIS VIEWS TO COMMERCE   335

HE PURCHASES PIPE-STICKS AND INSPIRES A HOPELESS PASSION   339

HE ACCOMPANIES A CARAVAN TO CONSTANTINOPLE   342

HAJJI MAKES A CONQUEST OF THE WIDOW OF AN EMIR   345

HE OBTAINS AN INTERVIEW WITH THE FAIR SHEKERLEB   351

FROM A VENDER OF PIPE-STICKS HE BECOMES A RICH AGA   355

A DESIRE TO EXCITE ENVY LAYS THE FOUNDATION OF DISGRACE   358

HE IS DISCOVERED; AND THE WIDE WORLD IS AGAIN BEFORE HIM   361

HE SEEKS CONSOLATION IN THE ADVICE OF OLD OSMAN   366

ENDEAVOURING TO GAIN SATISFACTION HE ACQUIRES A FRIEND 369

HE BECOMES USEFUL TO AN AMBASSADOR   373

OF HIS FIRST ESSAYS IN PUBLIC LIFE   377

HAJJI BABA WRITES THE HISTORY OF EUROPE   383

THE CEREMONY OF RECEIVING A FRANK AMBASSADOR   388

HAJJI IS NOTICED BY THE GRAND VIZIER   392

THE MANNER IN WHICH HE TURNED HIS INFLUENCE TO USE   396

THE CONCLUSION. NOW MISFORTUNE SEEMS TO TAKE LEAVE OF
    HAJJI BABA, WHO RETURNS TO HIS NATIVE CITY A GREATER
    MAN THAN WHEN HE FIRST LEFT IT   399

London, 1st December, 1823

The Reverend Doctor Fundgruben,
Chaplain to the Swedish Embassy
at the Ottoman Porte.

ESTEEMED AND LEARNED SIR,

*Y*OU *will be astonished to see yourself addressed by one, of whose existence you are perhaps ignorant, and whose name has doubtless long since been erased from your memory. But when I put you in mind of an English traveller, who (forgive my precision) sixteen years ago was frequently admitted to enjoy the pleasure of your conversation, and who was even honoured with a peculiar share of your attention, perhaps then you may indulgently recollect him, and patiently submit to peruse the following volumes, to which he now takes the liberty of prefixing your name.*

At the time to which I allude, your precious hours were employed in searching into the very depths of hieroglyphic lore, and you were then almost entirely taken up in putting together the fruits of those your researches, which have since appeared, and astonished the world in that very luminous work entitled "The Biography of celebrated Mummies." I have frequently since reflected upon the debt of gratitude which you imposed by allowing me to engross so much of your time, and that upon matters of comparatively trivial importance, when your mind must have been so much engaged upon those grave and weighty subjects, which you have treated with such vast learning, clearness, and perspicuity in your above-mentioned treatise. In particular I have ever borne in mind a conversation, when one beautiful moonlight night, reclining upon a sofa of the Swedish palace, and looking out of those windows which command so magnificent and extensive a view of the city and harbour of Constantinople, we discussed subjects which had reference to the life and manners of the extraordinary people its inhabitants.

Excuse me for reporting back your own words; but as the subject interested me much, I recollect well the observation you made, that no traveller had ever satisfied you in his delineation of Asiatic manners; 'for,' said you, 'in general their mode of treating the subject is by sweeping assertions, which leave no precise image on the mind, or by disjointed and insulated facts, which for the most part are only of consequence as they relate to the individual traveller himself.' We were both agreed, that of all the books which have ever been published on the subject, the "Arabian Nights' Entertainments" give the truest picture of the Orientals, and that for the best of all reasons, because it is the work of one of their own community. 'But,' said you, 'notwithstanding they have been put into a European dress, weeded of their numerous repetitions, and brought as near to the level of our ideas as can be, still few would be likely to understand them thoroughly who have not lived some time in the East, and who have not had frequent opportunities of associating with its inhabitants. For,' you added, opening a volume of that work at the same time, 'to make a random observation upon the first instance which occurs, here in the history of the three Calendars, I see that Amina, after having requested the porter whom she had met to follow her with his basket, stopped at a closed door, and having rapped, a Christian with a long white beard opened it, into whose hands she put some money without saying a single word. But the Christian, who knew what she wanted, went in again, and a little while after returned, bringing a large pitcher full of excellent wine.' You observed, 'that although we who lived in Turkey might know that wine was in most cities prohibited to be sold openly, and that if it was to be found it would be in the house of a Christian, many of whom disposed of it in a mysterious manner to the Mohamedans, yet that circumstance would not immediately occur to the mere European reader, who perhaps would expect something to be forthcoming in the future narrative, from what is in fact only a trait of common life.

I then suggested, that perhaps if a European would give a correct idea of Oriental manners, which would comprehend an account of the vicissitudes attendant upon the life of an Eastern, of his feelings about his government, of his conduct in domestic life, of his hopes and plans of advancement, of his rivalities and jealousies, in short, of everything that is connected both with the operations of the mind and those of the body, perhaps his best method would be to collect so many facts and anecdotes of actual life as would illustrate the different stations and ranks which compose a Mussulman community, and then work them into one connected narrative, upon the plan of that excellent picture of European life, "GilBlas" of LeSage.

To this you were pleased to object, because you deemed it almost impossible that a European, even supposing him to have rejected his own faith and adopted the Mohamedan, as in the case of Monsieur de Bonneval, who rose to high rank in the Turkish government, and of Messrs. C—— and B——, in more modern times (the former a Topchi Bashi, or general of artillery, the latter an attendant upon the Capitan Pasha), could ever so exactly seize those nice shades and distinctions of purpose, in action and manner, which a pure Asiatic only could. To support your argument, you illustrated it by observing, that neither education, time, nor talent, could ever give to a foreigner, in any given country, so complete a possession of its language as to make him pass for a native; and that, do what he would, some defect in idiom, or even some too great precision in grammar, would detect him. But, said you, if a native Oriental could ever be brought to understand so much of the taste of Europeans, in investigations of this nature, as to write a full and detailed history of his own life, beginning with his earliest education, and going through to its decline, we might then stand a chance of acquiring the desired knowledge.

This conversation, reverend sir, has remained treasured up in my mind; for, having lived much in Eastern countries, I never lost sight of the possibility of either falling in with a native who might have written his own adventures, or of forming such an intimacy with one, as might induce him faithfully to recite them, and thus afford materials for the work which my imagination had fondly conceived might be usefully put together. I have always held in respect most of the customs and habits of the Orientals, many of which, to the generality of Europeans, appear so ridiculous and disgusting, because I have ever con-

ceived them to be copies of ancient originals. For, who can think the custom of eating with one's fingers disgusting, as now done in the East, when two or more put their hands into the same mess, and at the same time read that part of our sacred history which records, 'He that dippeth his hand with me in the dish, &c.'? I must own, every time that, dining with my Eastern friends, I performed this very natural operation (although at the same time, let it be understood that I have a great respect for knives and forks), I could not help feeling myself to be a living illustration of an ancient custom, and a proof of the authenticity of those records upon which our happiness depends. Whenever I heard the exclamation so frequently used in Persia, on the occasion of little miseries, 'What ashes are fallen on my head!' instead of seeing anything ridiculous in the expression, I could not but meditate on the coincidence which so forcibly illustrated one of the commonest expressions of grief as recorded in ancient writ.

It is an ingenious expression which I owe to you, sir, that the manners of the East are as it were stereotype. Although I do not conceive that they are quite so strongly marked, yet, to make my idea understood, I would say that they are like the last impressions taken from a copperplate engraving, where the whole of the subject to be represented is made out, although parts of it, from much use, have been obliterated.

If I may be allowed the expression, a picturesqueness pervades the whole being of Asiatics, which we do not find in our own countries, and in my eyes makes everything relating to them so attractive as to create a desire to impart to others the impressions made upon myself. Thus, in viewing a beautiful landscape, the traveller, be he a draughtsman or not, tant bien que mal, endeavours to make a representation of it: and thus do I apologize for venturing before the public even in the character of a humble translator.

Impressed with such feelings, you may conceive the fullness of my joy, when, not very long after the conversation above mentioned, having returned to England, I was fortunate enough to be appointed to fill an official situation in the suite of an ambassador, which our government found itself under the necessity of sending to the Shah of Persia. Persia, that imaginary seat of Oriental splendour! that land of poets and roses! that cradle of mankind! that uncontaminated source of Eastern manners lay before me, and I was delighted with the opportunities which would be afforded me of pursuing my favourite subject. I had an undefined feeling about the many countries I was about to visit, which filled my mind with vast ideas of travel—

Sive per Syrtes iter aestuosas,
Sive facturus per inhospitalem
Caucasum, vel quae loca fabulosus
Lambit Hydaspes.

I was in some degree like a French lady of my acquaintance, who had so general a notion of the East, that upon taking leave she enjoined me to get acquainted with a friend of hers, living, as she said, quelque part dans les Indes, and whom, to my astonishment, I found residing at the Cape of Good Hope!

I will not say that all my dreams were realized, for perhaps no country in the world less comes up to one's expectation than Persia, whether in the beauties of nature, or the riches and magnificence of its inhabitants. But in what regards manners and customs, it appears to me that no Asiatics bear so strong the stamp of an ancient origin as they. Even in their features I thought to have distinguished a decided originality of expression, which was confirmed, when I remarked, that the numerous faces seen among the sculptures of Persepolis, so perfect as if chiselled but yesterday, were so many likenesses of modern Persians, more particularly of the natives of the province of Fars.

During my long residence there, I never lost the recollection of our conversation on the sofa of the Swedish palace, and every time I added an anecdote or an observation illustrative of Oriental manners to my store, or a sketch to my collection, I always thought of the Reverend Doctor Fundgruben, and sighed after that imaginary manuscript which some imaginary native of the East must have written as a complete exposition of the life of his countrymen.

I will not say, learned sir, that the years I passed in Persia were years of happiness; or that during that time I could so far keep up an illusion, that I was living among the patriarchs in the first ages of the world, or among those Persians whose monarchs gave laws to almost the whole of Asia: no, I sighed for shaven chins and swallow-tailed coats; and, to speak the truth, though addressing an antiquary of your celebrity, I felt that I would rather be one among the crowd in the Graben at Vienna, or in our own Bond Street, than at liberty to range in the ease of solitude among the ruins of the palaces of Darius.

At length the day of my departure came, and I left Persia with books filled with remarks, and portfolios abounding in original sketches. My ideas during the journey were wholly taken up with schemes for the future, and perhaps, like every other traveller, I nourished a sort of sly and secret conviction that I had seen and observed things which no one before me had ever done, and that when

I came to publish to the world the fruits of my discoveries, I should create a sensation equal at least to the discovery of a new planet.

I passed at the foot of the venerable Mount Ararat, and was fortunate enough to meet with a favourable moment for traversing the cold regions of Armenia, 'nec Armeniis in oris stat glacies iners menses per omnes'; and I crossed the dangerous borders of Turkey and Persia without any event occurring worthy of record. But I must request your indulgent attention to what befell me at Tocat, for it is to that occurrence you are indebted for this letter, and the world for the accompanying volumes.

It was at the close of a fatiguing day's journey, that I and my escort, consisting of two Tatars, two servants, and the conductors of our baggage and post-horses, entered the city of Tocat. Our approach was as usual announced by the howls of the Surujees, who I suppose more than usually exerted their lungs in my service, because they felt that these sounds, the harbingers of rest and entertainment, could not but be agreeable to weary and jaded travellers like ourselves. The moon was shining bright as our cavalcade was clattering over the long paved road leading to the city, and lighted up, in awful grandeur, the turret-topped peaks of the surrounding crags. On entering the post-house, I was immediately conducted into the travellers' room, where having disencumbered myself of my cloak, arms, and heavy boots, and putting myself at ease in my slippers and loose dress, I quietly enjoyed the cup of strong coffee and the chibouk, which were immediately handed to me, and after that my dish of rice, my tough fowl, and my basin of sour curds.

I was preparing to take my night's rest on the sofas of the post-house, where my bed had been laid, when a stranger unceremoniously walked into the room, and stood before me. I remarked that he was a Persian, and, by his dress, a servant. At any other moment I should have been happy to see and converse with him, because, having lived so long in Persia, I felt myself in some measure identified with its natives, and now in a country where both nations were treated with the same degree of contempt, my fellow-feeling for the sectaries of Ali became infinitely stronger.

I discovered that the stranger had a tale of misery to unfold, from the very doleful face that he was pleased to make on the occasion, and I was not mistaken. It was this—that his master, one Mirza Hajji Baba, now on his return from Constantinople, where he had been employed on the Shah's business, had fallen seriously ill, and that he had been obliged to stop at Tocat,—that he had taken up his abode at the caravanserai, where he had already spent a week, during which time he had been attended by a Frank doctor, an inhabitant of Tocat, who, instead of curing, had in fact brought him to his last gasp,—that having heard of my arrival from Persia, he had brightened up, and requested, without loss of time, that I would call upon him, for he was sure the presence of one coming from his own country would alone restore him to health. In short, his servant, as is usual on such occasions, finished his speech by saying, that with the exception of God and myself, he had nothing left to depend upon in this life.

I immediately recollected who Mirza Hajjî Baba was; for although I had lost sight of him for several years, yet once on a time I had seen much of him, and had taken great interest in everything that regarded him, owing to his having been in England, whither, in quality of secretary, he had accompanied the first ambassador which Persia had sent in modern times. He had since been employed in various ways in the government, sometimes in high and sometimes in lower situations, undergoing the vicissitudes which are sure to attend every Persian, and at length had been sent to Constantinople, as resident agent.

I did not hesitate an instant though tired and jaded to accompany his servant; and in the same garb in which I was, only throwing a cloak over my shoulders, I walked in all haste to the caravanserai.

There, on a bed laid in the middle of a small room, surrounded by several of his servants, I found the sick Mirza, looking more like a corpse than a living body. When I had first known him he was a remarkably handsome man, with a fine aquiline nose, oval face, an expressive countenance, and a well-made person. He had now passed the meridian of life, but his features were still fine, and his eye was full of fire. As soon as he saw he recognized me, and the joy which he felt at the meeting broke out in a great animation of his features, and in the thousand exclamations so common in a Persian's mouth.

'See,' said he, 'what a fortunate destiny is mine, that at a moment when I thought the angel of death was about to seize me for his own, the angel of life comes and blows a fresh existence into my nostrils!'

After his first transports were over, I endeavoured to make him explain what was the nature of his complaint, and how it had hitherto been treated. I saw well enough by his saffron hue, that bile was the occasion of his disorder, and as I had great experience in treating it during my stay in Persia, I did not hesitate to cheer up his hopes by an assurance of being able to relieve him.

'What can I say?' said he. 'I thought at first that I had been struck with the plague. My head ached intensely, my eyes became dim, I had a pain in my side, and a nauseous taste in my mouth, and expected to die on the third day; but no, the symptoms still continue, and I am alive. As soon as I arrived here, I inquired for a physician, and was told there were two practitioners in the town, a Jew and a Frank. Of course I chose the latter, but, 'tis plain, that my evil star had a great deal to say in the choice I made. I have not yet been able to discover to what tribe among the Franks he belongs,—certainly he is not an Englishman. But a more extraordinary ass never existed in this world, be his nation what it may. I began by telling him that I was very, very ill. All he said in answer, with a grave face, was, "Mashallah! Praise be to God!" and when, in surprise and rage, I cried out, "but I shall die, man!" with the same grave face he said "Inshallah! Please God!" My servants were about to thrust him from the room, when they found that he knew nothing of our language excepting these two words, which he had only learnt to misapply. Supposing that he still might know something of his profession, I agreed to take his medicine; but I might have saved myself the trouble, for I have been daily getting worse.'

Here the Mirza stopped to take breath. I did not permit him to exert himself further, but, without loss of time, returned to the post-house, applied to my medicine-chest, and prepared a dose of calomel, which was administered that evening with all due solemnity. I then retired to rest.

The next morning I repaired to his bed-side, and there, to my great satisfaction, found that my medicine had performed wonders. The patient's eyes were opened, the headache had in great measure ceased, and he was, in short, a different person. I was received by him and his servants with all the honours due to the greatest sage, and they could not collect words sufficiently expressive of their admiration of my profound skill. As they were pouring forth their thanks and gratitude, looking up I saw a strange figure in the room, whose person I must take the liberty to describe, so highly ludicrous and extravagant did it appear. He was of the middle size, rather inclined to be corpulent, with thick black eyebrows, dark eyes, a three days' beard, and mustachios. He wore the Turkish long dress, from his shoulders downwards, yellow pabouches, or slippers, shawl about his waist, and carried a long cane in his hand; but from his shoulders up he was a European, with a neckcloth, his hair dressed in the aile de pigeon fashion, a thick tail clubbed, and over all an old-fashioned, three-cornered laced hat. This redoubtable personage made me a bow, and at the same time accosted me in Italian. I was not long in discovering that he was my rival, the doctor, and that he was precisely what, from the description of the Mirza, I expected him to be, viz. an itinerant quack, who perhaps might once have mixed medicines in some apothecary's shop in Italy or Constantinople, and who had now set up for himself, in this remote corner of Asia, where he might physic and kill at his pleasure.

I did not shrink from his acquaintance, because I was certain that the life and adventures of such a person must be highly curious and entertaining, and I cordially encouraged him in his advances, hoping thus to acquire his confidence.

He very soon informed me who he was and what were his pursuits, and did not seem to take the least umbrage at my having prescribed for his patient without previously consulting him. His name was Ludovico Pestello, and he pretended to have studied at Padua, where he had got his diploma. He had not long arrived at Constantinople, with the intention of setting up for himself, where, finding that the city overflowed with Esculapii, he was persuaded to accompany a Pasha of two tails to Tocat, who had recently been appointed to its government, and was there now established as his body physician. I suspected this story to be fabrication, and undertook to examine his knowledge of physic, particularly in the case of my friend the Persian Mirza. The galimatias which he unfolded, as we proceeded, were so extremely ridiculous, and he puzzled himself so entirely by his answers to the plain questions which I put, that at length, not being able to proceed, he joined, most good-naturedly, in the horse laugh from which I could not refrain. I made him candidly confess that he knew nothing of medicine, more than having been servant to a doctor of some eminence at Padua, where he had picked up a smattering; and that, as all his patients were heretics and abominable Musulmans, he never could feel any remorse for those which, during his practice, he had dispatched from this world. 'But, caro Signor Dottore,' said I, 'how in the name of all that is sacred, how have you managed hitherto not to have had your bones broken? Turks are dangerous tools to play with.'

'Oh,' said he, in great unconcern, 'the Turks believe anything, and I take care never to give them medicine that can do harm.'

'But you must have drugs, and you must apply them,' said I. 'Where are they?'

'I have different coloured liquids,' said he, 'and as long as there is bread and water to be had I am never at a loss for a pill. I perform all my cures with them, accompanied by the words Inshallah and Mashallah!'

'*Bread and water! wonderful!*' did I exclaim.

'*Signor, si,*' said he, '*I sprinkle my pills with a little flour for the common people, cover them with gold leaf for my higher patients, the Agas and the Pasha, and they all swallow them without even a wry face.*'

I was so highly amused by the account which this extraordinary fellow gave of himself, of the life he led, and of the odd adventures which he had met with, that I invited him to dine; and were it not for the length which this letter has already run, I should perhaps have thought it right to make you partake of my entertainment by relating his narrative. I repaid him, as he said, over and above its price by presents from my medicine-chest, which he assured me would be plentifully sufficient to administer relief to the whole of Asia Minor.

I could not think of leaving the poor Persian in such hands; and feeling that I might be the means of saving his life, I determined to remain at Tocat until I saw him out of danger.

After three days' administration of calomel, Hajjî Baba's complexion was nearly restored to its original hue, and as he might now be said to be free from danger, and in a fair way of recovery, I proposed proceeding on my journey. The poor man could not find words for the expression of his gratitude, and I saw that he was labouring hard to discover a present worthy of my acceptance. At length, just before taking my leave, he desired his servants to leave us alone, and spoke to me in the following words:

'*You have saved my life; you are my old friend and my deliverer. What can I do to show my gratitude? Of worldly goods I have but few; it is long since I have received any salary from my government, and the little money I have here will barely suffice to take me to my own country. Besides, I know the English —they are above such considerations, it would be in vain to offer them a pecuniary reward. But I have that by me which, perhaps, may have some value in your eyes—I can assure you that it has in mine. Ever since I have known your nation, I have remarked their inquisitiveness, and eagerness after knowledge. Whenever I have travelled with them, I observed they record their observations in books; and when they return home, thus make their fellow countrymen acquainted with the most distant regions of the globe. Will you believe me, that I, Persian as I am, have followed their example, hence, during the period of my residence at Constantinople, I have passed my time in writing a detailed history of my life, which, although that of a very obscure and ordinary individual, is still so full of vicissitude and adventure, that I think it would not fail to* create an interest if published in *Europe*? I offer it to you; and in so doing, I assure you that I wish to show you the confidence I place in your generosity, for I never would have offered it to any one else. Will you accept it?'

Conceive, my dear sir, conceive my happiness upon hearing this—upon at length getting into my possession precisely the sort of work which you so long since had looked upon as a desideratum in the history of mankind, and which I had utterly despaired of ever seeing in reality.

My eyes, I am sure, glistened with pleasure when I expressed my sense of the *Mirza's* liberality; and as fast as I refused his offer (for I thought it but generous to do so upon the terms he proposed), the more he pressed it upon me.

As a further inducement, he said that he was going back to his country, uncertain if he enjoyed the favour of the *Shah*; and as he had freely expressed his sentiments, which included his observations upon *England*, he was afraid, should he be in disgrace, and his work be found upon him, that it might lead to his destruction.

Unable to withstand these entreaties, I acceded to his request, and became the possessor of the manuscript, which forms the subject of the following work; and tell me, can I dedicate it to any but him who first awakened my mind to its value? If you will do me the favour to peruse it, you will find I have done my best endeavour to adapt it to the taste of *European* readers, stripping it of the numerous repetitions, and the tone of exaggeration and hyperbole which pervade the compositions of the *Orientals*; but still you will no doubt discover much of that deviation from truth and perversion of chronology which characterize them. However, of the matter contained in the book, this I must say, that having lived in the country myself during the time to which it refers, I find that most of the incidents are grounded upon fact, which, although not adhered to with that scrupulous regard to truth which we might expect from a *European* writer, yet are sufficient to give an insight into manners. Many of them will no doubt appear improbable to those who have never visited the stage upon which they were acted; and it is natural it should be so, because, from the nature of circumstances, such events could only occur in *Eastern* countries.

A distinct line must be drawn between 'the nations who wear the hat and those who wear the beard'; and they must ever hold each other's stories as improbable, until a more general intercourse of common life takes place between them. What is moral and virtuous with the one, is wickedness with the other—that which the *Christian* reviles as abominable, is by the *Mohamedan* held sacred. Although the contrast between their respective manners may be very amusing, still it is most certain that the Christian will ever feel devoutly grateful that he is neither subject to Mohamedan rule, nor educated in Mohamedan principles; whilst the latter, in his turn looking upon the rest of mankind as unclean infidels, will continue to hold fast to his persuasion, until some powerful interposition of Providence shall dispel the moral and intellectual darkness which, at present, overhangs so large a portion of the Asiatic world.

Fearing to increase the size of the work, I have refrained adding the numerous notes which my long residence in Persia would have enabled me to do, and have only occasionally made explanations necessary to understand the narrative. In the same fear, I have not ventured to take Hajjî out of his own country. His remarks upon England during his residence there, and during his travels, may perhaps be thought worthy of future notice; and should they be called for, I will do my best endeavour to interpret his feelings as closely as possible.

I must now, dear sir, take my leave, expressing my regret at your absence from Constantinople on my return from Persia; for had I then been fortunate enough to meet you, no doubt, from the valuable hints which you would have afforded me, the work now presented to you would have been in every way more worthy of your acceptance. But you were far better engaged; you were seeking another Oasis in the wilds of the desert (that emblem of yourself in hieroglyphic lore), to which, so I was informed, you expected to have been guided by information gained in the inside wrappers of one of your most interesting mummies.

May your footsteps have been fortunate, and may I live to have the pleasure of assuring you by word of mouth how truly I am, esteemed and learned sir,

Your very devoted and

obliged humble servant

PEREGRINE PERSIC

THE VARIOUS INDIVIDUALS OF IMPORTANCE TO THE CURIOUS CAREER OF HAJJI BABA

Kerbelai Hassan, *Hajji's Father, the Celebrated Barber of Ispahan*

Ali Mohamed, *Capiji, Aged Door Keeper of the Caravanserai*

The Akhon, *Hajji's Schoolmaster*

Osman Aga, *Merchant of Bagdad, Dealer in Lambskins*
And his Fair Daughter, Dilaram

The Chaoûsh, *Leader of the Caravan from Tehran to Meshed*

Aslan Sultan, *the Lion Chief, Master of the Robber Turcomans*
And His Chief Wife, *the Banou*

Asker, *Melek Al Shoherah, Kermani, Prince of Poets,*
With the Court of the Prince of Shiraz

The Cadi of Galadoun

The Prince of Shiraz

Ali Katir, *Muleteer*

The Shah's Fifth Son, *Shahzadeh of Khorassan*

Dervish Sefer
And the Second Dervish, *His Accomplice*
The Third Dervish, Kessehgon, *the story-teller*

The Gis Sefid, *Oracel of Semnan*

THE SHAH, King of Kings, Centre of the Universe,
the Shadow of God Upon Earth

Mirza Ahmak, *the Hakim Bashi, Chief Physician to the Shah*
And His Khanum, *and* Nûr Jehan, *Her Black Slave*

Zeenab, *a Yezeedi, Fair Daughter of Okous Aga, a Curdish Chief*

Namerd Khan, *The Chief Executioner, Head of the Nasakchies*

The Governor of Erivan, *the Serdar, the Shah's General*

Yûsûf, *an Armenian of Gavinishlu, Son of Coja Petros*
And the Fair Mariam *of Geuklu*

Caliph *of the Monastery of Etchmiazin, Khalifeh of the Armenian Church*

Mirza Abdul Cossim, *Mushtehed*

Teez Negah, *the Conjuror, Expert Diviner of Isfahan*

The Mollah Nadan

The Mollah Bashi *of Tehran*
And His Widow

The Widow *of a Silversmith*
And the Second *Khanum*

Abdul Kerim, *the Daroga of Tehran, a Police Magistrate*

The Ked Khoda *of Seidabad*

Shekerleb, or Sugar-lips, *Fair Daughter of a Rich Aleppo Merchant,*
Widow of a Rich Emir
And Her Relations, *and* Her Maid, *Old Ayesha*

The Katib, *or Scribe of the Reis Effendi*

The British Elchi, *Ambassador from London*

Mirza Firouz, *Grand Vizier of All Persia*

Together with Merchants, Tribal Peoples, Dancing Girls, French Soldiers,
Pilgrims, Mollahs, Warriors, Russians and Other Friends
and Enemies too Numerous to Mention

IN THE LAND OF THE LION AND THE SUN
DURING THE EARLY DAYS OF THE
NINETEENTH CENTURY

CHAPTER I: OF HAJJI BABA'S BIRTH AND EDUCATION

Y FATHER, Kerbelai Hassan, was one of the most celebrated barbers of Ispahan. He was married, when only seventeen years of age, to the daughter of a chandler, who lived in the neighbourhood of his shop; but the connexion was not fortunate, for his wife brought him no offspring, and he, in consequence, neglected her. His dexterity in the use of the razor had gained for him, together with no little renown, such great custom, particularly among the merchants, that after twenty years' industry, he found he could afford to add a second wife to his harem; and succeeded in obtaining the daughter of a rich money-changer, whose head he had shaved, during that period, with so much success, that he made no difficulty in granting his daughter to my father. In order to get rid, for a while, of the importunities and jealousy of his first wife, and also to acquire the good opinion of his father-in-law (who, although noted for clipping money, and passing it for lawful, affected to be a saint), he undertook a pilgrimage to the tomb of Hosein, at Kerbelah. He took his new wife with him, and she was delivered of me on the road. Before the journey took place he was generally known, simply as 'Hassan the barber'; but ever after he was honoured by the epithet of Kerbelai; and I,

to please my mother, who spoilt me, was called *Hajjî* or the pilgrim, a name which has stuck to me through life, and procured for me a great deal of unmerited respect; because, in fact, that honoured title is seldom conferred on any but those who have made the great pilgrimage to the tomb of the blessed Prophet of Mecca.

My father having left his business during his absence to his chief apprentice, resumed it with increased industry on his return; and the reputation of a zealous Mussulman, which he had acquired by his journey, attracted the clergy, as well as the merchants, to his shop. It being intended that I should be brought up to the strap, I should perhaps have received no more education than was necessary to teach me my prayers, had I not been noticed by a *mollah* (or priest), who kept a school in an adjoining mosque, whom my father (to keep up the character he had acquired of being a good man) used to shave once a week, as he was wont to explain, purely for the love of God. The holy man repaid the service by teaching me to read and write; and I made such progress under his care, that in two years I could decipher the Koran, and began to write a legible hand. When not in school I attended the shop, where I learnt the rudiments of my profession, and when there was a press of customers, was permitted to practise upon the heads of muleteers and camel-drivers, who indeed sometimes paid dear for my first essays.

By the time I was sixteen it would be difficult to say whether I was most accomplished as a barber or a scholar. Besides shaving the head, cleaning the ears, and trimming the beard, I became famous for my skill in the offices of the bath. No one understood better than I the different modes of rubbing or shampooing, as practised in India, Cashmere, and Turkey; and I had an art peculiar to myself of making the joints to crack, and my slaps echo.

Thanks to my master, I had learnt sufficiently of our poets to enable me to enliven conversation with occasional apt quotations from Saadi, Hafiz, &c.; this accomplishment, added to a good voice, made me considered as an agreeable companion by all those whose crowns or limbs were submitted to my operation. In short, it may, without vanity, be asserted that Hajjî Baba was quite the fashion among the men of taste and pleasure.

My father's shop being situated near the Royal Caravanserai, the largest and most frequented in the city, was the common resort of the foreign, as well as of the resident, merchants; they not unfrequently gave him something over and above the usual price, for the entertainment they found in the repartees of his hopeful son. One of them, a Bagdad merchant, took great fancy to me, and always insisted that I should attend upon him, in preference even to my more experienced father. He made me converse with him in Turkish, of which I had acquired a slight knowledge, and so excited my curiosity by describing the beauties of the different cities which he had visited, that I soon felt a strong desire to travel. He was then in want of some one to keep his accounts, and as I associated the two qualifications of barber and scribe, he made me such advantageous offers, to enter into his service, that I agreed to follow him; and immediately mentioned my determination to my father. My father was very loath to lose me, and endeavoured to persuade me not to leave a certain profession for one which was likely to be attended with danger and vicissitudes; but when he found how advantageous were the merchant's offers, and that it was not impossible that I might become one myself in time, he gradually ceased to dissuade me from going; and at length gave me his blessing, accompanied by a new case of razors.

My mother's regret for the loss of my society, and her fears for my safety, derived no alleviation from the prospect of my expected future aggrandizement; she augured no good from a career begun in the service of a *Sûni*;[1] but still, as a mark of her maternal affection, she gave me a bag of

[1] It is perhaps almost needless to remind the reader, that the Mussulmans are divided into two inimical sects; viz. *Sûni* and *Shiah*; and that the Turks are of the former, and the Persians of the latter persuasion. The *Sûnies* hold, that Omar, Osman, and Abubekr were the lawful successors of Mohamed. The *Shiahs* assert that they were usurpers, and that Ali, his son-in-law, was the next in succession.

broken biscuit, accompanied by a small tin case of a precious unguent, which, she told me, would cure all fractures, and internal complaints. She further directed me to leave the house with my face towards the door, by way of propitiating a happy return from a journey undertaken under such inauspicious circumstances.

CHAPTER II: HAJJI BABA COMMENCES HIS TRAVELS HIS ENCOUNTER WITH THE TURCOMANS, AND HIS CAPTIVITY

OSMAN AGA, my master, was now on a journey to Meshed, the object of which was to purchase the lamb-skins of Bokhara, which he afterwards purposed to convey to Constantinople for sale. Imagine a short squat man, with a large head, prominent spongy nose, and a thick, black beard, and you will see my fellow traveller. He was a good Mussulman, very strict in his devotions, and never failed to pull off his stockings, even in the coldest morning, to wash his feet, in order that his ablutions might be perfect; and, withal, he was a great hater of the sect of Ali, a feeling he strictly kept to himself, as long as he was in Persia. His prevailing passion was love of gain, and he never went to sleep without having ascertained that his money was deposited in a place of safety. He was, however, devoted to his own ease; smoked constantly, ate much, and secretly drank wine, although he denounced eternal perdition to those who openly indulged in it.

The caravan was appointed to collect in the spring, and we made preparations for our departure. My master bought a strong, ambling mule for his own riding; whilst I was provided with a horse, which, besides myself, bore the *Kalian*[1] (for he adopted the Persian style of smoking), the fire-pan and leather bottle, the charcoal, and also my own wardrobe. A black slave, who cooked for us, spread the carpets, loaded and unloaded the beasts, bestrode another mule, upon which were piled the bedding, carpets, and kitchen utensils. A third, carrying a pair of trunks, in which was my master's wardrobe, and every other necessary, completed our equipment.

The day before our departure, the prudent Osman had taken the precaution to sew into the cotton wadding of his heavy turban fifty ducats, a circumstance known only to him and me, and these were to serve in case of accidents; for the remainder of his cash, with which he intended to make

[1] This is the Persian pipe, made upon the principle of the Indian hookah.

his purchases, was sewn up in small white leather bags, and deposited in the very centre of the trunks.

The caravan being ready to depart consisted of about five hundred mules and horses, and two hundred camels, most of which were laden with merchandize for the north of Persia, and escorted by about one hundred and fifty men, composed of merchants, their servants, and the conductors of the caravan. Besides these, a small body of pilgrims bound to the tomb of Imâm Reza at Meshed joined the caravan, and gave a character of sanctity to the procession of which its other members were happy to take advantage, considering in what high estimation persons bound upon so laudable a purpose as a pilgrimage are always supposed to be held.

Every man on these occasions is armed, and my master, who always turned his head away whenever a gun was fired, and became pale at the sight of a drawn sword, now appeared with a long carbine slung obliquely across his back, and a crooked sword by his side, whilst a pair of huge pistols projected from his girdle; the rest of his surface was almost made up of the apparatus of cartouch-boxes, powder-flasks, ramrods, &c. I also was armed cap-à-pie, only in addition to what my master carried, I was honoured by wielding a huge spear. The black slave had a sword with only half a blade, and a gun without a lock.

We started at break of day from the northern suburb of Ispahan, led by the *chaoûshes*[1] of the pilgrimage, who announced our departure by loud cries and the beating of their copper drums. We soon got acquainted with our fellow travellers, who were all armed; but who, notwithstanding their

[1] Officers whose duties are to find quarters for the pilgrims, establish the prices of provisions, make arrangements for their supply, regulate the hours of march, settle disputes, and announce the time of prayer, &c.

martial equipment, appeared to be very peaceably disposed persons. I was delighted with the novelty of the scene, and could not help galloping and curvetting my horse to the annoyance of my master, who in a somewhat crabbed tone, bid me keep in mind that the beast would not last the journey if I wore it out by unseasonable feats of horsemanship. I soon became a favourite with all the company, many of whom I shaved after the day's march was over. As for my master, it is not too much to say that I was a great source of comfort to him, for after the fatigue of sitting his mule was at an end, I practised many of the arts which I had acquired at the bath to do away the stiffness of his limbs, by kneading his body all over, and rubbing him with my hands.

We proceeded without impediment to Tehran, where we sojourned ten days to rest our mules, and to increase our numbers. The dangerous part of the journey was to come, as a tribe of Turcomans, who were at war with the king of Persia, were known to infest the road, and had lately attacked and plundered a caravan, whilst at the same time they had carried those who composed it into captivity. Such were the horrors related of the Turcomans, that many of our party, and my master in particular, were fearful of proceeding to Meshed; but the account he received of the enormous price of lamb-skins at Constantinople was so alluring, that, in spite of everything, he resolved not to be frightened out of his prospect of gain.

A *chaoûsh* had long been collecting pilgrims at Tehran and its vicinity, in the expectation of the arrival of our caravan, and as soon as we made our appearance, he informed us, that he was ready to join us with a numerous band, a reinforcement which he assured us we ought to receive with gratitude, considering the dangers which we were about to encounter. He was a character well known on the road between Tehran and Meshed, and enjoyed a great reputation for courage, which he had acquired for having cut off a Turcoman's head whom he had once found dead on the road. His appearance was most formidable, being in person tall and broad-shouldered, with a swarthy sunburnt face, ornamented by a few stiff hairs by way of beard at the end of a bony chin. Clad in a breastplate of iron, a helmet with a chain cape flapping over his shoulders, a curved sword by his side, pistols in his girdle, a shield slung behind his back, and a long spear in his hand, he seemed to bid defiance to danger. He made such boast of his prowess, and talked of the Turcomans with such contempt, that my master determined to proceed under his immediate escort. The caravan was ready to depart a week after the festival of the New Year's day,[1] and after having performed our devotions at the great mosque of the congregation on the Friday, we went to the village of Shahabdul Azim, whence the whole body was to proceed the next day on its journey.

We advanced by slow marches over a parched and dreary country, that afforded little to relieve the eye or cheer the heart. Whenever we approached a village, or met travellers on the road, invocations of Allah and of the Prophet were made by our conductors, in loud and shrill tones, accompanied by repeated blows with a leather thong on the drums suspended to their saddle-bow. Our conversation chiefly turned upon the Turcomans, and although we were all agreed that they were a desperate enemy, yet we managed to console ourselves by the hope that nothing could withstand our numbers and appearance, and by repeatedly exclaiming, 'In the name of God, whose dogs are they, that they should think of attacking us?' Every one vaunted his own courage. My master above the rest, with his teeth actually chattering from apprehension, boasted of what he would do, in case we were attacked; and, to hear his language, one would suppose that he had done nothing all his life but fight and slaughter Turcomans. The *chaoûsh*, who overheard his boastings, and who was jealous of being considered the only man of courage of the party, said aloud, 'No one can speak of the Turcomans until they have seen them—and none but an "eater of lions" (at the same time pulling up his moustaches toward his ears) ever came unhurt out of their clutches. Saadi speaks truth when he sayeth, "A young man, though he hath strength of arm, and the force of an elephant, will kick his heel ropes[2] to pieces with fear in the day of battle."'

But Osman Aga's principal hope of security, and of faring better than others in case we were attacked, was in the circumstance of his being a follower of Omar;[3] and, by way of proclaiming it, he wound a piece of green muslin round his cap, and gave himself out as an *emir*, or a descendant of the Prophet, to whom, as the reader may guess, he was no more allied than to the mule upon which he rode.

[1] This takes place in the spring, when the sun enters Aries, and is called the No Rûz, or the new day. The festival is not of Mohamedan origin, and dates from antiquity.
[2] By heel ropes is meant those fastenings which are used to secure horses in the East.
[3] The Turcomans, as well as the Turks, their descendants, are of the *Sûni* persuasion; with them green is a sacred colour; but it is not so among the *Shiahs*.

We had proceeded in this manner for several days, when the *chaoûsh* informed us, in a solemn and important manner, that we were now approaching to the places where the Turcomans generally lie in wait for caravans, and directed that we should all march in a compact body, and invited us to make preparations for a desperate resistance in case we were attacked. The first impulse of my master was to tie his gun, sword, and pistols on one of his baggage mules. He then complained of an affection in the bowels, and so abandoning all his former intentions of engaging in combat, wrapped himself up in the folds of his cloak, put on a face of great misery, took to counting his beads, ever and anon repeating the prayer of *Staferallah*, or 'God forgive me,' and, thus prepared, resigned himself to his destiny. His greatest dependence for protection he seemed to have placed upon the *chaoûsh*, who, among other reasons for asserting his indifference to danger, pointed to the numerous talismans and spells that he wore bound on his arms, and which, he boldly maintained, would avert the arrow of a Turcoman at any time.

This double-bladed sword of a man, and one or two of the boldest of the caravan, rode ahead, at some distance, as an advanced guard, and every now and then, by way of keeping up their courage, galloped their horses, brandishing their lances, and thrusting them forward into the air.

At length, what we so much apprehended actually came to pass. We heard some shots fired, and then our ears were struck by wild and barbarous shoutings. The whole of us stopped in dismay, and men and animals, as if by common instinct, like a flock of small birds when they see a hawk at a distance, huddled ourselves together into one compact body. But when we in reality perceived a body of Turcomans coming down upon us, the scene instantly changed. Some ran away; others, and among them my master, losing all their energies, yielded to intense fear, and began to exclaim, 'Oh Allah!—Oh Imams!—Oh Mohamed the prophet; we are gone! we are dying! we are dead!' The muleteers unloosed their loads from their beasts, and drove them away. A shower of arrows, which the enemy discharged as they came on, achieved their conquest, and we soon became their prey. The *chaoûsh*, who had outlived many a similar fray, fled in the very first encounter, and we neither saw nor heard any more of him. The invaders soon fell to work upon the baggage, which was now spread all over the plain.

My master had rolled himself up between two bales of goods to wait the event, but was discovered by a Turcoman of great size, and of a most ferocious aspect, who, taking him at first for part of the baggage, turned him over on his back, when (as we see a wood-louse do) he opened out at full length, and expressed all his fears by the most abject entreaties. He tried to soften the Turcoman by invoking Omar, and cursing Ali; but nothing would do; the barbarian was inexorable: he only left him in possession of his turban, out of consideration to its colour, but in other respects he completely stripped him, leaving him nothing but his drawers and shirt, and clothing himself with my master's comfortable cloak and trousers before his face. My clothes being scarcely worth the taking, I was permitted to enjoy them unmolested, and I retained possession of my case of razors, to my no small satisfaction.

The Turcomans having completed their plunder, made a distribution of the prisoners. We were blindfolded, and placed each of us behind a horseman, and after having travelled for a whole day in this manner, we rested at night in a lonely dell. The next day we were permitted to see, and found ourselves on roads known only to the Turcomans.

Passing through wild and unfrequented tracts of mountainous country, we at length discovered a large plain, which was so extensive that it seemed the limits of the world, and was covered with the black tents and the numerous flocks and herds of our enemies.

CHAPTER III: INTO WHAT HANDS HAJJI BABA FALLS, AND THE FORTUNE WHICH HIS RAZORS PROVED TO HIM

THE distribution of their prisoners which had been made by the Turcomans, turned out so far fortunate, that Osman Aga and I fell into the hands of one master, the savage robber whom I have before mentioned. He was called *Aslan Sultan*,[1] or the Lion Chief, and proved to be the captain of a considerable encampment, which we reached almost immediately after descending from the mountains into the plain. His tents were situated on the borders of a deep ravine, at the bottom of which flowed

[1] The word *Sultan*, which in Europe is generally used to designate the sovereign of Turkey, among the Tartars, Turcomans, &c., means captain or chief, and is given frequently to subalterns, as well as to those of higher rank.

a stream that took its rise in a chain of neighbouring hills; and green pastures, teeming with cattle, were spread around as far as the eye could reach. Our other fellow sufferers were carried into a more distant part of the country, and distributed among the different tribes of Turcomans who inhabit this region.

At our appearance the whole encampment turned out to look at us, and whilst our conqueror was greeted with loud welcomes, we were barked at and nearly devoured by a pack of large sheep dogs, who had soon selected us out as strangers. My master's green shawl had hitherto procured him some degree of respect; but the chief wife, or the *Banou*,[1] as she was called, was seized, at first sight, with a strong desire to possess it; so he was left with no other covering to his head than his padded *caoûk*, or tiara, which contained his money. That too was longed for by another wife, who said that it would just do to stuff the pack-saddle which had galled her camel's back, and it was taken from his head and thrown, among other lumber, into a corner of the tent. He did all he could to keep possession of this last remnant of his fortune, but to no purpose; in lieu of it he received an old sheep-skin cap, which had belonged to some unfortunate man, who, like us, had been a prisoner, and who had lately died of grief and wretchedness.

My master having been installed in the possession of the dead man's cap, was soon appointed to fill the situation, which was that of tending the camels, when they were sent to feed upon the mountains, and, as he was fat and unwieldy, there was no apprehension of his running away. As for me, I was not permitted to leave the tents, but was, for the present, employed in shaking the leather bags which contained the curds from which butter was made.

In order to celebrate the success of the expedition, an entertainment was given by the chief to the whole encampment. A large cauldron, filled with rice, was boiled, and two sheep were roasted whole. The men, consisting of our chief's relations, who came from the surrounding tents, and most of whom had been at the attack of our caravan, were assembled in one tent, whilst the women were collected in another. After the rice and the sheep had been served up to the men, they were carried to the women,

---

[1] *Banou* implies a female head or chief; thus in the Arabian Nights, *Paribanou*, or more properly *Peribanou*, means the chief of the fairies. The king of Persia's principal wife is styled *Banou Harem*, chief of the harem.

and when they had done, the shepherds' boys were served, and, after they had devoured their utmost, the bones and scrapings of dishes were given to us and the dogs. But, when I was waiting with great anxiety for our morsel, having scarcely tasted food since we were taken, I was secretly beckoned to by one of the women, who made me screen myself behind a tent, and setting down a dish of rice, with a bit of sheep's tail in it, which was sent, she said, by the chief's wife, who pitied my misfortune, and bade me be of good courage, hurried away without waiting for my acknowledgements.

The day was passed by the men in smoking, and relating their adventures, and by the women in singing and beating the tambourine, whilst my poor master and I were left to ponder over our forlorn situation. The mark of favour which I had just received had set my imagination to work, and led me to consider my condition as not entirely desperate. But in vain I endeavoured to cheer up the spirits of my companion; he did not cease to bewail his hard fate. I brought to his mind that constant refuge of every true Mussulman in grief, '*Allah kerim!*—God is merciful!' His answer was, '*Allah kerim, Allah kerim*, is all very well for you who had nothing to lose; but in the meantime I am ruined for ever.' His greatest concern seemed to be, the having failed to secure the profits which he had expected to make on his lamb-skins, and he passed all his time in calculating, to the utmost farthing, what had been his losses on this occasion. However, we were soon to be parted. He was sent off the next day to the mountains, in charge of a string of fifty camels, with terrible threats from the chief that his nose and ears should pay for the loss of any one of them, and that if one died, its price should be added to the ransom money which he hereafter expected to receive for him. As the last testimony of my affection for him, I made him sit down on a camel's pack-saddle, and, with some water from a neighbouring spring, and a piece of soap, which, together with my razors, I had saved from the wreck of our fortunes, shaved him in the face of the whole camp. I very soon found that this exhibition of my abilities and profession might be productive of the greatest advantage to my future prospects. Every fellow who had a head to scratch immediately found out that he wanted shaving,[1] and my reputation soon reached the ears of the chief, who called

[1] All Mohamedans shave the crown of the head. In Persia two patches of hair are left behind each ear by way of curls. In Turkey a tuft is left on the summit of the head.

me to him, and ordered me to operate upon him without loss of time. I soon went to work upon a large head that exhibited the marks of many a sword cut, and which presented as rough a surface as that of the sheep dogs aforementioned. He who had been accustomed to have his hair clipped, perhaps, with the same instrument that sheared his sheep, and who knew of no greater luxury than that of being mutilated by some country barber, felt himself in paradise under my hand. He freely expressed his satisfaction and his approbation of my services, said, on feeling his head, that I had shaved him two days' march under the skin, swore that he never would accept of any ransom for me, be it what it might, and that I should, henceforth, be entitled to the appointment of his own body barber. I leave the gentle reader to guess what were my feelings upon this occasion. Whilst I stooped down and kissed the knee of this my new master, with every appearance of gratitude and respect, I determined to make use of the liberty which the confidence reposed in me might afford, by running away on the very first favourable opportunity. From being so often near the person of the chief, I soon began to acquire great ascendancy over him; and although I was still watched with care, yet I could already devise plans, which appeared to me to be practicable, for escaping from this hateful servitude into which I was thrown, and I felt in a less degree than another would have done the drudgery and wretchedness of my situation.

CHAPTER IV: OF HIS INGENUITY IN RESCUING
HIS MASTER'S MONEY FROM THE TURCOMAN, AND OF
HIS DETERMINATION TO KEEP IT

ONE of the first objects which I had in view for the furtherance of my plan of escape was to obtain possession of the money which was sewed in the padding of my former master's turban. But it had been thrown into a corner of the women's tent, to which I had no access, and it required much ingenuity to get at it without creating suspicion. I had established my reputation as a barber throughout ours and the neighbouring encampments, and had become a favourite of the men; but although I had reason to believe that the *Banou* of my master would fain become more intimately acquainted with me than she hitherto had been, yet as neither she nor any of the other women could employ me in my profession as a shaver, our intercourse hitherto had been confined to tender glances, occasional acts of kindness on her part, and of corresponding marks of thankfulness and acknowledgement on mine. But as they knew enough of civilized life to be aware that in Persia barbers were also surgeons—that besides shaving and rubbing in the bath, they could bleed, draw teeth, and set a broken limb; the Banou soon discovered that she wanted to be bled, and sent a deputation to ask me if I could perform that service for her. Looking upon this as a favourable opportunity to learn some tidings of the object of my solicitude, or perhaps to gain possession of it, I immediately answered that provided I was furnished with a penknife, I hoped that I could bleed as dexterously as the best of my profession. The instrument was produced, and one of the elders of the tribe, who pretended to a smattering of astrology, announced that a conjunction of the planets favourable to such an operation would take place on the following morning. At that auspicious moment, I was introduced into the women's tent, where I found the Banou seated on a carpet on the ground, waiting for me with great impatience. She was not a person to excite sensations of a tender nature in a novice like me; for, in the first place, she was of an unwieldy size[1] (so different from the slim forms that we are taught to prize in Persia) that I looked upon her with disgust; and, in the next, I lived in such terror of Aslan Sultan, that had I aspired to her favour, it must have been in the constant dread of the loss of my ears. However, I was much noticed by her, and received great attentions from her companions, who, looking upon me as a being of a superior order, all wanted to have their pulses felt. Whilst making my preparations for bleeding the Banou, I cast my eyes about the tent, in the hopes of seeing the prize, which I was anxious to possess. It struck me that I might make the very operation in which I was engaged subservient to my views, and demanding to feel the patient's pulse once more, which I did with a look of intense meditation, I observed that this was a complicated disorder —that the blood must not be allowed to flow upon the ground, but be collected in a vessel, that I might examine it at leisure. This strange proposal of mine raised an immediate outcry amongst the women; but with the

[1] The Turks differ materially from the Persians in their tastes for women, the one admiring corpulency, whilst the latter show greater refinement, and esteem those forms which are mostly prized in Europe.

Banou a deviation from the usual practice only served to confirm her opinion of my superior skill. Here, however, a new difficulty arose. The scanty
stock of a Turcoman could ill afford to sacrifice any utensil by applying it
to a service which would defile it for ever. They were recapitulated one by
one, and all found too precious to be thrown away. I was hesitating whether
I might venture to go straight to my point, when the Banou bethought
herself of an old leather drinking-cup, which she desired one of the women
to search for in a corner of the tent. 'This will never do: you can see the
light through it,' said I, holding it up towards the tent door, and pointing
to the seams with the penknife, which I held in my hand, and with which
I cut, at the same time, half a dozen of the stitches. 'Where is the cap of
that old Emir?' cried out the Banou. 'It is mine,' said the second wife; 'I
want it to stuff my saddle with,' 'Yours!' returned the other in a fury.
'There is but one God! Am not I the Banou of this harem? I will have it.'
'You shall not,' retorted the other. Upon this an uproar ensued which became so loud and threatening, that I feared it would come to the ears of
Aslan Sultan, who very probably would have settled the dispute by taking
at once the bone of contention from the contending parties. But luckily the
astrologer interfered, and when he had assured the second wife that the
blood of the Banou would be upon her head if anything unfortunate happened on this occasion, she consented to give up her pretensions. I accordingly prepared to bleed my patient; but when she saw the penknife, the
cap underneath to receive her blood, and the anxious faces of those about
her, she became frightened, and refused to permit me to proceed. Fearing
after all that I should lose my prize, I put on a very sagacious look, felt her
pulse, and said that her refusal was unavailing, for that it was her fate to
be bled, and that she and every one knew nothing could avert an event
which had been decreed since the beginning of the world. To this there
was no reply; and all agreeing that she would commit a great sin were she
to oppose herself to the decrees of Providence, she put out her bare arm,
and received the stab from my penknife with apparent fortitude. The blood
was caught, and, when the operation was over, I ordered that it should be
conveyed to a little distance from the camp, and that none but myself
should be permitted to approach it, as much of the good or evil that might
accrue to the patient from bleeding depended upon what happened to the
blood after it had flown from the body. I waited until night, when every-

body was asleep, and then with great anxiety ripped up the lining, where to my joy I found the fifty ducats, which I immediately concealed in an adjacent spot, and then dug a hole for the cap, which I also concealed. In the morning I informed the Banou, that having seen some wolves prowling about the tents, I feared that something unlucky might happen to her blood, and that I had buried it, caouk[1] and all. This appeared to satisfy her; and by way of recompense for the service I had rendered, she sent me a dish made with her own hands, consisting of a lamb roasted whole, stuffed with rice and raisins, accompanied by a bowl of sour milk with salt in it.

I must confess that when I became possessed of the fifty ducats, a recollection of my poor former master, who was leading a melancholy life in the mountains with the camels, whilst I was living in comparative luxury, came across my mind, and I half resolved to restore them to him; but by little and little I began to argue differently with myself. 'Had it not been for my ingenuity,' said I, 'the money was lost for ever; who therefore has a better claim to it than myself? If he was to get possession of it again, it could be of no use to him in his new profession, and it is a hundred to one but what it would be taken from him, therefore, I had best keep it for the present: besides, it was his fate to lose, and mine to recover it.' This settled every difficulty, and I looked upon myself as the legitimate possessor of fifty ducats, which I conceived no law could take from me. Meanwhile, I made an attempt to convey to him half of the roasted lamb which I had just received, through the means of a shepherd's boy who was going into the mountains, and who promised not to eat any of it by the wayside. Although I doubted his word, yet, after my deliberation about the ducats, my conscience wanted some quietus: 'I cannot do less,' said I, 'than make my fellow sufferer in adversity a partaker of my prosperity.' But alas! the boy had scarcely crossed the deep ravine that bordered the encampment ere I could perceive him carrying the meat to his mouth, and I made no doubt that every bone was picked clean before he was out of sight. It would have been a useless undertaking to have pursued him, considering the distance that already separated us, so I contented myself by discharging a stone and a malediction at his head, neither of which reached their destination.

[1] Padded cap round which the turban was wound.

CHAPTER V: HAJJI BABA BECOMES A ROBBER
IN HIS OWN DEFENCE, AND INVADES HIS NATIVE CITY

I HAD now been above a year in the hands of the Turcomans, during which I had acquired the entire confidence of my master. He consulted me upon all his own affairs, as well as those of his community, and as he considered that I might now be depended upon, he determined to permit me to accompany him in a predatory excursion into Persia—a permission, which, in hopes of a good opportunity to escape, I had frequently entreated of him to grant. Hitherto I had never been allowed to stray beyond the encampment and its surrounding pastures, and as I was totally ignorant of the roads through the great salt desert which separated us from Persia, I knew that it would be in vain for me to attempt flight, as many before me had done, and had invariably perished or returned to their masters, who treated them with more rigour than before. I therefore rejoiced that I now had an opportunity of observing the country we were about to cross, and determined with myself that if I could not get away during this expedition, nothing should hinder my attempting it on our return. The Turcomans generally make their principal excursions in the spring, when they find pasturage for their horses in

the highlands, and fresh corn in the plains, and because they then are almost certain of meeting caravans to plunder on their march. This season
being now near at hand, Aslan called together the chiefs of his tribe, the
heads of tens and the heads of hundreds, and all those who were skilled in
plunder, and proposed a plan to them of an incursion into the very heart
of Persia. Their object was to reach Ispahan itself, to enter the city in the
night, when all was quiet, and to sack the caravanserai, to which the richest merchants were known to resort. Our guide through the great salt
desert was to be my master in person, whose experience and local knowledge were greater than that of any of his contemporaries; and he proposed
to the council that as no one amongst them, except myself, knew the streets
and bazaars of Ispahan, I should lead the way, when once we had entered
the city. This was opposed by several, who said that it was imprudent to
trust a stranger and a native of the very place they intended to attack, who
would be likely to run off the moment he could do so with safety. At length,
after much discussion, it was agreed that I should be their guide in Ispahan;
that two men should ride close on each side of me, and in case I showed the
least symptom of treachery in my movements, kill me on the spot. This
being settled, the Turcomans put their horses in training, and one was appointed for my use, which had the reputation of having twice borne away
the flag at their races.[1] I was equipped as a Turcoman, with a large sheep-
skin cap on my head, a sheep-skin coat, a sword, a bow and arrows, and a
heavy spear, the head of which was taken off or put on as the occasion
might require. I had a bag of corn tied behind on my horse, besides ropes
to tether him with when we made a halt,—and for my own food I carried
several flaps of bread,[2] and half a dozen of hard eggs, trusting to the
chapter of accidents, and to my own endurance of hunger, for further sus-
tenance. I had already made a very tolerable apprenticeship to a hard life
since I had first been taken, by sleeping on the ground with the first thing
that I could seize for a pillow, and thus I looked upon the want of a bed as
no privation. My companions were equally hardy, and in point of bodily
fatigue, perhaps, we were a match for any nation in the world.

[1] The races that take place among the Turcomans and the Persians are intended to try
the *bottom*, rather than the actual speed of their horses.
[2] The bread here alluded to is baked on small and convex iron plates, and when prepared is about the thickness of brown paper.

I took previous care to unbury the fifty ducats, which I tied very carefully in my girdle, and I promised my former master, who from fretting had worn himself down to a skeleton, that if ever I had an opportunity, I would do all in my power to make his friends ransom him. 'Ah,' said he, 'no one will ever ransom me. As for my son, he will be happy to get my property; and as for my wife, she will be happy to get another husband: so no hope is left. There is only one favour I beg of you, which is, to inquire what is the price of lamb-skins at Constantinople.'

Here I had another struggle with my conscience on the subject of the ducats. Should I restore them? Would it not be more advantageous, even to my master, that I should keep them? My ability to take advantage of this opportunity to escape might depend upon my having a little money in my purse—and what chance had he of being relieved but through my interference? All things considered, I let them remain in my girdle.

The astrologer having fixed upon a lucky hour for our departure, we mounted at nightfall. Our party consisted of Aslan Sultan, who was appointed chief of the expedition, and of twenty men, myself included. Our companions were composed of the principal men of the different encampments in our neighbourhood, and were all, more or less, accomplished cavaliers. They were mounted upon excellent horses, the speed and bottom of which are so justly celebrated throughout Asia; and as we rode along in the moonlight, completely armed, I was persuaded that we looked as desperate a gang of ruffians as ever took the field. For my part, I felt that nature had never intended me for a warrior, and although I thought that I could keep up appearances as well as most men in my predicament, and indeed I believe did act my part so perfectly, as to make both my master and his companions believe that they had got a very *Rustam*[1] in me, yet I dreaded the time when I should be put to the trial.

I was surprised to observe the dexterity with which our chief led us through the thick forests that clothe the mountains which border the plains of Kipchâk. The dangers of the precipices and the steep ascents were something quite appalling to a young traveller like me; but my companions rode over everything with the greatest unconcern, confident in the sure-

---

[1] Rustam is the fabulous hero of Persian history, so much celebrated in the Shahnameh as a paragon of strength and courage. His duel with *Asfendiar*, which lasted two whole days, is the theme of Persian romance.

footedness of their horses. Having once ascended the mountains, we entered upon the arid plains of Persia, and here my master's knowledge of the country was again conspicuous. He knew every summit the moment it appeared, with the same certainty as an experienced *Frank* sailor recognizes a distant headland at sea. But he showed his sagacity most in drawing his inferences from the tracks and footsteps of animals. He could tell what sort of travellers they belonged to, whence coming, whither going, whether enemy or friend, whether laden or unladen, and what their probable numbers, with the greatest precision.

We travelled with much precaution as long as we were in the inhabited parts of the country, lying by during the day, and making all expedition at night. Our stock of provender and provisions was renewed at the last encampment of the wandering tribes which we visited before we reached the great salt desert, and when we entered it, we urged our horses on with as much haste as we knew their strength was likely to support. At length, after travelling about 120 parasangs,[1] we found ourselves in the environs of Ispahan. The moment for reaping the fruit of our fatigue, and for trying my courage, was now at hand, and my heart quite misgave me when I heard of the plan of attack which my companions proposed.

Their scheme was to enter the city through one of the unguarded avenues, which were well known to me, and at midnight to make straight for the Royal Caravanserai, where we were sure to find a great many merchants, who at this season of the year collect there with ready money to make their purchases. We were at once to carry off all the cash we could find, then to seize and gag each a merchant if we were able, that before the city could be alarmed, we might be on the road to our encampment again. I found the plan so hazardous, and so little likely to succeed, that I gave it as my opinion that we ought not to attempt it; but my master, putting on his most determined look, said to me, 'Hajjî! open your eyes—this is no child's play!—I swear by the beard of the Prophet, that if you do not behave well, I'll burn your father. We have succeeded before, and why should we not be as successful now? He then ordered me to ride near him, and placed another ruffian at my side, and both vowed, if I flinched, that they would immediately run me through the body. We then took the lead, and, from my knowledge of Ispahan, I easily picked my way through the ruins

[1] A parasang is equivalent to about three and a half geographical miles.

which surround it, and then entered into the inhabited streets, which were at that time of night entirely forsaken. When near the scene of action, we stopped under the arches of one of the ruined houses, which are so frequently to be met with even in the most inhabited parts of the city, and dismounting from our horses, picketed them to the ground with pegs and heelropes,[1] and left them under the care of two of our men. By way of precaution we appointed a rendezvous in a lonely dell about five parasangs from Ispahan, to which it was determined we should retreat as circumstances might require. Once on foot, we proceeded without noise in a body, avoiding as much as we could the bazaars, where I knew that the officers of the police kept watch, and by lanes reached the gate of the caravanserai. Here was a place, every square inch of which I knew by heart, namely, my

father's shaving shop. Being aware that the gate of the caravanserai would be locked, I made the party halt there, and, taking up a stone, knocked, and called out to the doorkeeper by name: 'Ali Mohammed,' said I, 'open, open: the caravan is arrived.'

Between asleep and awake, without showing the least symptom of opening, 'What caravan?' said he.

'The caravan from Bagdad.'

'From Bagdad? why that arrived yesterday. Do you laugh at my beard?'

Seeing myself entrapped, I was obliged to have recourse to my own name, and said, 'Why, a caravan to be sure with Hajjî Baba, Kerbelai Hassan the barber's son, who went away with Osman Aga, the Bagdad merchant. I bring the news, and expect the present.'

'What, Hajjî?' said the porter, 'he who used to shave my head so well? His place has long been empty. You are welcome.'

[1] A fully-equipped horseman in the **east** generally carries with him an iron peg, to which is affixed a rope terminated by a noose, with which he pickets his horse wherever he may alight. The rope is buttoned to the fore leg, whilst the peg is driven into the ground with a stone.

Upon which he began to unbolt the heavy gates of the entrance porch, which, as they creaked on their hinges, discovered a little old man in his drawers with an iron lamp in his hand, which shed enough light to show us that the place was full of merchants and their effects.

One of our party immediately seized upon him, and then we all rushed in and fell to work. Expert in these sort of attacks, my companions knew exactly where to go for plunder, and they soon took possession of all the gold and silver that was to be found; but their first object was to secure two or three of the richest merchants, whose ransom might be a further source of wealth to them. Ere the alarm had been spread, they had seized upon three, who from their sleeping upon fine beds, covered with shawl quilts, and reposing upon embroidered cushions, they expected would prove a good prize. These they bound hand and foot after their fashion, and forcing them away, placed them upon their best horses behind riders, who immediately retreated from the scene of action to the rendezvous.

From my knowledge of the caravanserai itself, and of the rooms which the richest merchants generally occupied, I knew where cash was to be found, and I entered one room as softly as I could (the very room which my first master had occupied), and seizing upon the small box in which the merchants generally keep their money, I made off with it.—To my joy, I found it contained a heavy bag, which I thrust into my bosom, and carried it about with me as well as I could; although, on account of the darkness, I could not ascertain of what metal it was.

By the time we had nearly finished our operations the city had been alarmed. Almost all the people within the caravanserai, such as servants, grooms, and mule-drivers, at the first alarm had retreated to the roof; the neighbouring inhabitants then came in flocks, not knowing exactly what to do: then came the police magistrate and his officers, who also got on the roof of the caravanserai, but who only increased the uproar by their cries, exclaiming, 'Strike, seize, kill!' without in fact doing anything to repulse the enemy. Some few shots were fired at random; but, owing to the darkness and the general confusion, we managed to steal away without any serious accident. During the fray I was frequently tempted to leave the desperate gang to which I belonged, and hide myself in some corner until they were gone; but I argued thus with myself: If I should succeed in getting away, still my dress would discover me, and before I could explain

who I really was, I should certainly fall a sacrifice to the fury of the populace, the effects of which more than once I had had occasion to witness. My
father's shop was before me; the happy days I had passed in that very caravanserai were in my recollection, and I was in the act of deliberating
within myself what I should do, when I felt myself roughly seized by the
arm, and the first thing which I recognized on turning round was the grim
face of Aslan Sultan, who threatened to kill me on the spot, if I did not
render myself worthy of the confidence he had placed in me. In order to
show him my prowess, I fastened upon a Persian who had just rushed by
us, and, throwing him down, I exclaimed that, if he did not quietly submit

to be taken prisoner and to follow me, I would put him to death. He began
to make the usual lamentations, 'For the sake of Iman Hossein, by the soul
of your father, by the beard of Omar, I conjure you to leave me!' and immediately I recognized a voice that could belong to no one but my own
father. By a gleam from a lantern, I discovered his well-known face. It was
evident, that hearing the commotion, he had left his bed to secure the property in his shop, which altogether did not consist of more than half-a-dozen
of towels, a case of razors, soap, and a carpet. The moment I recognized
him, I let go his beard, of which I had got a fast hold, and, owing to that
habit of respect which we Persians show to our parents, would have kissed
his hand and stood before him; but my life was in danger if I appeared to
flinch, so I continued to struggle with him, and in order to show myself in
earnest, pretending to beat him, I administered my blows to a mule's pack-
saddle that was close to where he lay. This while I heard my father mutter-

ing to himself, 'Ah, if Hajji was here, he would not permit me to be served in this way!' which had such an effect upon me, that I immediately let him go, and exclaimed in Turkish to the surrounding Turcomans: 'He won't do for us; he's only a barber.' So without more ceremony I quitted the scene of action, mounted my horse, and retreated in full gallop through the city.

CHAPTER VI: CONCERNING THE THREE PRISONERS TAKEN BY THE TURCOMANS, AND OF THE BOOTY MADE IN THE CARAVANSERAI

WHEN we had reached our place of rendezvous, we dismounted from our horses, and made a halt to rest them, and to recruit ourselves after the fatigues of the night. One of the party had not forgotten to steal a lamb as we rode along, which was soon put into a fit state to be roasted. It was cut up into small pieces, which were stuck on a ram-rod, and placed over a slow fire made of what underwood we could find, mixed up with the dung of the animals, and, thus heated, was devoured most ravenously by us all.

Our next care was to ascertain the value of our prisoners. One was a tall thin man, about fifty years of age, with a sharp eye, a hollow aguish cheek, a scanty beard, wearing a pair of silken drawers, and a shawl under-coat. The other was a short round man, of a middle age, with a florid face, dressed in a dark vest, buttoning over his breast, and looked like an officer of the law. The third was stout and hairy, of rough aspect, of a strong vigorous form, and who was bound with more care than the others on account of the superior resistance which he had made.

After we had finished our meal, and distributed the remains of it to the prisoners, we called them before us, and questioned them as to their professions and situations in life. The tall thin man, upon whose rich appearance the Turcomans founded their chief hope, was first examined, and as I was the only one of our party who could talk Persian, I stood interpreter. 'Who and what are you?' said Aslan Sultan. 'I,' said the prisoner, in a very subdued voice, 'I beg to state, for the good of your service, that I am nothing—I am a poor man.'

'What's your business?'

'I am a poet, at your service; what can I do more?'

'A poet!' cried one of the roughest of the Turcomans; 'what is that good for?'

'Nothing,' answered Aslan Sultan, in a rage; 'he won't fetch ten tomauns; poets are always poor, and live upon what they can cozen from others. Who will ransom a poet? But if you are so poor,' said Aslan Sultan, 'how do you come by those rich clothes?'

'They are part of a dress of honour,' returned the poet, 'which was lately conferred upon me by the Prince of Shiraz, for having written some verses in his praise.'

Upon which the clothes were taken from him, a sheep-skin cloak given to him in return, and he was dismissed for the present. Then came the short man. 'Who are you?' said the chief: 'what is your profession?'

'I am a poor Cadi,' answered the other.

'How came you to sleep in a fine bed, if you are poor?' said his interrogator. 'You father of a dog, if you lie, we'll take your head off! Confess that you are rich! All Cadies are rich: they live by selling themselves to the highest bidder.'

'I am the Cadi of Galadoun, at your service,' said the prisoner. 'I was ordered to Ispahan by the governor to settle for the rent of a village which I occupy.'

'Where is the money for your rent?' said Aslan.

'I came to say,' answered the Cadi, 'that I had no money to give, for that the locusts had destroyed all my last year's crops, and that there had been a want of water.'

'Then after all, what is this fellow worth?' said one of the gang.

'He is worth a good price,' replied the chief, 'if he happens to be a good Cadi, for then the peasants may wish him back again; but if not, a *dînar*[1] is too much for him. We must keep him: perhaps he is of more value than a merchant. But let us see how much this other fellow is likely to fetch.'

They then brought the rough man before them, and Aslan Sultan questioned him in the usual manner—'What are you?'

'I am a *ferash*' (a carpet-spreader), said he, in a very sulky manner.

'A *ferash!*' cried out the whole gang—'a ferash! The fellow lies! How came you to sleep in a fine bed?' said one.

'It was not mine,' he answered, 'it was my master's.'

[1] The *dînar* is the smallest denomination of money in Persia.

'He lies! he lies!' they all cried out: 'he is a merchant—you are a merchant. Own it, or we'll put you to death.'

In vain he asserted that he was only a carpet-spreader, nobody believed him, and he received so many blows from different quarters, that at last he was obliged to roar out that he was a merchant.

But I, who judged from the appearance of the man that he could not be a merchant, but that he was what he owned himself to be, assured my companions that they had got but a sorry prize in him, and advised them to release him; but immediately I was assailed in my turn with a thousand maledictions, and was told, that if I chose to take part with my countrymen, I should share their fate, and become a slave again—so I was obliged to keep my peace and permit the ruffians to have their own way.

Their speculation in man-stealing having proved so unfortunate, they were in no very good humour with their excursion, and there was a great difference of opinion amongst them, what should be done with such worthless prisoners. Some were for keeping the Cadi, and killing the poet and the ferash, and others for preserving the Cadi for ransom, and making the ferash a slave; but all seemed to be for killing the poet.

I could not help feeling much compassion for this man, who in fact appeared to be from his manners, and general deportment, a man of consequence, although he had pleaded poverty; and seeing it likely to go very hard with him, I said, 'What folly are you about to commit! Kill the poet! why it will be worse than killing the goose with the golden egg. Don't you know that poets are sometimes very rich, and can, if they choose, become rich at all times, for they carry their wealth in their heads? Did you never hear of the king who gave a famous poet a *miscal*[1] of gold for every stanza which he composed? Is not the same thing said of the present Shah? and—who knows?—perhaps your prisoner may be the King's poet himself.'

'Is that the case?' said one of the gang; 'then let him make stanzas for us immediately, and if they don't fetch a miscal each, he shall die.'

'Make on! make on!' exclaimed the whole of them to the poet, elated by so bright a prospect of gain; 'if you don't, we'll cut your tongue out.'

At length it was decided that all three should be preserved, and that as soon as they had made a division of the booty, we should return to the plains of Kipchâk.

[1] Twenty-four grains make one miscal.

Aslan then called us together, and every man was obliged to produce what he had stolen. Some brought bags of silver and others gold. Nor did they confine themselves to money only; gold heads of pipes, a silver ewer, a sable pelisse, shawls, and a variety of other things, were brought before us. When it came to my turn, I produced the heaviest bag of tomauns that had yet been given in, which secured to me the applause of the company.

'Well done! well done! Hajjî,' said they all to me; 'he has become a good Turcoman: we could not have done better ourselves.'

My master in particular was very loud in his praises, and said, 'Hajjî, my son, by my own soul, by the head of my father, I swear that you have done bravely, and I will give you one of my slaves for a wife, and you shall live with us—and you shall have a tent of your own, with twenty sheep, and we'll have a wedding, when I will give an entertainment to all the encampment.'

These words sunk deep in my mind, and only strengthened my resolution to escape on the very first opportunity; but in the meanwhile I was very intent upon the division of the spoil which was about to be made, as I hoped to be included for a considerable portion of it. To my great mortification they gave me not a single dînar. In vain I exclaimed, in vain I entreated; all I could hear was, 'If you say a word more, we will cut your head off.' So I was obliged to console myself with my original fifty ducats, whilst my companions were squabbling about their shares. At length it became a scene of general contention, and would have finished by bloodshed, if a thought had not struck one of the combatants, who exclaimed, 'We have got a Cadi here; why should we dispute? He shall decide between us.'

So immediately the poor Cadi was set in the midst of them, and was made to legislate upon goods, part of which belonged in fact to himself, without even getting the percentage due to him as judge.

CHAPTER VII: HAJJI BABA EVINCES A FEELING DISPOSITION
THE HISTORY OF THE POET ASKER

WE made our retreat by the same road we came, but not with the same expedition, on account of our prisoners. They sometimes walked, and sometimes rode.

The general appearance of the poet had, from the first moment, interested me in his misfortunes; and being a smatterer in learning myself, my vanity, perhaps, was flattered with the idea of becoming the protector of a man of letters in distress. Without appearing to show any particular partiality to him, I succeeded in being appointed to keep watch over him, under the plea that I would compel him to make verses; and conversing in our language, we were able to communicate with each other with great freedom without the fear of being understood. I explained my situation, and informed him of my intentions to escape, and assured him that I would do everything in my power to be useful to him. He seemed delighted to meet with kind words, where he expected nothing but ill-treatment; and when I had thus acquired his confidence, he did not scruple to talk to me freely about himself and his concerns. I discovered what I had before suspected, that he was a man of consequence, for he was no less a personage than the court poet, enjoying the title of *Melek al Shoherah*, or the Prince of Poets. He was on his road from Shiraz (whither he had been sent by the Shah on business) to Tehran, and had that very day reached Ispahan, when he had fallen into our hands. In order to beguile the tediousness of the road through the Salt Desert, after I had related my adventures, I requested him to give me an account of his, which he did in the following words:

'I was born in the city of Kerman, and my name is Asker. My father was for a long time governor of that city, during the reign of the eunuch Aga Mohammed Shah; and although the intrigues that were set on foot against him to deprive him of his government were very mischievous, still such was his respectability, that his enemies never entirely prevailed against him. His eyes were frequently in danger, but his adroitness preserved them; and he had at last the good fortune to die peaceably in his bed in the present Shah's reign. I was permitted to possess the property which he left, which amounted to about 10,000 tomauns. In my youth I was remarkable for the attention which I paid to my studies, and before I had arrived at the age of sixteen I was celebrated for writing a fine hand. I knew Hafiz entirely by heart, and had myself acquired such a facility in making verses, that I might almost have been said to speak in numbers. There was no subject that I did not attempt. I wrote on the loves of Leilah[1] and Majnoun; I never heard the note of a nightingale, but I made it pour

[1] The loves of these personages have been treated by various oriental writers. Majnoun as the model of a lover, and Leilah as the most beautiful and perfect of her sex.

out its loves to the rose; and wherever I went I never failed to produce my poetry and chant it out in the assembly. At this time the king was waging war with Sadik Khan, a pretender to the throne, and a battle was fought, in which his majesty commanded in person, and which terminated in the defeat of the rebel. I immediately sang the king's praises. In describing the contest I made Rustam appear standing in a cloud over the field of battle; who seeing the king lay about him desperately, exclaims to himself, "Lucky wight am I to be here instead of below, for certainly I should never escape from *his* blows." I also exerted my wit, and was much extolled when I said, that Sadik Khan and his troops ought not to repine after all; for although they were vanquished, yet still the king, in his magnanimity, had exalted their heads to the skies. In this, I alluded to a pillar of skulls which his majesty had caused to be erected of the heads of the vanquished. These sayings of mine were reported to the Shah, and he was pleased to confer upon me the highest honour which a poet can receive; namely, causing my mouth to be filled with gold coin in the presence of the

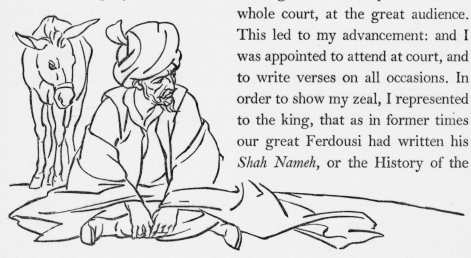

whole court, at the great audience. This led to my advancement: and I was appointed to attend at court, and to write verses on all occasions. In order to show my zeal, I represented to the king, that as in former times our great Ferdousi had written his *Shah Nameh*, or the History of the Kings, it behooved him, who was greater than any monarch Persia ever possessed, to have a poet who should celebrate his reign; and I entreated permission to write a *Shahin Shah Nameh*, or the History of the King of Kings; to which his majesty was most graciously pleased to give his consent. One of my enemies at court was the lord high treasurer, who, without any good reason, wanted to impose upon me a fine of 12,000 tomauns, which the king, on the plea that I was the first poet of the age, would not allow. It happened one day, that in a large assembly, the subject of discussion was the liberality of Mahmoud Shah Ghaznevi to Ferdousi, who gave him a miscal of gold for every couplet in the *Shah Nameh.* Anxious that the king should hear what I was about to say, I exclaimed: "The liberality of his present majesty is equal to that of Mahmoud Shah—equal did I say?—nay greater; because in the one case, it was exercised towards the most celebrated poet of Persia; and in my case, it is exercised towards the humble individual now before you."

'All the company were anxious to hear how and when such great favours had been conferred upon me. "In the first place," said I, "when my father died, he left a property of 10,000 tomauns; the king permitted me to inherit it; he might have taken it away—there are 10,000 tomauns. Then the lord high treasurer wanted to fine me 12,000 tomauns; the king did not allow it—there are 12,000 more. Then the rest is made up of what I have subsisted upon ever since I have been in the Shah's service, and so my sum is made out." And then I took to my exclamations of "May the king live for ever!—may his shadow never be less!—may he conquer all his enemies!"—all of which I flattered myself was duly reported to his majesty: and some days after I was invested with a dress of honour, consisting of a brocade coat, a shawl for the waist, and one for the head, and a brocade cloak trimmed with fur. I was also honoured with the title of Prince of Poets, by virtue of a royal firman, which, according to the usual custom, I wore in my cap for three successive days, receiving the congratulations of my friends, and feeling of greater consequence than I had ever done before. I wrote a poem, which answered the double purpose of gratifying my revenge for the ill-treatment I had received from the lord high treasurer, and of conciliating his good graces; for it had a double meaning all through: what he in his ignorance mistook for praise, was in fact satire; and as he thought that the high-sounding words in which it abounded (which, being mostly Arabic, he did not understand) must contain an eulogium, he did not in the least suspect that they were in fact expressions containing the grossest disrespect. In truth, I had so cloaked my meaning, that, without my explanation, it would have been difficult for any one to have discovered it. But it was not alone in poetry that I excelled. I had a great turn for mechanics, and several of my inventions were much admired at court. I contrived a wheel for perpetual motion, which only wants one little addition to make it go round for ever. I made different sorts of col-

oured paper; I invented a new sort of ink-stand; and was on the high road
to making cloth, when I was stopped by his majesty, who said to me,
"Asker, stick to your poetry: whenever I want cloth, my merchants bring
it from Europe." And I obeyed his instructions; for on the approaching
festival of the new year's day, when it is customary for each of his servants
to make him a present, I wrote something so happy about a toothpick,
which I presented in a handsome case, that the principal nobleman of the
court, at the great public audience of that sacred day, were ordered to kiss
me on the mouth for my pains. I compared his majesty's teeth to pearls,
and the toothpick to the pearl-diver; his gums to a coral-bank, near which
pearls are frequently found; and the long beard and mustachios that en-
circled the mouth to the undulations of the ocean. I was complimented by
everybody present upon the fertility of my imagination. I was assured that
Ferdousi was a downright ass when compared to me. By such means, I enjoyed great favour with the Shah; and his majesty being anxious to give
me an opportunity of acquiring wealth as well as honours, appointed me to
be the bearer of the usual annual dress of honour which he sends to his son,
the prince of the province of Fars. I was received at Shiraz with the greatest distinctions, and presents were made to me to a considerable amount;
which, in addition to what I had levied from the villages on the road, made
a handsome sum. The event of last night has deprived me of all: all has
been stolen from me, and here you see me the most miserable of human
beings. If you do not manage to help me to escape, I fear that I shall die a
prisoner. Perhaps the king may be anxious to release me, but certainly he
will never pay one farthing for my ransom. The lord high treasurer is not
my friend; and since I told the grand vizier, that with all his wisdom he
did not know how to wind up a watch, much less how it was made, I fear
that he also will not care for my loss. The money, with which I might have
purchased my ransom, the barbarians have taken; and where to procure a
similar sum I know not. It is my fate to have fallen into this disaster, therefore I must not repine; but let me entreat you, as you are a fellow Mussulman—as you hate Omar, and love Ali—let me entreat you to help me in
my distress.'[1]

[1] In sketching the history of the poet Asker, the author has attempted to record part
of the life of the late Fatteh Ali Khan, poet-laureate to the Shah, a most ingenious and
amiable man, well known to the English who were at Tehran in 1812 and 1813.

CHAPTER VIII: HAJJI BABA ESCAPES FROM THE TURCOMANS

THE MEANING OF 'FALLING FROM THE FRYING-PAN

INTO THE FIRE' ILLUSTRATED

SSOON as the poet had finished his narrative, I assured him that I would do everything in my power to serve him; but I recommended patience to him for the present, as I had not yet devised the means of procuring my own liberty, and foresaw great difficulties in saving him at the same time. It would be impossible to evade the watchfulness of our masters, as long as we were in the open desert: their horses were as good as mine, and they were much better acquainted with the country than I was. To run away from them under these circumstances would be madness; therefore it was only left us to watch any opportunity that might be given us of escape.

We had reached the limits of the Salt Desert, and were about crossing the high road that leads from Tehran to Meshed, about twenty parasangs to the east of Damgan, when Aslan Sultan made a halt, and proposed that we should remain concealed for a day in the broken ground that borders the road, in the hopes that fortune might throw us in the way of a passing caravan, which it was his intention that we should pillage. At the very dawn of the following day, a spy, who had been stationed on an adjacent hill, came in great haste to report that he saw clouds of dust rising in the direction of Damgan, and approaching towards us, on the road leading to Meshed.

Immediately we were all upon the alert. The Turcomans left their prisoners, bound hand and foot, on the spot where we had rested, with the intention of returning to take them up as soon as we should have rifled the caravan, and, fully equipped, we sallied forth with great caution, determined on blood and plunder.

Aslan himself proceeded before the rest, in order to reconnoitre; and calling me to him, said, 'Now, Hajjî, here is an opportunity for distinguishing yourself. You shall accompany me; and you will observe the precautions I use previous to showing our whole body, which it may be necessary for you to know, in order that you may be able to conduct such an enterprise yourself on some future occasion. I take you with me, in case I should be obliged to use an interpreter; for frequently in these caravans, there is not a person who understands our language. We will approach as near as we can, perhaps have a parley with the conductor, and if we cannot make terms with him, we will fall on with our whole party.'

As the travellers approached, I perceived that Aslan Sultan became uneasy. 'This is no caravan, I fear,' said he; 'they march in too compact a body: besides, I hear no bells; the dust is too great in one spot. I see spears!—it is an immense cavalcade—five led horses!—this is no game for us.'

In fact, as they approached, it was easy to discover that it was no caravan, but some great personage, the governor of a province at least, who was travelling, attended by a numerous escort of horsemen and servants, and with all the pomp and glitter usual on such occasions.

My heart leaped within me when I saw this, for here was an excellent opportunity for escape. Could I approach near enough to be taken prisoner by them, without exciting any previous suspicion in my master, I should be safe; and although I might be ill-treated at first, still I trusted to my eloquence to make my story believed. Accordingly, I said to my companion, 'Let us approach nearer'; and, without waiting for his permission, I excited my horse onwards. He immediately followed, with an intention of stopping me; but we had no sooner cleared the small elevated ground behind which we had posted ourselves, than we came in full view of the whole party, and were scarcely a bow-shot from them. As soon as we were discovered, some six or seven of their best horsemen were detached from the rest of the body, and, at the fullest speed of their horses, came towards us. We turned about to fly: as much as Aslan urged on his steed, so much did I restrain mine; and by this manœuvre I was very soon overtaken and seized. To be knocked off my horse, disarmed, plundered of my fifty ducats, my razors and all my other effects, was but the business of a few seconds; and although I assured my new masters that I was in no intention to leave them, still they persisted in tying my arms behind me, with my own shawl, which they took from round my waist for that purpose. Thus pinioned, and receiving blows every now and then, because I did not move fast enough, I was dragged before their chief, who had made a halt, surrounded by his attendants.

From the sort of attentions which he received, and the low inclinations of the body that were made before him, I imagined that he must be a royal personage, and I was soon informed as much, when I came near; for several blows on the head were given me, as hints to make me prostrate myself before a *shahzadeh*, or prince. A large circle being made, he ordered me to be released, and, as soon as I felt myself free, at one bound I disengaged myself from those near me, and seizing upon the skirt of his cloak, as he was seated on his horse,[1] exclaimed, '*Penah be shahzadeh!* protection from the prince.' One of the guards rushed forward to punish my audacity; but the prince would not allow the sacred custom to be infringed, and promised me his protection. Ordering his servants not to molest me, he, at the same time, commanded me to relate how I came to be placed in the predicament in which I now stood.

Falling on my knees, and kissing the ground, I related my story in as concise a manner as possible; and, to corroborate all that I had said, added, that if he would order his horsemen to attack the party of Turcomans, who still were close at hand, they might release the king's poet, with two other Persians, who were prisoners in their hands, and they would fully confirm all that I had asserted.

---

[1] Seizing the skirt of a man in authority, or the heel-ropes of his horses in the stable, are as great protection to a culprit in Persia as the precincts of a church are in Roman Catholic countries.

I had no sooner said this than the horsemen, who had pursued Aslan Sultan, returned, with looks of great dismay, swearing by Ali and by the head of the king, that an immense body of Turcomans, at least 1,000 strong, were marching down upon us, and that the prince must prepare to fight. In vain I explained to them that they were only twenty in number—nobody would believe me; I was treated as a spy and a liar, and every one said that if the Turcomans did attack, they would put me to death on the spot. The party then proceeded onwards at a good pace, looking about in all directions for the expected enemy, and betraying all those symptoms of apprehension which the very name of Turcoman excites throughout the whole of Persia.

My own horse had been taken from me, and I was permitted to ride upon a baggage mule, where I had time to ponder over my wretched fate and miserable prospects. Without a farthing in my pocket, without a friend, I saw nothing before me but starvation. I had not yet become a sufficiently good Mussulman to re-ceive comfort from predestination, and I absolutely sobbed aloud at my own folly, for having voluntarily been the cause of my present misery. That fond partiality for my own country-men, which used to predominate so powerfully in my breast when I was a prisoner, entirely forsook me here, and I cursed them aloud.

'You call yourselves Mussulmans!' said I to those around me: 'you have not the feelings of dogs. Dogs did I say? You are worse than Chris-tian dogs—the Turcomans are men compared to you.'

Then when I found that this sort of language only produced laughter in my auditors, I tried what entreaty would do. 'For the love of Imam Hossein, for the sake of the Prophet, by the souls of your children, why do you treat a stranger thus? Am I not a Mussulman like yourselves? What have I done that I should be made to devour this grief? I sought refuge amongst you as friends, and I am thrust away as an enemy.'

For all this I got no consolation, excepting from an old muleteer, by name Ali Katir, who had just lighted his *kalian*, or water pipe, and giving it to me to smoke, said, 'My son, everything in this world is in the hand of God.' Pointing to the mule upon which he rode, he added, 'If God has made this animal white, can Ali Katir make it black? It one day gets a feed of corn; on the next it growses upon a thistle. Can we contend with fate? Smoke your pipe now and be happy, and be thankful that it is no worse with you. Hafiz says, "Every moment of pleasure that you enjoy, account it gain: who can say what will be the event of any thing?" '[1]

This speech of the muleteer soothed me a little, and as he found that I was as well versed in Hafiz as he, and not backward in permitting myself to be comforted, he treated me with much kindness, and made me a partaker of his mess during the remainder of the journey. He informed me that 'the prince, into whose hands I had fallen, was the Shah's fifth son, who had lately been installed in the government of the province of Khorassan, and was now on his road to Meshed, the seat of his jurisdiction. He was escorted by a greater number of attendants than ordinary, on account of the alarming state of the Turcoman frontier, and it was said that he had instructions to commence very active operations against that people, as many of whose heads as possible he was invited to send to Tehran, to be piled up before the gate of the royal palace; and you may account yourself very fortunate,' added the muleteer, 'that yours was not taken off your shoulders. Had you happened to be fair, with little eyes, and without much hair, instead of being a dark man, as you are, you certainly would have been put to death, and your head have been pickled, and made to pass for that of a Turcoman.'

When we had reached our resting-place at night, which was a lonely caravanserai half in ruins, situated on the skirts of the desert, I determined to endeavour to procure admittance to the prince, and to make an effort to regain my fifty ducats, and my horse and arms, which I made no scruple in claiming as my own, notwithstanding a certain little voice within me, which told me that another had almost as much right to them as I had. I accordingly watched an opportunity, just before the evening prayer, of presenting myself to him. He was seated on a carpet that had been spread

---

[1] It is no uncommon circumstance in Persia to find men of the lowest estate well versed in their poets. The Persians are eminently a poetical people.

on the terrace of the caravanserai, reposing himself on his cushion, and
before his attendants had time to beat me off, I exclaimed, '*Arzi darum*, I
have a petition to make.' Upon which he ordered me to approach, and
asked me what I wanted? I complained of the treatment I had received
from his servants who had first seized me—related how they had robbed
me of my fifty ducats; and then entreated that my horse and arms might
be restored to me. He inquired of those surrounding him who the men
were that I complained of, and when their names were mentioned, he sent
his chief tent-pitcher to conduct them to him. As soon as they appeared,
for they were two, I recognized the aggressors, and affirmed them to be
such to the prince.

'Sons of dogs,' said he to them, 'where is the money you stole from
this man?'

'We took nothing,' they immediately exclaimed.

'We shall soon see that,' answered he. 'Call the *ferashes*,' said he to one
of his officers, 'and let them beat the rogues on the soles of their feet till
they produce the fifty ducats.'

They were immediately seized, and when their feet were in the air,
strongly tied in the noose, and after receiving a few blows, they confessed
that they had taken the money, and produced it. It was forthwith carried
to the prince, who deliberately counted it over, and, putting it under the
cushion upon which he was reclining, released the culprits, and said in a
loud voice to me, 'You are dismissed.' I stood with my mouth wide open,
hoping to see the money handed over to me, when his master of the ceremonies took me by the shoulders and pushed me away. I exclaimed, 'And
my money, where is it?'

'What does he say?' said the prince: 'give him the shoe if he speaks
again.' When the master of the ceremonies, taking off his high green
slipper, struck me over the mouth with the heel of it, shod with iron, saying, 'Do you speak to a king's son thus? Go in peace, and keep your eyes
open, or you'll have your ears cut off'; and so I was pushed and dragged
violently away.

I returned in utter despair to my muleteer, who appeared not in the
least surprised at what had happened and said, 'What could you expect
more? After all, is he not a prince? When once he or any man in power gets
possession of a thing, do you think that they will ever restore it? You might

We all rushed in and fell to work

as well expect a mule to give up a mouthful of fresh grass, when once it has got it within its mouth, as a prince to give up money that has once been in his hands.'

CHAPTER IX: HAJJI BABA IN HIS DISTRESS, BECOMES A SAKA OR WATER-CARRIER

WE reached Meshed in due time, and the prince made his solemn entry amidst all the noise, parade, and confusion, attendant upon such ceremonies. I found myself a solitary being, in a strange city, distant from my friends, and from any creature to whom I might look for assistance, and without even a pair of razors to comfort me. When I looked at my present means, I found that they consisted of five tomauns—which I had managed to secrete from the sack I had stolen in the caravanserai, and which I put between the lining of my cap—of a brown woollen coat, of a sheep-skin jacket, a shirt, a pair of trousers, and a heavy pair of boots. I had lived upon the muleteer as long as he enjoyed the daily allowance of provisions that he received during the time when he was attached to the suite of the prince; but now that he and his mules were discharged, I could not expect that he should continue to support me. I thought of again taking to my profession; but who would trust their throats to a man who had the reputation of being a Turcoman spy? Besides, although I might purchase razors, yet my means were not large enough to set up a shop, and I was determined not to become a journeyman.

My friend the muleteer, who knew the ways and means of Meshed, recommended me strongly to become a *saka*, or water-carrier. 'You are young, and strong,' said he: 'you have a good voice, and would entice people to drink by a harmonious cry. You have besides a great talent for cant and palaver, and for laughing at one's beard. The number of pilgrims who come to Meshed to perform their devotions at the tomb of the Imâm is great, and charity being one of the principal instruments which they use for the salvation of their souls, they give freely to those who promise them the best reward. You must sell each draught in the name and for the sake of Imam Hossein, our favourite saint. Always offer it gratis; but be sure you get money in hand before you pour it out; and when your customer has drunk, say, with great emphasis, 'May your draught be propitious!

May the holy Imam take you under his protection! May you never suffer the thirst of the blessed Hossein!' and such like sort of speeches, which you must chant out so loud that everybody may hear you. In short, to devotees who come some hundreds of parasangs to say their prayers, you may say anything and everything, and you will be sure to be believed. I myself have been a *saka* at Meshed, and know the trade. It has enabled me to buy a string of mules, and to be the man you see.'

I followed my friend's advice. I forthwith laid out my money in buying a leather sack, with a brass cock, which I slung round my body, and also a bright drinking cup. After having filled my sack with water, and let it soak for some time, in order to do away the bad smell of the leather, I sallied forth, and proceeded to the tomb, where I immediately began my operations. The cry I adopted was 'Water, water! in the name of the Imâm, water.' This I chanted with all the force and swell of my lungs, and having practised under the tuition of the muleteer for two days before, I was assured that I acquitted myself as well as the oldest practitioners. As soon as I appeared, I immediately drew the attention of the other sakas, who seemed to question the right I had to exercise their profession. When I showed myself at the reservoir, to draw water, they would have quarrelled  with me, and one attempted to push me in; but they found I was resolute, and that my resolution was backed by a set of strong and active limbs, and therefore confined themselves to abusive language, of which being the entire master, I soon got the lead, and completely silenced them. Nature, in fact, seemed to have intended me for a saka. The water which I had a moment before drawn from a filthy reservoir, I extolled as having flowed from a spring created by Ali in person, equal to the sacred well of *Zem*

Zem, and a branch of the river which flows through Paradise. It is inconceivable how it was relished, and how considerable was the money I received for giving it gratis. I was always on the watch to discover when a new set of pilgrims should arrive, and before they had even alighted from their mules, all dusty from the road, and all happy at having escaped the Turcomans, I plied them in the name of the Prophet with a refreshing draught, and made them recollect that, this being the first devotional act which they performed on reaching Meshed, so out of gratitude for their safe arrival, they ought to reward me liberally; and my admonitions were scarcely ever disregarded.

The commemoration of the death of Hossein, which is so religiously kept throughout Persia, was now close at hand, and I determined to put myself into training to appear as the water-carrier, who on the last day of the festival, which is held the most sacred, performs a conspicuous character in the tragedy. This was to be acted in public before the prince in the great open square of the city, and I expected to acquire much reputation and profit from the feat of strength which I should perform, which consists of carrying an immense sack full of water on the back, accompanied by additional exertions. I had a rival, who accomplished the task on the last festival; but as the sack I was about to carry contained infinitely more water than he could support, my claim to superiority was not to be disputed. However, I was advised to be on my guard, for he was of a jealous character, and would not lose an opportunity of doing me an injury if he could. When the day arrived, the prince being seated in an upper room situated over the gate of his palace, and the whole population of the city assembled to witness the religious ceremonies, I appeared naked to the waist, with my body streaming with blood, slowly walking under the weight of my immense sack. Having reached the window at which the prince was seated, I attracted his notice by loud exclamations for his happiness and prosperity. He threw me down a gold coin, and expressed himself pleased with my performance. In my exultation I invited several boys, who were near at hand for the purpose, to pile themselves upon my load, which they did, to the astonishment of the crowd, who encouraged me by their cries and applause. I called for another boy, when my rival, who had watched his opportunity, sprang forwards and mounted himself on the very top of all, hoping, no doubt, to crush me: but, exerting myself to the utmost of my strength, I carried my burden clean off, amidst the animating shouts of the staring multitude. But although in the heat of the exertion I felt no inconvenience, yet when I was disencumbered I found that my back was sprained so severely, that I was totally unfitted for the trade of a water-carrier for the future. I therefore sold my sack and other articles, and, with the money that I had gained in water-selling, found myself well off, compared to the deplorable situation in which I was on my arrival at Meshed. My friend the muleteer had departed some time before the festival with a caravan for Tehren, so I was deprived of his counsels. I should have demanded justice for the injury done me by my rival, and might have dragged him before the cadi; but I was assured that in the Mohammedan law there is no provision made for a sprain. It is written an eye for an eye, and a tooth for a tooth; but there is no sprain for a sprain. Had I had some powerful protector, who would have prosecuted the business for me, perhaps I might have got redress; but a miserable creature like myself, unknown and unfriended, I could have gained nothing, and should perhaps have stood a chance of losing the little money I had acquired.

CHAPTER X: HE MAKES A SOLILOQUY
AND BECOMES AN ITINERANT VENDER OF SMOKE

I HELD a consultation with myself as to what I should do next for my livelihood. Various walks in life were open to me. The begging line was an excellent one in Meshed, and, judging from my success as a water-carrier, I should very soon have been at the head of the profession. I might also have become a *lûti*,[1] and kept a bear; but it required some apprenticeship to learn the tricks of the one, and to know how to tame the other: so I gave that up. Still I might have followed my own profession, and have taken a shop; but I could not bear the thoughts of settling, particularly in so remote a town as Meshed. At length I followed the bent of my inclination, and, as I was myself devotedly fond of smoking, I determined to become an itinerant seller of smoke. Accordingly I bought pipes of various sizes, a wooden tray, containing the pipe-heads, which was strapped round my waist, an iron pot for fire, which I carried in my hand, a pair of iron pincers, a copper jug for water, that was suspended by a hook,

[1] The *lûties* are privileged buffoons, usually keeping monkeys, bears, and other animals.

behind my back, and some long bags for my tobacco. All these commodities were fastened about my body, and when I was fully equipped, I might be said to look like a porcupine with all its quills erect. My tobacco was of various sorts—Tabas, Shiraz, Susa, and Damascus. It is true that I was not very scrupulous about giving it pure; for with a very small quantity of the genuine leaf I managed to make a large store, with the assistance of different sorts of dungs. I had a great tact in discovering amongst my customers the real connoisseur, and to him I gave it almost genuine. My whole profits, in fact, depended upon my discrimination of characters. To those of the middling ranks, I gave it half-mixed; to the lower sort, three-quarters; and to the lowest, almost without any tobacco at all. Whenever I thought I could perceive a wry face, I immediately exerted my ingenuity in favour of the excellence of my tobacco. I showed specimens of the good, descanted on its superior qualities, and gave the history of the very gardener who had reared it, and pledged myself to point out the very spot in his grounds where it grew.

I became celebrated in Meshed for the excellence of my pipes. My principal customer was a dervish, who was so great a connoisseur that I never dared to give him any but pure tobacco; and although I did not gain much by his custom, as he was not very exact in his payments, yet his conversation was so agreeable, and he recommended so many of his friends to me, that I cultivated his good will to the utmost of my power.

Dervish Sefer (for that was his name) was a man of peculiar aspect. He had a large aquiline nose, piercing black eyes, a thick beard, and a great quantity of jet black hair flowing over his shoulders. His conical cap was embroidered all over with sentences from the Koran, and holy invocations: the skin of a red deer was fastened loosely upon his back, with the hairy side outwards: he bore in hand a long steel staff, which he generally carried on his shoulder, and in the other a calabash, suspended by three chains, which he extended whenever he deigned to ask the charity of passengers. In his girdle he wore large agate clasps, from which hung a quantity of heavy wooden beads; and, as he swung himself along through the streets and bazaars, there was so much of wildness and solicitude in all his words and actions, that he did not fail to inspire a certain awe in all beholders. This, I afterwards learnt, was put on, in order to suit the character which he had adopted; for when he smoked my pipes, if no one chanced to be present, he was the most natural and unreserved of beings. Our acquaintance soon improved into intimacy, and at length he introduced me into a small circle of dervishes, men of his own turn and profession, with whom he lived almost exclusively, and I was invited to frequent their meetings. It is true that this did not suit my views in the smoking line, for they amongst them consumed more of my good tobacco than all the rest of my other customers put together; but their society was so agreeable that I could not resist the temptation.

Dervish Sefer, one evening when we had smoked more than usual, said to me, 'Hajjî Baba, you are too much of a man to be a seller of smoke all your life: why do you not turn dervish, like us? We hold men's beards as cheap as dirt; and although our existence is precarious, yet it is one of great variety, as well as of great idleness. We look upon mankind as fair game—we live upon their weakness and credulity; and, from what I have seen of you, I think you would do honour to our profession, and in time become as celebrated as even the famous Sheikh Saadi himself.' This speech was applauded by the other two, who pressed my entering upon their profession. I was nothing loath, but I pleaded my ignorance of the necessary qualifications. 'How is it possible,' said I, 'that a being so ignorant and unexperienced as I am can at once attain to all the learning requisite for a dervish? I know how to read and write, 'tis true; I have gone through the Koran, and have my Hafiz and Saadi nearly by heart; besides which, I have read a great part of the *Shah Nameh* of Ferdûsi, but beyond that I am totally ignorant.' 'Ah, my friend,' said Dervish Sefer, 'little do you know of dervishes, and still less of humankind. It is not great learning that is required to make a dervish: assurance is the first ingredient. With one-fiftieth part of the accomplishments that you have mentioned, and with only a common share of effrontery, I promise you, that you may command not only the purses, but even the lives of your hearers. By impudence I have been a prophet, by impudence I have wrought miracles, by impudence I have restored the dying to health—by impudence, in short, I lead a life of great ease, and am feared and respected by those who, like you, do not know what dervishes are. If I chose to give myself the trouble, and incur the risks which Mahomed himself did, I might even now become as great a prophet as he. It would be as easy for me to cut the moon in two with my finger as it was for him, provided I once made my hearers have confidence in me; and impudence will do that, and more, if exerted in a proper manner.' When Dervish Sefer had done talking, his companions applauded what he had said, and they related so many curious anecdotes of the feats which they had performed, that I became very anxious to know more of these extraordinary men. They promised to relate the history of their lives at our next meeting, and, in the meanwhile, recommended me strongly to turn my thoughts to a line of life more dignified, and fuller of enjoyment, than that of a vagabond seller of adulterated smoke.

CHAPTER XI: HISTORY OF DERVISH SEFER, AND
OF THE TWO OTHER DERVISHES

WHEN we had again collected ourselves together, each with a pipe in his hand, seated with our backs against the wall, in a room, the window of which opened into a small square planted with flowers, Dervish Sefer, as the acknowledged chief of our society, began his story in the following words:

'I am the son of the Lûti Bashi, or head Merry-Andrew of the Prince of Shiraz, by a celebrated courtezan of the name of *Taous*, or the Peacock. With such parents, I leave you to imagine the education which I received. My principal associates, during my infancy, were the monkeys and bears that belonged to my father and his friends, and, perhaps, it is to the numerous tricks in which they were instructed, and to the facility with which they learnt them, that I am indebted for the talent of mimicry that has been of so much use to me through life. At fifteen I was an accomplished lûti. I could eat fire, spout water, and perform all sorts of sleight of hand, and I should very probably have continued to prosper in this profession, had not the daughter of the prince's general of camel artillery become en-amoured of me, as I danced on the tight-rope before the court on the festival of the new year's day. A young camel-driver under his orders had a sister who served in the harem of the general: he was my most intimate friend, and his sister gave him the intelligence of the effect my appearance had produced upon her mistress. I immediately went to a mîrza or scribe, who lived in a small shed in a corner of the bazaar, and requested of him to write a love-letter for me, with as much red ink in it as possible, and crossed and re-crossed with all the complication he could devise. Nothing could be better than this composition—for at the very outset it informed my mistress that I was dead, and that my death was owing to the fire of her eyes, that had made roast meat of my heart. Notwithstanding this assertion, I ventured at the end to say that as I had never yet seen her, I hoped that she would contrive to grant me an interview. In the joy of my heart for the possession of such a letter, in great confidence I told the scribe who my charmer was, which he had no sooner heard, than hoping to receive a present for his trouble, he went forthwith and informed the general himself of the fact. That the son of the *Lûti Bashi* should dare to look up to the daughter of *Zambûrekchi Bashi* was a crime not to be forgiven, and as the latter had influence at court, he procured an order for my instant removal from Shiraz. My father did not wish to incur the prince's displeasure, and fearing, from my growing celebrity, that I should very soon rival him in his own profession, rather urged than delayed my departure. On the morning when I was about quitting Shiraz, and was bidding adieu to my friends the monkeys, bears, and other animals under his care, he said to me, "Sefer, my son, I should be sorry to part with you; but with the education which you have received, and the peculiar advantages which you have had of living almost entirely in the society of me and my beasts, it is impossible but that you will succeed in life. I now endow you with what will ensure you a rapid fortune. I give you my chief ape, the most accomplished of his species. Make a friend of him for your own sake, and love him for mine; and I hope in time that you will reach the eminence to which your father has attained." Upon this he placed the animal upon my shoulder, and thus accompanied I left the paternal roof.

'I took the road to Ispahan, in no very agreeable mood, for I scarcely knew whether to be happy or sorry for this change in my circumstances. A monkey and independence were certainly delightful things; but to leave my associates, and the places that were endeared to me from my infancy, and, above all, to abandon that fair unknown, whom my imagination had pictured to me as lovely as *Shireen* herself, were circumstances which appeared to me so distressing, that by the time I had reached the hut of the dervish, at the *Teng Allah Akbar*, my mind sank into a miserable fit of despondency. I seated myself on a stone, near the hut, and, with my monkey by my side, I gave vent to my grief in a flood of tears, exclaiming, *"Ah wahi! Ah wahi!"* in accents the most piteous that can be imagined.

'These brought the dervish out, and when he had heard my tale, invited me into the hut, where I found another dervish, of much more commanding aspect than the former. He was clad nearly in the same manner that I am now (indeed, the cap I wear was his); but there was a wildness about his looks that was quite imposing.

'At the sight of me and my companion, he appeared struck by a sudden thought. He and the other dervish having talked together in private, he proposed that I should accompany him to Ispahan, promised that he would be kind to me, and, if I behaved well, would put me into the way of making my fortune. I readily agreed, and after the dervish of the hut had given us a pipe to smoke, we departed, walking at a good pace, without much being said between us during some time. *Dervish Bideen*, for that was his name, at length began to question me very closely about my former life, and hearing in what my accomplishments consisted, seemed to be well pleased. He then descanted upon the advantages attending the life of a dervish, proved them to be superior to the low pursuits of a *lûti*, and at length persuaded me to embrace his profession. He said, that if I would look upon him as my master, he would teach me all he knew, and *that*, he assured me, was no small portion of knowledge, inasmuch as he was esteemed the most perfect dervish in Persia. He began to talk of magic and astrology, and gave me various receipts for making spells and charms, to serve on every occasion in life; by the sale of which alone I should be able to make my fortune. The tail of a hare, placed under the pillow of a child, he assured me, produces sleep; and its blood, given to a horse, makes him fleet and long-winded. The eye and the knuckle-bones of a wolf, attached to a boy's person, give him courage; and its fat, rubbed on a woman, will convert her husband's love into indifference: its gall, used in the same manner, produces fruitfulness. But the article which bore the greatest price in the seraglios was the *kûs keftar*, the dried skin of a female hyena; which, if worn about the person, conciliated the affection of all to the wearer. He discoursed long upon these and such-like subjects, until he gradually excited so much interest in my heart, by thus placing my fortune apparently in full view, that at length he ventured to make a proposal, which he easily judged would be disagreeable.

'"Sefer," said he to me, "you know not the treasure you possess in that ape,—I do not mean as he stands now alive, but dead. If he were dead, I could extract such ingredients from him to make charms, which would sell for their weight in gold in the harem of the Shah. You must know, that the liver of an ape, and only of that particular species which you possess, is sure to bring back the love of a desired object to the person who may possess it. Then the skin of its nose, if worn round the neck, is a decisive preventive against poison; and the ashes of the animal itself, after it has been burnt over a slow fire, will, if taken internally, give all the qualities of the ape, cunning, adroitness, and the powers of imitation." He then proposed that we should kill the beast.

'I was certainly alarmed at the proposal. I had been brought up with my ape; we had hitherto gone through life together in prosperity as well as in adversity; and to lose him in this barbarous manner was more than I could bear. I was about to give a flat refusal to the dervish, when I observed that his countenance, which hitherto had been all smiles and good humour, had changed to downright furiousness; and fearing that he would take by force that which I could not protect, I, with all the reluctance imaginable, consented to the execution of his project. We then deviated from the road; and having got into a solitary glen, we gathered together some dry stubble and underwood, made a fire, striking a light with a flint and steel, which my companion carried about him. He took my poor ape into his hands, and, without further ceremony, put it to death. He then dissected it; and having taken from it the liver, and the skin off its nose, burnt it in the pile we had made; and when all was over, carefully collected the ashes, which having packed in a corner of his handkerchief, we proceeded on our journey.

'We reached Ispahan in due time, where I exchanged such parts of my dress as belonged to the *lûti* for the garb of a dervish, and then we proceeded to Tehran. Here my master's appearance produced great effect; for no sooner was it known that he was arrived, than all sorts of people flocked to consult him.—Mothers wanted protection for their children against the evil eye; wives a spell against the jealousy of their husbands; warriors talismans to secure them from harm in battle. But the ladies of the king's seraglio were his principal customers. Their most urgent demand was some powerful charm to ensure the attention of the king. The collection of materials for this purpose, which the Dervish Bideen had made, was very great. He had the hairs of a lynx, the back-bone of an owl, and bear's grease in various preparations. To one of the ladies, who, owing to her advanced age, was more pressing than the others, he sold the liver of my monkey, assuring her, that as soon as she appeared wearing it about her person, his majesty would distinguish her from her rivals. To another, who complained that she was never in favour, and frustrated in all her schemes to attract notice, he administered a decoction of the monkey's ashes; and to a third, who wanted a charm to drive away wrinkles, he gave an ointment, which, if property applied, and provided she did not laugh, or otherwise move the muscles of her face, would effectually keep them smooth.

'I was initiated into all these mysteries, and frequently was a party concerned in a fraud, whenever my master was put to the necessity of doing something supernatural to support his credit, if by chance his spells were palpably of no avail. But whatever profit arose either from these services, or from the spoils of my monkey, he alone was the gainer, for I never touched a *ghauz*[1] of it.

'I accompanied the Dervish Bideen into various countries, where we practised our art: sometimes we were adored as saints, and at others stoned for vagrants. Our journeys being performed on foot, I had good opportunities to see every place in detail. We travelled from Tehran to Constantinople, and from that capital to Grand Cairo, through Aleppo and Damascus. From Cairo we showed ourselves at Mecca and Medina; and taking ship at Jedda, landed at Surat, in the Guzerat, whence we walked to Lahore and Cashmire.

'At this last place, the dervish, according to custom, endeavoured to deceive the natives; but they were too enlightened for us, and we were obliged to steal away in disgrace; and we at length fixed ourselves at Herat, where we were repaid for our former want of success by the credu-

---

[1] A *ghauz* is a small copper coin.

lity of the Affghans, who were good enough to admit all that we chose to tell them. But here, as the dervish was getting up a plan to appear as a prophet, and when our machinery for performing miracles was nearly completed, he, who had promised eternal youth to thousands, at length paid the debt of nature himself. He had shut himself up in a small hut, situated at the top of a mountain near Herat, where we made the good people believe he was living upon no other food than that which the *Gins* and *Peris* brought to him; but unfortunately he actually died of a surfeit, having ate more of a roast lamb and sweetmeats than his nature could support. For my own credit, I was obliged to say, that the Gins, jealous of us mortals for possessing the society of so wonderful a person, had so inflated him with celestial food, that, leaving no room for his soul, it had been completely blown out of his body, and carried away into the fifth heaven by a strong north-east wind, which was blowing at the time. This wind, which lasts for 120 days during the summer months, and without which the inhabitants would almost die with heat, I endeavoured to make them believe was a miracle performed by the dervish in their favour, as a parting legacy to them and their descendants for ever. The old men, indeed, who recollected the wind ever since their youth, were incredulous; but their testimony bore but little weight, compared to the influence which we had acquired. He was buried with the greatest honours; and the prince of Herat himself, *Eshek Mirza*, lent his shoulder to bear his coffin to the grave. A mausoleum was erected over it by some of the most pious of the Affghans, and it has ever since been a place of pilgrimage from all the country round.

'I remained at Herat for some time after the death of my companion, in order to enjoy the advantages which might accrue to me from being the friend and disciple of one of such high reputation, and I did not repent of my resolution. I disposed of my spells at great prices, and moreover made a considerable sum by selling the combings of my deceased friend's beard, and the cuttings of his nails, which I assured my purchasers had been carefully preserved during the time of his retirement in the mountains; although in fact they were chiefly collected from my own person. When I had sold of these relics enough to make several respectable beards, and a proportionate quantity of nails, I felt that if I persisted in the traffic, notwithstanding the inordinate credulity of the Affghans, I might be discovered for a cheat, therefore I took my departure, and, having travelled into

various parts of Persia, I at length fixed myself among the Hezareh, a
large tribe, living for the most part in tents, and which occupy the open
country between Caboul and Candahar. My success among them was
something quite beyond my expectation, for I put into practice what the
Dervish Bideen had planned at Herat, and actually appeared in the character of a prophet.'

The Dervish Sefer then, laying his hand upon the shoulder of the dervish who sat next to him, said, 'My friend, here, was my accomplice on
that occasion, and he will remember how ingeniously we managed to make
the Hezareh believe that we possessed a cauldron which was always full of
boiled rice—a miracle which even the most incredulous did not fail to believe, as long as they got their share of it. In short, I am the celebrated
Hazret Ishan himself; he of whom you have lately heard so much in Khorassan;
and although my sacred character was not proof against the attacks made
upon it by the arms of the Shah, yet, while it lasted, I collected enough
from the zeal and credulity of my disciples to enable me to pass the remainder of my life in comfort. I have lived at Meshed for some time; and
it is but a week ago that we contrived to perform the miracle of giving
sight to a blind girl; so now are held in the highest veneration.'

Here the Dervish Sefer ended his history, and then called upon his
next neighbour to give an account of himself.

This was the dervish who had been his accomplice among the Hezareh,
and he began as follows:

'My father was a celebrated man of the law, of the city of Kom, enjoying the reputation of saying his prayers, making his ablutions, and keeping his fasts more regularly than any man in Persia; in short, he was the

cream of Shîahs, and the model of Mussulmans. He had many sons, and we were brought up in the strictest practice of the external parts of our religion. The rigour and severity with which we were treated were combated on our part by cunning and dissimulation. These qualities gradually fixed themselves in our character; and without any consideration for our circumstances, we were early branded as a nest of hypocrites, and as the greatest cheats and liars of our birth-place. I, in particular, was so notorious that in my own defence I became a dervish, and I owe the reputation which I have acquired in that calling to the following fortunate circumstance.

'I had scarcely arrived at Tehran, and had taken up my quarters opposite to a druggist's shop, when I was called up in a great hurry by an old woman, who informed me that her master, the druggist, had just been taken exceedingly ill, after having eaten more than usual; that the medicine which he had taken had not performed its office; and that his family wished to try what a talisman would do for him: she therefore invited me to write one suited to his case. As I had neither paper, pens, nor ink, I insisted upon going into his *anderûn*, or woman's apartments, and writing it there, to which she consented. I was introduced into a small square yard, and then into a room, where I found the sick man extended on his bed on the ground, surrounded by as many women as the place could hold, who cried aloud, and exclaimed, "*Wahi, wahi*, in the name of God he dies, he dies!" The implements of medicine were spread about, which showed that everything had been done either to kill or save him. A large basin, which had contained the prescription, was seen on the shelf; the long glass tube, that instrument of torture, was in a corner; and among other furniture, the

doctor himself was seen seated, unconcernedly enjoying his pipe, and who, having found that human means were inefficient, had had recourse to supernatural, and had prescribed, as a last resource, the talisman, which it was my fate to write. A new dervish excited new hopes, for I saw that I produced much stir as I entered the sick room, I asked for paper with an air of authority, as if I felt great confidence in my own powers, (although, in fact, I had never written a talisman before), and a large piece was produced, which seemed to have been the wrapper to some drug or other. Pen and ink were also given me; and then calling up all my gravity, I scrawled the paper over in a variety of odd characters, which here and there contained the names of Allah, Mohamed, Ali, Hassan, and Hossein, and all the Imâms, placing them in different anagrams, and substituting here and there figures instead of letters. I then handed it over with great ceremony to the doctor, who, calling for water and a basin, washed the whole from off the paper into the basin, whilst the bystanders offered up prayers for the efficacy of the precious writing. The doctor then said, "In the name of the prophet, let the patient take this; and if fate hath decreed that he is to live, then the sacred names which he will now swallow will restore him: but if not, neither my skill, nor that of any other man, can ever be of the least avail."

'The draught was administered, and every eye was immediately fixed upon the wretched man's face, as if a resuscitation was expected to ensue. He remained for some time without showing any symptom of life; when, to the astonishment of all, not excepting myself and the doctor, he groaned, opened his eyes, raised his head on his arm, then called for a basin, and at length vomited in a manner that would have done credit to the prescription of Abu Avicenna himself. In short, he recovered.

'In my own mind, I immediately attributed the happy change to the drug which had once been wrapped in the paper, and which, with the nausea of the ink, had produced the effect just described; but I took care to let the bystanders know that the cure was entirely owing to the interference and to the handwriting of one of my sanctity; and that but for me he would have died.

'The doctor, on the other hand, took all the merit of the case to himself; for as soon as his patient had opened his eyes, he exclaimed, "Did I not tell you so?" and in proportion as the draught operated, he went on

I became anxious to know more of these extraordinary men

exulting thus: "There, there, see the efficacy of my prescription! Had it not been for me, you would have seen the druggist dead before you."

'I, however, would not allow him to proceed, and said: "If you are a doctor, why did you not cure your patient without calling for me? Keep to your blisters and to your bleedings, and do not interfere with that which doth not belong to you."

'He answered, "Mr. Dervish, I make no doubt that you can write a very good talisman, and also can get a very good price for it; but every one knows who and what dervishes are; and if their talismans are ever of use, it is not their sanctity which makes them so."

'"Whose dog are you," exclaimed I, in return, "to talk to me after this manner? I, who am a servant of the prophet. As for you doctors, your ignorance is proverbial: you hide it by laying all to fate: if by chance your patient recovers, then you take all the credit of the cure to yourselves; should he die, you say, God hath decreed thus; what can the efforts of man avail? Go to, go to; when you have nearly killed your next patient, and then know not what more to ordain, send for me again, and I will cover your impudent ignorance by curing him as I have just done the druggist."

'"By my head, and by your death," returned the doctor, "I am not a man to hear this from any one, much less from a dog of a dervish:" and immediately he got up and approached me in a threatening attitude, making use of every epithet of abuse that he could think of.

'I received him with suitable expressions of contempt, and we very soon came to blows; he so effectually fastened upon my hair, and I upon his beard, that we plucked out whole handfuls from each other: we bit and spat, and fought with such fury, heedless of the sick man and the cries of the women, that the uproar became very great, and perhaps would have terminated in something serious, if one of the women had not run in to us, in great agitation, assuring us that the *Darogah's* officers (police men) were then knocking at the door of the house, and inquiring whence proceeded all the disturbance.

'This parted us; and then I was happy to find that the bystanders were in my favour, for they expressed their contempt of the skill of the physician, whose only object was to obtain money without doing his patients any good, whilst they looked upon me in the light of a divine person, who in handwriting alone possessed the power of curing all manner of disease.

'The doctor, seeing how ill matters were going for him, stole away with the best face he could; but before he left the room, he stooped down, and collecting as many of the hairs of his beard, which I had plucked from him, as he could find, to which he cunningly added some of my own hair, he brandished them in my face, saying, "We shall see on whose side the laugh will be when you are brought before the Cadi to-morrow; for beards are worth a ducat[1] per hair in Tehran, and I doubt, with all your talismans, whether you can buy these that I hold in my hand."

'It was evident, that when his anger was cooled, out of regard to his own reputation, he would not put his threat into execution; so the fear of being dragged before the justice gave me no uneasiness, and I therefore only considered how to make the most of the fortunate circumstance which had just taken place. The report that the druggist (who was the first in Tehran) had been brought to life, when on the point of death, by a newly arrived dervish, was soon spread about, and I became the object of general concern. From morning to night I was taken up in writing talismans, for which I made my customers pay according to their means, and in a short time I found myself the possessor of some hundreds of piastres. But unfortunately for me, I did not meet with a dying druggist and a piece of his paper every day; and feeling myself reduced to live upon the reputation of this one miracle, which I perceived to my sorrow daily diminished, I made a virtue of necessity, and determining to make the tour of Persia, I immediately left Tehran. To whichsoever city I bent my steps, I managed matters so adroitly, that I made my reputation precede my arrival there. The druggist had given me an attestation under his seal, that he had been restored to life by virtue of a talisman written by my hand, and this I exhibited wherever I went, to corroborate the truth of the reports which had been circulated in my favour. I am now living upon this reputation: it supports me very tolerably for the present, but whenever I find that it begins to fail, I shall proceed elsewhere.'—The dervish here ended his history.

When the third dervish came to his turn to speak, he said: 'My tale is but short, although story-telling is my profession. I am the son of a schoolmaster, who, perceiving that I was endowed with a very retentive memory, made me read and repeat to him most of the histories with which our

---

[1] A beard is held so sacred in the East, that every hair which grows upon a Mohamedan's chin is protected from molestation by a heavy fine.

language abounds; and when he found that he had furnished my mind with a sufficient assortment, he turned me out into the world under the garb of dervish, to relate them in public to such audiences as my talents might gather round me.

'My first essays were anything but successful. My auditors heard my stories, and then walked away without leaving me any reward for my pains. Little by little I acquired experience. Instead of being carried away, as I had at first permitted myself to be, by the interest of the story, I made a pause when the catastrophe drew near, and then, looking around me, said, "All ye that are present, if you will be liberal towards me, I will tell you what follows;" and I seldom failed in collecting a good handful of copper coin. For instance, in the story of the Prince of Khatai and the Princess of Samarcand, when the Ogre *Hezar Mun* seizes the prince, and is about to devour him; when he is suspended in the ogre's mouth, between his upper and lower jaw; when the princess, all dishevelled and forlorn, is on her knees praying that he may be spared; when the attendants couch their lances, and are in dismay; when the horses start back in fright; when the thunder rolls, and the ogre growls; then I stop, and say, "Now, my noble hearers, open your purses, and you shall hear in how miraculous a manner the Prince of Khatai cut the ogre's head off!" By such arts, I manage to extract a subsistence from the curiosity of men; and when my stock of stories is exhausted in one place, I leave it, travel to another, and there renew my labours.'

CHAPTER XII: HAJJI BABA FINDS THAT FRAUD DOES NOT REMAIN UNPUNISHED, EVEN IN THIS WORLD HE MAKES FRESH PLANS

THE dervishes having finished their narratives, I thanked them for the entertainment and instruction which they had afforded me, and I forthwith resolved to learn as much from them as possible, in order to become a dervish myself, in case I should be obliged to abandon my present business. Dervish Sefer instructed me in the numerous tricks which he practised, to impose himself upon the world as a person of great sanctity; I learned the art of writing talismans from the second; and the story-teller taught me some of the tales with which his head was stored, lent me his books, and gave me general rules how to lead on the curiosity of an audi-ence, until their money should insensibly be enticed from their pockets.

In the meanwhile, I continued to sell my tobacco and my pipes; but ow-ing to my intimacy with the dervishes, who smoked away all my profits, I was obliged to adulterate the tobacco of my other customers considerably more than usual; so that in fact they enjoyed little else than the fumes of dung, straw, and decayed leaves.

One evening, when it was dusk, and about the time of closing the ba-zaars, an old woman in rags, apparently bent double with age, stopped me, and requested me to dress a pipe for her to smoke. She was closely veiled, and scarcely uttered a word beyond her want. I filled her one of my very worst mixtures: she put it to her mouth; and at her spitting, coughing, and exclamations, half a dozen stout fellows, with long twigs in their hands, immediately came up, seized me, and threw me on my back. The supposed old woman then cast off her veil, and I beheld the *Mohtesib*[1] in person.

'At length, wretch of an *Ispahani!*' said he, 'I have caught you—you, that have so long been poisoning the people of Meshed with your abom-inable mixtures. You shall receive as many strokes on your feet as you have received *shahies*[2] for your pipes. Bring the *felek*,[3] said he, to his offi-cers, 'and lay on till his nails drop off.'

My feet were instantly inserted into the dreaded noose, and the blows fell upon them so thick, that I soon saw the images of ten thousand Mohte-sibs, intermixed with ten thousand old women, dancing before my eyes, apparently enjoying my torture, and laughing at my writhing and contor-tions. I implored the mercy of my tormentor by the souls of his father, mother, and grandfather—by his own head—by that of his child—and by that of his prince; by the Prophet—by Ali—and by all the Imâms. I cursed tobacco, I renounced smoking. I appealed to the feelings of the surround-ing spectators, to my friends the three dervishes, who stood there stirring neither limb nor muscle for me; in short, I bawled, cried, entreated, until I entirely lost all sensation and all recollection.

[1] The *Mohtesib* is an officer who perambulates the city, and examines weights and measures, and qualities of provisions.
[2] Twenty *shahies* make the *groust* or piastre, which is worth about two shillings British.
[3] The *felek* is a long pole, with a noose in the middle, through which the feet of him who is to be bastinadoed are passed, whilst its extremities are held up by two men, for the two others, who strike.

At length, when I came to myself, I found myself seated with my head against the wall on the side of the road, surrounded by a crowd gaping at my miserable situation. No one seemed to pity me. My pipes, my jug, and everything that I possessed, had been taken from me, and I was left to crawl to my home as well as I was able. Luckily it was not far off, and I reached it on my hands and knees, making the most piteous moans imaginable.

After I had remained a day in horrid torment, with my feet swelled into a misshapen mass of flesh and gore. I received a visit from one of the dervishes, who ventured to approach me, fearful, as he told me, of being taken up as my accomplice, in case he had come sooner to my help. He had, in his early career, undergone a similar beating himself, and, therefore, knew what remedies to apply to my limbs which, in a short time, restored them to their former state.

During my confinement, I had time to reflect upon my situation. I determined to leave Meshed, for I felt that I had entered it at an unlucky hour. Once my back had been sprained, and once I had been bastinadoed. I had managed to collect a small sum of money, which I kept carefully buried in a corner near my room; and with this I intended to make my way to Tehran by the very first caravan that should be on its departure. I communicated my plan to the dervishes, who applauded it; and, moreover, the Dervish Sefer offered to accompany me; 'for,' said he, 'I have been warned that the priesthood of Meshed are jealous of my increasing influence, and that they are laying a plot for my ruin; and, as it is impossible to withstand their power, I will try my fortunes elsewhere.'

It was agreed that I should put on the dress of a dervish; and having made my purchases, in the bazaar, of a cap, some beads, and a goat's skin, which I slung across my shoulder, I was ready to begin my journey at a moment's warning.

We became so impatient to depart, that we had almost made up our minds to set off without any other companions, and trust to our good fortune to find our road, and escape the dangers of it; but we determined to take a *fall*[1] out of Saadi, before we came to a resolution. Dervish Sefer, after making the usual prayer, opened the book, and read: 'It is contrary to reason, and to the advice of the wise, to take medicine without confidence, or to travel an unknown road without accompanying the caravan.' This extraordinary warning settled our minds, and we determined to be guided by it.

On making inquiries about the departure of caravans for Tehran, I was delighted to meet my friend Ali Kâtir, the muleteer, who had just arrived at Meshed, and was then making a bargain with a merchant, to convey merchandise, consisting of the lambs' skins of Bokhara, to the capital. As soon as he saw me, he uttered an exclamation of delight, and immediately lighted his *nargil*, or water pipe, which he invited me to smoke with him. I related all my adventures since we last parted, and he gave me an account of his. Having left Meshed with a caravan for Ispahan, with his mules loaded partly with bars of silver, and partly with lambs' skins; and having undergone great fears on account of the Turcomans—he reached his destination in safety. That city was still agitated with the recollections of the late attack of the caravanserai, of which I have given an account; and the general belief was, that the invaders had made their approach in a body, consisting of more than a thousand men; that they had been received with great bravery, and that one Kerbelai Hassan, a barber, had, with his own hand, wounded one of the chiefs so severely, that he had escaped with the greatest difficulty. I had always kept this part of my adventures secret from everybody; so I hid any emotion that might appear on my face from the muleteer, by puffing out a sufficient volume of smoke in his face.

From Ispahan he carried cotton stuffs, tobacco, and copper ware to Yezd, where he remained some time, until a caravan was collected for Meshed, when he loaded his mules with the manufactures of the former city. Ali Kâtir agreed that Dervish Sefer and I should return with him to Tehran, and that whenever we were tired with walking, he would willingly assist us, by permitting us to mount his mules.

[1] *Saadi*, *Hafiz*, and the *Koran*, are the three books to which the Persians most willingly refer for this mode of divination. It resembles that of the *Sortes Virgilianæ*.

CHAPTER XIII: HAJJI BABA LEAVES MESHED,

IS CURED OF HIS SPRAIN

AND RELATES A STORY WITH A MORAL

WHEN I had cleared the gate which leads out of Meshed to Tehran, I shook the collar of my coat, and exclaimed to myself: 'May Heaven send thee misfortunes!' for had I been heard by any one of the pilgrims, who were now on their return—it very probably would have gone ill with me. My companion, Dervish Sefer, whom I knew to be of my mind, entered into my feelings, and we both vented our spleen against the inhabitants of that place; I for the drubbings which had been inflicted upon me, he for the persecutions he had undergone from the Mollahs.

'As for you, my friend,' said he to me, 'you are young; you have much to suffer before you gain the experience necessary to carry you through life: do not repine at the first beating; it will probably save you many more, and will teach you another time to discover a *Mohtesib*, although hid under a woman's veil: but' (taking hold of his beard) 'for a man of my age, one who has seen so much of the world, to be obliged to set out upon his travels again, is truly a great misfortune.'

'But it would have been easy for you,' said I, 'to remain at Meshed, if you had chosen it: had you been regular in your prayers and ablutions, you might have bid defiance to the Mollahs.'

'That is true enough,' said the Dervish; 'but the fact is, that the festival of the Ramazan is now close at hand, when I should have been more closely watched than ever by them; and as I cannot and will not fast (smoking being as necessary to me as air, and wine as daily bread), I have thought it better to make a journey during that time, for the sake of the indulgence which is permitted to travellers. I might perhaps have deceived them, as I have frequently done before, by eating and smoking in secret; but one so notorious as I, who lives by the supposed sanctity of his character, being narrowly watched, cannot take such liberties.'

We arrived at Semnan without the occurrence of anything remarkable, excepting, that a day or two before we reached it, when I was helping my friend Ali Kâtir to load one of his mules, I sprained my back again in its old place: the pain was so great, that it became impossible for me to proceed with the caravan, and I determined to remain where I was until I was cured; particularly, as all danger from the Turcomans having passed, it was needless to make myself any longer a dependant upon a caravan. Dervish Sefer, who was anxious to get to the wine and pleasures of the capital, continued his journey.

I took up my abode in a tomb on the skirts of the town; and having spread my goat's skin in a corner of it, I proclaimed my arrival, according to the custom adopted by travelling dervishes, blowing my horn, and making my exclamations of *Hak*, *Hû*, *Allah Akbar*, in a most sonorous and audible manner. I had allowed my person to acquire a wild and extravagant appearance, and flattered myself that I did credit to the instructions which had been given me in the arts of deception.

I was visited by several women, for whom I wrote talismans, and they repaid me by small presents of fruit, milk, honey, and other trifles. My back became so painful, that I was obliged to inquire if no one at Semnan could afford me relief. The barber and the farrier were the only two supposed to possess any medical talents; the one skilled in bleeding, drawing teeth, and setting a limb; the other, from his knowledge in the diseases of horses, being often consulted in human ailments. There was also a *gis sefid*, or grey wig, an old woman of a hag-like and decrepit appearance, who was looked up to as an oracle in all cases where the knowledge of the barber and farrier was of no avail, and who had besides a great many nostrums and recipes for all sorts of aches. Each came to me in succession: all were agreed that my disorder proceeded from cold; and as fire was the hottest thing in opposition to cold that they knew of, they as unanimously agreed that the actual cautery should immediately be applied to the part; and the farrier, on account of his dealings in hot and cold iron, was appointed operator. He accordingly brought a pan of charcoal, a pair of bellows, and some small skewers; and seating himself in a corner, made his fire, and heated his skewers: when they were red hot, I was placed on the ground flat on my face, and then, with great solemnity, my back was seared with the burning iron, whilst all the bystanders, at every touch, exclaimed, with great earnestness, 'Khoda shefa mídehed,' God gives relief. My medical attendants, in their united wisdom, out of compliment to the prophet and the twelve Imâms, marked me in thirteen different places; and although, when I had endured half the operation, I began to cry out most lustily with the pain, still I was not let off until the whole was gone through. It was long before the wounds which they had inflicted were cured; and as they never would heal unless I was kept in perfect quiet, I confined myself to my cell for a considerable time; at the end of which, my sprain had entirely taken its leave, and strength was restored to my whole frame. Of course, my recovery was attributed to the thirteen worthies, who had presided over the operation, and all the town became more than ever persuaded of the efficacy of hot iron; but I could not but think that long repose had been my best doctor—an opinion which I took care to keep to myself; for I had no objection that the world should believe that I was a protégé of so many holy personages.

I now determined to pursue my journey to Tehran; but before I ventured to produce myself as a dervish upon that stage, I resolved to try my talent in relating a story before a Semnan audience. Accordingly, I went to a small open space, that is situated near the entrance of the bazaars, where most of the idlers of the town flock about noon; and making the sort of exclamations usual upon such occasions, I soon collected a crowd, who settled themselves on the ground, round the place which I had fixed upon for my theatre. A short story, touching a barber at Bagdad (which I had heard when I was myself in that profession), luckily came into my memory; and, standing in the middle of a circle of louts with uplifted eyes and open mouths, I made my debut in the following words:

'In the reign of the Caliph Haroun al-Rashid, of happy memory, lived in the city of Bagdad a celebrated barber, of the name of Ali Sakal. He was so famous for a steady hand, and dexterity in his profession, that he could shave a head, and trim a beard and whiskers, with his eyes blindfolded, without once drawing blood. There was not a man of any fashion at Bagdad who did not employ him; and such a run of business had he, that at length he became proud and insolent, and would scarcely ever touch a head, whose master was not at least a *Beg* or an *Aga*. Wood for fuel was always scarce and dear at Bagdad; and as his shop consumed a great deal, the wood-cutters brought their loads to him in preference, almost sure of meeting with a ready sale. It happened one day, that a poor wood-cutter, new in his profession, and ignorant of the character of Ali Sakal, went to his shop, and offered him for sale a load of wood which he had just brought from a considerable distance in the country, on his ass: Ali immediately offered him a price, making use of these words, *"for all the wood that was upon the ass."* The woodcutter agreed, unloaded his beast, and asked for the money. "You have not given me all the wood yet," said the barber; "I must have the pack-saddle (which is chiefly made of wood) into the bargain; that was our agreement." "How!" said the other, in great amazement—"who ever heard of such a bargain?—it is impossible." In short, after many words and much altercation, the overbearing barber seized the pack-saddle, wood and all, and sent away the poor peasant in great distress. He immediately ran to the Cadi, and stated his griefs: the Cadi was one of the barber's customers, and refused to hear the case. The wood-cutter applied to a higher judge: he also patronized Ali Sakal, and made light of the complaint. The poor man then appealed to the Mûfti himself; who, having pondered over the question, at length settled, that it was too difficult a case for him to decide, no provision being made for it in the Koran, and therefore he must put up with his loss. The wood-cutter was not disheartened; but forthwith got a scribe to write a petition to the Caliph himself, which he duly presented on Friday, the day when he went in state to the mosque. The Caliph's punctuality in reading petitions is well known, and it was not long before the wood-cutter was called to his presence. When he had approached the Caliph, he kneeled and kissed the ground, and then placing his arms straight before him, his hands covered with the sleeves of his cloak, and his feet close together, he awaited the decision of his case. "Friend," said the Caliph, "the barber has words on his side—you have equity on yours. The law must be defined by words, and agreements must be made by words: the former must have its course, or it is nothing; and agreements must be kept, or there would be no faith between man and man; therefore the barber must keep all his wood; but—" Then calling the wood-cutter close to him, the Caliph whispered something in his ear, which none but he could hear, and then sent him away quite satisfied.'

Here then I made a pause in my narrative, and said whilst I extended a small tin cup which I held in my hand), 'Now, my noble audience, if you will give me something I will tell you what the Caliph said to the wood-cutter.' I had excited great curiosity, and there was scarcely one of my hearers who did not give me a piece of money.

'Well then,' said I, 'the Caliph whispered to the wood-cutter what he was to do, in order to get satisfaction from the barber, and what that was I will now relate. The wood-cutter having made his obeisances, returned to his ass, which was tied without, took it by the halter, and proceeded to his home. A few days after, he applied to the barber, as if nothing had happened between them, requesting that he, and a companion of his from the country, might enjoy the dexterity of his hand; and the price at which both operations were to be performed was settled. When the wood-cutter's crown had been properly shorn, Ali Sakal asked where his companion was. "He is just standing without here," said the other, "and he shall come in presently." Accordingly he went out, and returned, leading his ass after him by the halter. "This is my companion," said he, "and you must shave him." "Shave him!" exclaimed the barber, in the greatest surprise; "it is enough that I have consented to demean myself by touching you, and do you insult me by asking me to do as much to your ass? Away with you, or I'll send you both to *Jehanum;*" and forthwith drove them out of his shop.

'The wood-cutter immediately went to the Caliph, was admitted to his presence, and related his case. "'Tis well," said the commander of the faithful: "bring Ali Sakal and his razors to me this instant," he exclaimed to one of his officers; and in the course of ten minutes the barber stood before him. "Why do you refuse to shave this man's companion?" said the Caliph to the barber: "Was not that your agreement?" Ali, kissing the ground, answered: "'Tis true, O Caliph, that such was our agreement; but who ever made a companion of an ass before? or who ever before thought of treating it like a true believer?" "You may say right," said the Caliph: "but, at the same time, who ever thought of insisting upon a pack-saddle being included in a load of wood? No, no, it is the wood-cutter's turn now. To the ass immediately, or you know the consequences." The barber was then obliged to prepare a great quantity of soap, to lather the beast from head to foot, and to shave him in the presence of the Caliph and of the whole court, whilst he was jeered and mocked by the taunts and laughing of all the bystanders. The poor wood-cutter was then dismissed with an appropriate present of money, and all Bagdad resounded with the story, and celebrated the justice of the commander of the faithful.'

CHAPTER XIV: OF THE MAN HE MEETS,
AND OF THE CONSEQUENCES OF THE ENCOUNTER

I LEFT Semnan with a light heart—my sprain was cured—I was young and handsome—twenty tomauns, my savings at Meshed, clinked in my purse—I had acquired some experience in the world; and I determined, as soon as I reached Tehran, to quit the garb of a dervish, to dress myself well from head to foot, and to endeavour to push my fortunes in some higher walk in life.

About a day's journey from Tehran, as I was walking onward, chanting, with all my throat, a song on the loves of *Leilah* and *Majnoun*, I was overtaken by a courier, who entered into conversation with me, and invited me to partake of some victuals which he had brought with him. The heat of the day being overpowering, I willingly accepted his invitation. We settled ourselves on the borders of a rivulet, near a cornfield, whilst the courier took off his horse's bridle, and permitted it to feed on the new wheat. He then groped up, from the deep folds of his riding trousers, a pocket handkerchief, in which were wrapped several lumps of cold boiled rice, and three or four flaps of bread, which he spread before us, and then added some sour curds, which he poured from a small bag that hung at his saddle-bow. From the same trousers, which contained his shoes, a provision of tobacco, a drinking cup, and many other useful articles, he drew

half a dozen raw onions, which he added to the feast; and we ate with such
appetite, that very soon we were reduced to the melancholy dessert of
sucking our fingers. We washed the whole down with some water from
the rivulet, and only then (such had been our voracity) we thought of
questioning each other concerning the object of our respective journeys.
From my dress, he perceived me to be a dervish, and my story was soon
told: as for himself, he was a courier belonging to the governor of Asterabad, and, to my joy and surprise, was carrying the happy intelligence of
the release of my former companion, Asker Khan, the Shah's poet, from
his captivity among the Turcomans. I did not let the courier know how
much I was interested in his errand, for experience had taught me how
wise it was, in the affairs of life to keep one's own counsel; and, therefore,
I pretended ignorance of even the existence of such a person.

My companion informed me
that the poet had managed to reach
Asterabad in safety, and that, being destitute of everything, he, in
the meanwhile, had been dispatched
to give intelligence of his situation to his family. He showed me
the letters with which he was entrusted, which he drew forth from
his breast, wrapped up in a handkerchief; and being a very inquisitive fellow, though unable to read,
he was happy to find in me one who
might give him some account of
their contents. The first which I
inspected was a memorial from the
poet to the King of Kings, in which
he set forth, in language the most
poetic, all the miseries and tortures

which he had endured since he had been thrown into the hands of the
Turcomans: that the hunger, the thirst, and the barbarous treatment which
he had experienced, were nothing, when compared with the privation of
the all-gracious and refulgent presence of that pearl of royalty, that gem

of magnificence, the quintessence of all earthly perfection, the great King of Kings! that as the vilest reptile that crawls is permitted to enjoy the warmth of the glorious sun, so he, the meanest of the king's subjects, hoped once more to bask in the sunshine of the royal countenance; and, finally, he humbly prayed, that his long absence might not deprive him of the shadow of the throne; that he might aspire to reoccupy his former post near his majesty's person, and once again be permitted to vie with the nightingale, and sing of the charms and perfections of his lovely rose.

The next letter was addressed to the prime vizier, in which that notorious minister, decrepit in person, and nefarious in conduct, was called a planet among the stars, and the sheet-anchor of the state, and in which the poet sues for his protection. There was nearly a similar one to his former enemy, the lord high treasurer. I then inspected the letters addressed to his family, of which one was to his wife, another to his son's tutor, and a third to his steward. To his wife, he talked of the interior arrangements of his *anderûn*; hoped that she had been economical in her dress, that she had kept the female slaves in good order, and desired her immediately to set herself and them about making clothes for him, as he was destitute of everything.

To the tutor, he enjoined great attention to his son's manners; hoped that he had been taught all the best forms of cant and compliment; that he never omitted to say his prayers; that he was by this time able to sit a horse, to perform the spear exercise, and to fire a gun on the full gallop.

To his steward, he gave some general instructions concerning the administration of his affairs—enjoined great economy;—that he should daily go and stand before the prime vizier; praise him to the skies; and make all sorts of professions, on his part, to his excellency; that he should keep a good watch upon his women and slaves; that his wife should not go too often to the bath; that when she and her slaves went abroad to take the air, he should accompany them. He hoped that no intriguing old women, particularly Jewesses, had been admitted into his harem; and that the walls, which surrounded the women's apartments, had always been kept in good repair, in order to prevent gadding on the housetop with the neighbours. He ordered that his black slave, Johur, was now no longer to be allowed free access into the *anderûn*; and if ever seen to be familiar with any of the female slaves, he and they were to be whipped: finally, he desired the steward to give the courier a handsome reward, for being the bearer of such good news to his family.

I folded up the letters again;—those which had been sealed, I again sealed,[1] and returned to the courier. He seemed to reckon a great deal upon the reward that he was to get for bringing the first intelligence of the poet's safety, and told me that, fearing some other might get the start of him, he had travelled day and night; and added, that the horse, which he now bestrode, belonged to a peasant, from whom he had taken it forcibly on the road, having left his own, which was knocked up, to be brought on after him.

After we had conversed a little more, he seemed entirely overpowered by fatigue, and fell into a profound sleep. As he lay extended on the grass, I looked upon him, and I began to reflect how easy it would be to forestall him. I knew the whole of the poet's history;—in fact, I was in some measure identified with it.—I began to think that I had a right to the first relation of it.—Then as to the horse, it was as much mine as his; particularly since the peasant, with his own, must now be close at hand:—so without more ceremony, I unfolded the handkerchief, which still lay in his lap, and taking out the letter to the steward, I mounted the horse: I applied the stirrups[2] to his sides; I galloped off; and in a very short time had left the sleeper far behind me, and had made considerable progress on the road to the capital.

As I rode along, I considered what was now my best line of conduct, and in what manner I should best introduce myself to the poet's family, so as to make my story good, and secure for myself the reward which had been destined for the courier. I calculated that I should have at least a good day's start of him; for when he awoke, he probably would be obliged to walk some distance before he got another horse, should he not regain his own, which was very doubtful; and appearing on foot as he did, it would be a hundred to one if anybody would believe his story, and he, most probably, would now be refused the loan of a beast to carry him on. I resolved,

[1] A Persian letter is folded up like a lady's thread paper, and fastened in the middle by a slip of adhesive paper, which is moistened with the tongue, and then stamped with the seal of the writer. Thus, letters are frequently opened and reclosed without detection.
[2] The stirrup, which is a sort of iron shovel, sharp at the edge, in Persia as well as in Turkey, is used by way of spur.

therefore, immediately upon reaching Tehran, to sell the horse, and its accoutrements, for what they would fetch; I would then exchange my dervish's dress for the common dress of the country; and making myself up as
one come from off a long journey, present myself at the gate of the poet's
house, and there make the best story I could, which would be a sufficiently
easy matter, considering how well I was acquainted with every circumstance relating to him.

CHAPTER XV: HAJJI BABA REACHES TEHRAN,
AND GOES TO THE POET'S HOUSE

I ENTERED Tehran early in the morning by the *Shah Abdul Azîm*
gate, just as it was opened, and immediately exhibited my horse for
sale at the market, which is daily held there, for that purpose. I had proved
it to be a good beast, from the rate at which I had travelled since taking my
hasty leave of the courier; but a horse-dealer, to whom I showed it, made
out so clearly that it was full of defects, that I thought myself in luck, if I
got anything at all for it. It was *chup*[1]—it had the *ableh*—it was old, and its
teeth had been burnt;—in short, it seemed to have every quality that a
horse ought not to have. I was therefore surprised when he offered me five
tomauns for it, provided I threw him the bridle and saddle into the bargain; and he seemed as surprised when I took him at his word, and accepted of his offer. He paid me down one half of the money, and then of-

[1] The Persians have a particular aversion to horses which have white legs on one side,
which they call *chup*; and they also very much undervalue a horse that has the *ableh*,
which consists of white leprous marks on its nose, round the eyes, and under the tail.

fered me a half-starved ass in payment of the remainder; but this I refused, and he promised to pay me in full when we met again. I was too much in haste to continue bargaining any longer; so going straightway to the bazaar, I bought a black cap, laid by my dervish's tiara, and having equipped myself in a manner to be taken for one come from off a journey, I inquired my way to the house of the poet.

It was situated in a pleasant quarter of the town, surrounded by gardens filled with poplars and pomegranate trees, and in a street through which ran a stream of water, bordered by beautiful *chenars*.[1] But the house itself seemed indeed to speak the absence of its master: the gate was half closed; there was no stir about it; and when I entered the first court, I could perceive but few indications of an inhabitant. This looked ill for my promised reward. At length, making my way to the upper room, that was situated over the gate, I there saw a man of about fifty years old, seated on a felt carpet, smoking his *kaliân*, whom I found to be the very person I was in search of, viz. the *Nazir* or steward.

I immediately exclaimed, 'Good news! the khan is coming.'

'*Yani cheh?* what do you mean?' said he; 'which khan? where? when?'

When I had explained myself, and had presented the letter addressed to him, he seemed to be thrown into a mixed state of feigned joy and real sorrow, amazement, and apprehension.

'But are you very sure,' said he, 'that the khan is alive?'

'Very sure,' returned I; 'and before to-morrow is over, you will receive another courier, who will give you many more particulars of his safety, and who will bring letters to the king, viziers, and others.'

He then began to make all sorts of incoherent exclamations; 'This is a wonderful business! What dust has fallen upon our heads!—Where shall I go?—What shall I do?'

When he had a little recovered himself, I endeavoured to persuade him to give me an explanation of his emotions on this occasion, and tell me why he felt so agitated, and apparently distressed, at what ought only to be a matter of joy. All I could hear from him was, 'He must be dead; everybody says he is dead; his wife dreamt that she had lost her largest tooth, the one that gave her such aching pain, and therefore he is dead; besides the king has settled it so. He cannot be alive; he must not be alive.'

[1] The *chenar* tree is a species of sycamore.

'Well,' said I, 'if he is dead, be it so; all I can say is, that he was one of the true believers at Asterabad, not six days ago; and that he will soon prove in person, by showing himself at Tehran, in the course of another week.'

After the Nazir had sat, and wondered, and ruminated for some time, he said, 'You will not be surprised at my perplexity when I tell you of the state of things here, in consequence of the report of my master's death. In the first place, the Shah has seized all his property: his house, furniture, and live stock, including his Georgian slaves, are to be given to Khur Ali Mirza, one of the king's younger sons: his village now belongs to the prime vizier: his place is about to be bestowed upon Mirza Fûzûl; and, to crown all, his wife has married his son's tutor. Say, then, whether or no I have not a right to be astonished and perplexed?'

I agreed that there was no disputing his right; 'but, in the meanwhile,' said I, 'what becomes of my reward?'

'O, as for that,' answered the Nazir, 'you cannot expect anything from me; for you have brought me no joyful tidings: you may claim it from my master, when he comes, if you choose, but I can give you nothing.'

Upon which, promising to return on some future day, I left the Nazir to his own reflections, and quitted the house.

CHAPTER XVI: HE MAKES PLANS FOR THE FUTURE, AND IS INVOLVED IN A QUARREL

I DETERMINED to wait the arrival of the poet, and through his inter-ference to endeavour to get into some situation, where I might gain my bread honestly, and acquire a chance of advancing myself in life, without having recourse to the tricks and frauds which I had hitherto practised: for I was tired of herding with the low and the vulgar; and I saw so many instances before me of men rising in the world, and acquiring both riches and honour, who had sprung from an origin quite as obscure as my own, that I already anticipated my elevation, and even settled in my own mind how I should act when I was a prime vizier.

'Who,' said I to myself, 'was the Shah's chief favourite, Ismael Beg *tellai*, or the golden, but a *ferash*, or a tent pitcher? He is neither hand-somer nor better spoken than I; and if ever there should be an opportunity of comparing our horsemanship, I think one who has been brought up amongst the Turcomans would show him what riding is, in spite of his reputation. Well; and the famous lord high treasurer, who fills the king's coffers with gold, and who does not forget his own—who and what was he? A barber's son is quite as good as a greengrocer's, and, in our respective cases, a great deal better too; for I can read and write, whereas his excellency, as report says, can do neither. He eats and drinks what he likes; he puts on a new coat every day; and after the Shah, has the choice of all the beauties of Persia; and all this without half my sense, or half my abilities: for to hear the world talk, one must believe him to be little better than a *khûr be teshdeed*, i. e. a doubly accented ass.'

I continued wrapt up in these sort of meditations, seated with my back against the wall of one of the crowded avenues which lead to the gate of the royal palace, and had so worked up my imagination by the prospect of my future greatness, that on rising to walk away, I instinctively pushed the crowd from before me, as if such respect from them was due to one of my lofty pretensions. Some stared at me, some abused me, and others took me for a madman; and indeed when I came to myself, and looked at my tattered clothes and my beggarly appearance, I could not help smiling at their surprise, and at my folly; and straightway went into the cloth bazaar in the determination of fitting myself out in decent apparel, as the first step towards my change of life.

Making my way through the crowd, I was stopped by a violent quarrel between three men, who were abusing each other with more than ordinary violence. I pushed into the circle which surrounded them, and there, to my

dismay, discovered the courier, whom I had deceived, seconded by a peasant, attacking the horsedealer, whom they had just pulled off the horse,
which I had sold him.

'That is my horse,' said the peasant.

'That is my saddle,' said the courier.

'They are mine,' exclaimed the horse-dealer.

I immediately saw the danger in which I stood, and was about to slink
away, when I was perceived by the horse-dealer, who seized hold of my
girdle, and said, 'This is the man I bought the horse of.' As soon as I was
recognized by the courier, immediately the whole brunt of the quarrel,
like a thunder-cloud, burst on my head, and I was almost overwhelmed by
its violence. Rascal, thief, cheat, were epithets which were dinned into my
ears without mercy.

'Where's my horse?' cried one.—'Give me my saddle,' vociferated the
other.—'Return me my money,' roared
out a third.—'Take him to the cadi,'
said the crowd.

In vain I bawled, swore, and bade defiance; in vain I was all smooth-
ness and conciliation: it was impossible for the first ten minutes to gain a
hearing: every one recited his griefs. The courier's rage was almost un-
governable; the peasant complained of the injustice which had been done
him; and the horse-dealer called me every sort of name, for having robbed
him of his money. I first talked to the one, then coaxed the other, and endeavoured to bully the third. To the courier I said, 'Why are you so angry?
there is your saddle safe and sound, you can ask no more.' To the peasant
I exclaimed, 'You could not say more if your beast had actually been

killed; take him and walk away, and return thanks to Allah that it is no worse.' As for the horse-dealer, I inveighed against him with all the bitterness of a man who had been cheated of his property: 'You have a right to talk indeed of having been deceived, when to this moment you know that you have only paid me one-half of the cost of the horse, and that you wanted to fob me off with a dying ass for the other half.'

I offered to return him the money; but this he refused: he insisted upon my paying him the keep of the horse besides: upon which a new quarrel ensued, in which arguments were used on both sides which convinced neither party, and consequently we immediately adjourned to the *daroga* or police magistrate, who, we agreed, should decide the question.

We found him at his post, at the cross streets in the bazaar, surrounded by his officers, who, with their long sticks, were in readiness to inflict the bastinado on the first offender. I opened the case, and stated all the circumstances of it; insisting very strongly on the evident intention to cheat me, which the horse-dealer had exhibited. The horse-dealer answered me, and showed that as the horse did not belong to him, it being stolen from another, he had no right to pay for its keep.

The question puzzled the daroga so much, that he declined interfering, and was about ordering us to the tribunal of the cadi, when a decrepit old man, a bystander, said, 'Why do you make so much difficulty about a plain question?—when the horse-dealer shall have paid the Hajjî the remaining half of the price of the horse, then the Hajjî shall pay for the keep of the beast, as long as it was in the horse-dealer's possession.'

Every one cried *Barîk Allah! Barîk Allah!* Praise be to God! and right or wrong, they all appeared so struck by the specious justice of the decision, that the daroga dismissed us, and told us to depart in peace.

I did not lose a moment in repaying to the horse-dealer the purchase-money of the horse, and in getting from him a receipt in full: it was only after he had settled with me that he began to ponder over the merits of the decision, and seemed extremely puzzled to discover why, if he was entitled to the horse's keep at all, he was not entitled to it, whether he had paid me half or the whole of the money? He seemed to think, that he for once had been duped; and very luckily his rage was averted from me to the daroga, who he very freely accused of being a puzzle-headed fool, and one who had no more pretension to law than *he* had to honesty.

CHAPTER XVII: HE PUTS ON NEW CLOTHES,
GOES TO THE BATH AND APPEARS IN A NEW CHARACTER

I NOW looked upon myself as clear of this unpleasant business, which I had entirely brought on my own head, and congratulated myself that I had got off at so cheap a rate. I again made my way to the cloth bazaar, and going to the first shop near the gate of it, I inquired the price of red cloth, of which it was my ambition to make a *barûni*, or cloak; because I thought that it would transfer to me that respect which I always felt for those who wore it. The shopkeeper, upon looking at me from head to foot, said 'A *barûni* indeed! and for whom do you want it, and who is to pay for it?'

'For myself, to be sure,' answered I.

'And what does such a poor devil as you want with such a coat? Mirzas and Khans only wear them, and I am sure you are no such personage.'

I was about to answer in great wrath, when a *dalal* or broker went by, loaded with all sorts of second-hand clothes, which he was hawking about for sale, and to him I immediately made application, in spite of the reiterated calls of the shopkeeper, who now too late repented of having driven me off in so hasty a manner. We retreated to a corner in the gateway of the adjacent mosque, and there the dalal, putting his load down, spread his merchandise before me. I was struck by a fine shot silk vest, trimmed in front with gold lace and gold buttons, of which I asked the price. The dalal extolled its beauty and my taste; swore that it had belonged to one of the king's favourite Georgians, who had only worn it twice, and having made me try it on, walked around and around me, exclaiming all the while '*Mashallah, Mashallah!*' Praise be to God! I was so pleased with this, that I must needs have a shawl for my waist to match, and he produced an old Cashmerian shawl full of holes and darns, which he assured me had belonged to one of the ladies in the king's harem, and which, he said, he would let me have at a reasonable price. My vanity made me prefer this commodity to a new *Kermân* shawl, which I might have had for what I was about to pay for the old worn-out Cashmere, and adjusting it so as to hide the defects, I wound it about my waist, which only wanted a dagger stuck into it, to make my dress complete. With this the dalal also supplied me, and when I was thus equipped I could not resist expressing my satisfaction to the broker, who was not backward in assuring me, that there was not a handsomer nor better-dressed man in Tehran.

When we came to settle our accounts, the business wore a more serious aspect. The dalal began by assuring me of his honesty, that he was not like other dalals, who asked a hundred and then took fifty, and that when he said a thing, I might depend upon its veracity. He then asked me five tomauns for the coat, fifteen for the shawl, and four for the dagger, making altogether twenty-four tomauns.

Upon hearing this, my delight subsided, for I had barely twenty tomauns in my pocket, and I was about stripping myself of my finery, and returning again to my old clothes, when the dalal stopped me, and said, 'You may perhaps think that price a little too much, but, by my head and by your soul, I bought them for that—tell me what you will give?' I answered, that it was out of the question dealing with him upon such high terms, but that if he would give them to me for five tomauns I would be a purchaser. This he rejected with disdain, upon which I stripped, and returned him his property. When he had collected his things again, and apparently when all dealings between us were at an end, he said, 'I feel a friendship for you, and I will do for you, what I would not do for my brother—you shall have them for ten tomauns.' I again refused, and we stood higgling, until we agreed that I should pay him six, and one by way of a dress for himself. This was no sooner said than done.

He then left me, and I packed up my bargain, with the intention of first going to the bath, and there equipping myself. On my road, I bought a pair of high-heeled green slippers, a blue silk shirt, and a pair of crimson silk trousers, and having tied up the whole in my handkerchief, I proceeded to the bath.

No one took notice of me as I entered, for one of my mean appearance could create no sensation, and I comforted myself by the reflection, that the case would be changed as soon as I should put on my new clothes. I deposited my bundle in a corner, where I also undressed, and having wrapt myself round with a towel, I entered the bath.

Here all ranks were on a level, in appearance at least, and I now flattered myself that my fine form, my broad chest, and narrow waist, would make me an object of admiration. I called to one of the *dalâks* (bathing men) to wait upon me, and to go through the different operations of rubbing with the hand, and of the friction with the hair bag, and I also ordered him to shave my head, to get ready the necessary materials for dying my beard, moustaches, and curls, as well as my hands and the soles of my feet, and also to prepare the depilatory; in short, I announced my intention of undergoing a complete lustration.

The dalâk, as soon as he began rubbing me, expressed his admiration at my broad chest by his repeated exclamations; and bearing in mind the influence which new clothes were likely to create, I behaved like one who had been accustomed to this sort of praise and attention. He said that I could not have come at a luckier hour, for that he had just operated upon a Khan, who having received a dress of honour from the Shah, upon the occasion of bringing the first melons from Ispahan, had been sent to the bath by the astrologers at this particular time, as the most fortunate for putting on a new dress.

As soon as all was over, the dalâk brought me some dry linen, and conducted me to the spot where I had left my clothes. With what pleasure I opened my bundle and inspected my finery! It appeared that I was renovated in proportion as I put on each article of dress. I had never yet been clothed in silk. I tied on my trousers with the air of a man of fashion, and when I heard the rustling of my vest, I turned about in exultation to see who might be looking at me. My shawl was wound about me in the newest style, rather falling in front, and spread out large behind, and when the dagger glittered in my girdle, I conceived that nothing could exceed the finish of my whole adjustment. I indented the top of my cap in the true *Kajari* or royal style, and placed it on my head considerably on one side. When the bathing man at length brought me the looking-glass, as a signal for paying the bath, I detained him for the purpose of surveying myself, arranging my curls to twist up behind the ear, and pulling my moustaches up towards my eyes. I then paid him handsomely, and leaving my old clothes under his charge, I made my exit with the strut of a man of consequence.

CHAPTER XVIII: THE POET RETURNS FROM CAPTIVITY. THE CONSEQUENCES OF IT FOR HAJJI BABA

I TOOK my road towards the poet's house, in the hope of gaining some intelligence about him. From the head of the street, I perceived a crowd surrounding the gate, and I was soon informed that he had just arrived, and had gone through the ceremony of making his entrance over the roof instead of through the door; for such is the custom when a man who has been thought dead returns home alive.

I immediately pushed through the crowd, made my way into the room where the poet was seated, and with every demonstration of great joy, congratulated him upon his safe arrival. He did not recognize me, and even when I had explained who I was, he could scarcely believe that one so trim and smart as I then was could be the same dirty ragged ruffian whom he had known before.

The apartment was filled with all sorts of people, some happy at his return, others full of disappointment. Among the latter, and those who paid him the finest compliments, was Mirza Fûzûl, the man who had been nominated to succeed him in his situation, and who did not cease exclaiming, 'Your place has been empty, and our eyes are enlightened,' as long as he remained in the room. At length, a great bustle was heard, the doors were opened, and an officer from the king was announced, who commanded the poet forthwith to repair to the presence, which he did in the very clothes, boots, dust and all, in which he had travelled.

The party then broke up, and I left the house in the determination of returning the next day; but as I was going out of the yard, I met the Nazir, with whom I had had a conversation as before related. He did not appear to me to be among the happy ones. 'In the name of Allah,' said I, 'you see that my words have proved true: the Khan is alive!' 'True enough,' answered he, with a sigh; 'he is alive; and may his life be a long one! but God is great!' and then making two or three more similar exclamations, he left me, apparently full of care and misery.

I passed the remainder of the day in strolling about, and building castles in the air. I walked through the bazaars, went to the mosques, and lounged among the idlers, who are always to be found in great numbers about the gate of the royal palace. Here, the news of the day was the poet's return, and the reception which he had met with from the Shah. Some said, that his majesty, upon hearing of his arrival had ordained that it could not be; that he was dead, and must be so. Others, that, on the contrary, the king was happy at the intelligence, and had ordered ten tomauns to be given to the bearer of it. The truth, however, was this; the king had been disappointed at the poet's resurrection, because it destroyed the arrangements he had made with respect to his house and effects, and he was not disposed to give him a good reception; but Asker who well knew his majesty's passion for poetry, and particularly of that kind which sings the royal praises, had long since foreseen the event, and had provided himself with an impromptu, which he had composed even when he was living an exile among the Turcomans. This he repeated at the proper moment; and thus the tide of the king's favour, which was running full against him, he entirely turned, and made it flow to his advantage. In short, he had his mouth filled with gold for his pains, was invested with a magnificent dress, and was reinstated in his situation and his possessions.

I lost no time in again congratulating my adopted patron, and did not miss a single morning in attending his levee. Finding that he was favourably inclined towards me, I made known to him my situation, and entreated him either to give me a place in his household, or to recommend me as a servant to one of his acquaintance. I had found out that the Nazir's despondency at his master's return proceeded from the fear of being detected in certain frauds which he had committed on his property; and, as I hoped that I might eventually succeed to his situation, I expressed the greatest zeal for the poet's interest, and disclosed all that I knew concerning the delinquency of his servant. However, I did not succeed; for whether he had a clearer insight into characters than I gave him credit for, or whether the Nazir managed to prove his innocence, and make me suspected, I know not; but the fact was, that he kept his place, and I continued to be an attendant at the levees.

At length, one morning Asker called me to him, and said, 'Hajjî, my friend, you know how thankful I have always expressed myself for your kindness to me when we were prisoners together in the hands of the Turcomans, and now I will prove my gratitude. I have recommended you strongly to Mirza Akmak, the king's *Hakîm Bashi*, or chief physician, who is in want of a servant; and I make no doubt, that if you give him satisfaction, he will teach you his art, and put you in the way of making your fortune. You have only to present yourself before him, saying that you come from me, and he will immediately assign you an employment.'

I had no turn for the practice of physic, and recollecting the story which had been related to me by the dervish, I held the profession in contempt: but my case was desperate; I had spent my last *dînar*, and therefore I had nothing left me but to accept of the doctor's place. Accordingly, the next morning I proceeded to his house, which was situated in the neighbourhood of the palace; and as I entered a dull, neglected court-yard, I there found several sick persons, some squatted against the wall, others supported by their friends, and others again with bottles in their hands, waiting the moment when the physician should leave the women's apartments to transact business in public. I proceeded to an open window, where those who were not privileged to enter the room stood, and there I took my station until I should be called in. Within the room were several persons who came to pay their court to the doctor (for every man who is an officer of the court has his levee), and from remarking them, I learnt how necessary it was, in order to advance in life, to make much of everything, even the dog or the cat, if they came in my way, of him who can have access to the ear of men in power. I made my reflections upon the miseries I had already undergone, and was calculating how long it would take me to go through a course of cringing and flattery to be entitled to the same sorts of attention myself, when I perceived, by the bows of those near me, that the doctor had seated himself at the window, and that the business of the day had commenced.

The Hakîm was an old man, with an eye sunk deep in his head, high
cheek bones, and a scanty beard. He had a considerable bend in his back,
and his usual attitude, when seated, was that of a projecting chin, his head
reclining back between his shoulders, and his hands resting on his girdle,
whilst his elbows formed two triangles on each side of his body. He made
short snappish questions, gave little hums at the answers, and seemed to
be thinking of anything but the subject before him. When he heard the account of the ailments of those who had come to consult him, and had said
a few words to his little circle of parasites, he looked at me, and after I had
told him that I was the person of whom the poet had spoken, he fixed his
little sharp eyes upon me for a second or two, and then desired me to wait,
for that he wished to speak to me in private. Accordingly, he soon after
got up, and went out of the
room, and I was called upon
to attend him in a small separate court, closely walled
on all sides, except on the
one where was situated the
khelwet, or private room,
in which the doctor was
seated.

CHAPTER XIX: HAJJI BABA GETS INTO THE
SERVICE OF THE KING'S PHYSICIAN. OF THE MANNER
HE WAS FIRST EMPLOYED BY HIM

AS soon as I appeared, the doctor invited me into the room, and requested me to be seated; which I did with all the humility which is
the etiquette for an inferior to show towards his superior for so great an
honour. He informed me that the poet had spoken very favourably of me,
and had said that I was a person to be depended upon, particularly on ac-

count of my discretion and prudence; that I had seen a great deal of life; that I was fertile in expedients; and that if any business in which circumspection and secrecy were necessary was intrusted to me, I should conduct it with all the ability required. I bowed repeatedly as he spoke, and kept my hands respectfully before me, covered with the border of my sleeve, whilst I took care that my feet were also completely hid. He then continued, and said, 'I have occasion for a person of your description precisely at this moment, and as I put great confidence in the recommendation of my friend Asker, it is my intention to make use of your good offices; and if you succeed according to my expectations, you may rest assured that it will be well for you, and that I shall not remain unmindful.'

Then requesting me to approach nearer to him, and in a low and confidential tone of voice, he said, looking over his shoulders as if afraid of being overheard: 'Hajjî, you must know that an ambassador from the Franks is lately arrived at this court, in whose suite there is a doctor. This infidel has already acquired considerable reputation here. He treats his patients in a manner quite new to us, and has arrived with a chest full of medicines, of which we do not even know the names. He pretends to the knowledge of a great many things of which we have never yet heard in Persia. He makes no distinction between hot and cold diseases, and hot and cold remedies, as Galenus and Avicenna have ordained, but gives mercury by way of a cooling medicine; stabs the belly with a sharp instrument for wind in the stomach;[1] and, what is worse than all, pretends to do away with the small-pox altogether, by infusing into our nature a certain extract of cow, a discovery which one of their philosophers has lately made. Now this will never do, Hajjî. The smallpox has always been a comfortable source of revenue to me; I cannot afford to lose it, because an infidel chooses to come here and treat us like cattle. We cannot allow him to take the bread out of our mouths. But the reason why I particularly want your help proceeds from the following cause. The grand vizier was taken ill, two days ago, of a strange uneasiness, after having eaten more than his usual quantity of raw lettuce and cucumber, steeped in vinegar and sugar. This came to the Frank ambassador's ears, who, in fact, was present at the eating of the lettuce, and he immediately sent his doctor to him, with

---

[1] This alludes to tapping in cases of dropsy; an operation unknown among the Persians, until our surgeons taught it them.

a request that he might be permitted to administer relief. The grand vizier and the ambassador, it seems, had not been upon good terms for some time, because the latter was very urgent that some demand of a political nature might be conceded to him, which the vizier, out of consideration for the interests of Persia, was obliged to deny; and, therefore, thinking that this might be a good opportunity of conciliating the infidel, and of coming to a compromise, he agreed to accept of the doctor's services. Had I been apprised of the circumstance in time, I should easily have managed to put a stop to the proceeding; but the doctor did not lose an instant in administering his medicine, which, I hear, only consisted of one little white and tasteless pill. From all accounts, and as ill luck would have it, the effect it has produced is something quite marvellous. The grand vizier has received such relief that he can talk of nothing else; he says, 'that he felt the pill drawing the damp from the very tips of his fingers'; and that now he has discovered in himself such newness of strength and energy, that he laughs at his old age, and even talks of making up the complement of wives permitted to him by our blessed Prophet. But the mischief has not stopped here; the fame of this medicine, and of the Frank doctor, has gone throughout the court; and the first thing which the king talked of at the *selam* (the audience) this morning, was of its miraculous properties. He called upon the grand vizier to repeat to him all that he had before said upon the subject; and as he talked of the wonders that it had produced upon his person, a general murmur of applause and admiration was heard throughout the assembly. His majesty then turned to me, and requested me to explain the reason why such great effects should proceed from so small a cause, when I was obliged to answer, stooping as low as I could to hide my confusion, and kissing the earth—"I am your sacrifice: O king of kings, I have not yet seen the drug which the infidel doctor has given to your majesty's servant, the grand vizier; but as soon as I have, I will inform your majesty of what it consists. In the meanwhile, your humble slave beseeches the Centre of the Universe to recollect that the principal agent, on this occasion, must be an evil spirit, an enemy to the true faith, since he is an instrument in the hands of an infidel; of one who calls our holy Prophet a cheat, and who disowns the all-powerful decrees of predestination."

'Having said this, in order to shake his growing reputation, I retired in deep cogitation how I might get at the secrets of the infidel, and particularly inquire into the nature of his prescription, which has performed such miracles; and you are come most opportunely to my assistance. You must immediately become acquainted with him; and I shall leave it to your address to pick his brain and worm his knowledge out of him; but as I wish to procure a specimen of the very medicine which he administered to the grand vizier, being obliged to give an account of it to-morrow to the Shah, you must begin your services to me by eating much of lettuce and raw cucumbers, and of making yourself as sick to the full as his highness the vizier. You may then apply to the Frank, who will, doubtless, give you a duplicate of the celebrated pill, which you will deliver over to me.'

'But,' said I, who had rather taken fright at this extraordinary proposal, 'how shall I present myself before a man whom I do not know? besides, such marvellous stories are related of the Europeans, that I should be puzzled in what manner to behave: pray give me some instructions how to act.'

'Their manners and customs are totally different to ours, that is true,' replied Mirza Ahmak, 'and you may form some idea of them, when I tell you, that instead of shaving their heads, and letting their beards grow, as we do, they do the very contrary, for not a vestige of hair is to be seen on their chins, and their hair is as thick on their heads as if they had made a vow never to cut it off: then they sit on little platforms, whilst we squat on the ground; they take up their food with claws made of iron, whilst we use our fingers; they are always walking about, we keep seated; they wear tight clothes, we loose ones; they write from left to right, we from right to left; they never pray, we five times a day; in short, there is no end to what might be related of them; but most certain it is, that they are the most filthy people on the earth, for they hold nothing to be unclean; they eat all sorts of animals, from a pig to a tortoise, without the least scruple, and that without first cutting their throats; they will dissect a dead body, without requiring any purification after it, and perform all the brute functions of their nature, without ever thinking it necessary to go to the hot bath, or even rubbing themselves with sand after them.'

'And is it true,' said I, 'that they are so irascible, that if perchance their word is doubted, and they are called liars, they will fight on such an occasion till they die?'

'That is also said of them,' answered the doctor; 'but the case has not happened to me yet; however, I must warn you of one thing, which is, that if they happen to admire anything you possess, you must not say to them, as you would to one of us, "It is a present to you, it is your property," lest they should take you at your word and keep it, which you know would be inconvenient, and not what you intended; but you must endeavour as much as possible to speak what you think, for that is what they like.'

'But then, if such is the case,' said I, 'do not you think that the Frank doctor will find me out with a lie in my mouth; pretending to be sick when I am well; asking medicine from him for myself, when I want it for another?'

'No, no,' said the Mirza; 'you are to be sick, really sick, you know, and then it will be no lie. Go, Hajjî, my friend,' said he, putting his arm round my neck: 'go, eat your cucumbers immediately, and let me have the pill by this evening.' And then coaxing me, and preventing me from making any further objections to his unexpected request, he gently pushed me out of the room, and I left him, scarcely knowing whether to laugh or to cry at the new posture which my affairs had taken. To sicken without any stipulated reward was what I could not consent to do, so I retraced my steps, with a determination of making a bargain with my patron; but, when I got to the room, he was no longer there, having apparently retreated into his harem; and, therefore, I was obliged to proceed on my errand.

CHAPTER XX: HE SUCCEEDS IN DECEIVING
TWO OF THE FACULTY, GETTING A PILL FROM ONE
AND A PIECE OF GOLD FROM THE OTHER

I INQUIRED my way to the ambassador's house, and actually set off with the intention of putting the doctor's wishes into execution, and getting, if possible, a writhing disorder on the road; but, upon more mature reflection, I recollected that a stomach-ache was not a marketable commodity which might be purchased at a moment's notice; for although lettuce and cucumber might disagree with an old grand vizier, yet it was a hundred to one but they would find an easy digestion in a young person like me. However, I determined to obtain the pill by stratagem, if I could not procure it in a more direct manner. I considered that if I feigned to be ill, the doctor would very probably detect me, and turn me out of his house for a cheat, so I preferred the easier mode of passing myself off for one of the servants of the royal harem, and then making out some story by which I might attain my end. I accordingly stepped into one of the old clothes' shops in the bazaar, and hired a cloak for myself, such as the scribes wear; and then substituting a roll of paper in my girdle instead of a dagger, I flattered myself that I might pass for something more than a common servant.

I soon found out where the ambassador dwelt. Bearing in mind
all that Mirza Ahmak had told me,
I rather approached the door of the
doctor's residence with fear and
hesitation. I found the avenues to it
crowded with poor women, bearing infants in their arms, who, I
was told, came to receive the new-
fashioned preservative against the
smallpox. This, it was supposed
for political reasons, the Franks
were anxious to promote; and, as
the doctor performed the operation
gratis, he had no lack of patients,
particularly of the poorer sort, who

could not approach a Persian doctor without a present, or a good fee in their hand.

On entering, I found a man seated in the middle of the room, near an elevated wooden platform, upon which were piled boxes, books, and a variety of instruments and utensils, the uses of which were unknown to me. He was in dress and appearance the most extraordinary looking in-fidel I had ever seen. His chin and upper lip were without the vestige of a hair upon them, as like a eunuch as possible. He kept his head most disre-spectfully uncovered, and wore a tight bandage round his neck, with other contrivances on the sides of his cheeks, as if he were anxious to conceal some wound or disease. His clothes were fitted so tight to his body, and his outward coat in particular was cut off at such sharp angles, that it was evident cloth was a scarce and dear commodity in his country. The lower part of his dress was particularly improper, and he kept his boots on in his room, without any consideration for the carpet he was treading upon, which struck me as a custom subversive of all decorum.

I found that he talked our language; for, as soon as he saw me, he asked me how I did, and then immediately remarked that it was a fine day, which was so self-evident a truth, that I immediately agreed to it. I then thought it necessary to make him some fine speeches, and flattered him to the best of my abilities, informing him of the great reputation he had already acquired in Persia; that Locman[1] was a fool when compared to one of his wisdom; and that as for his contemporaries, the Persian physicians, they were not fit to handle his pestle for him. To all this he said nothing. I then told him that the king himself, having heard of the wonderful effects of his medicine upon the person of his grand vizier, had ordered his historian to insert the circumstance in the annals of the empire, as one of the most extraordinary events of his reign—that a considerable sensation had been produced in his majesty's seraglio, for many of the ladies had immediately been taken ill, and were longing to make a trial of his skill— that the king's favourite Georgian slave was, in fact, at this moment in great pain—that I had been deputed by the chief eunuch, owing to a special order from his majesty, to procure medicine similar to that which the first minister had taken—and I concluded my speech by requesting the doctor immediately to furnish me with some.

He seemed to ponder over what I had told him; and, after reflecting a short time, said that it was not his custom to administer medicine to his patients without first seeing them, for by so doing he would probably do more harm than good; but that if he found that the slave was in want of his aid, he should be very happy to attend her.

I answered to this, that as to seeing the face of the Georgian slave, that was totally out of the question, for no man ever was allowed that liberty in Persia, excepting her husband. In cases of extreme necessity, perhaps a doctor might be permitted to feel a woman's pulse, but then it must be done when a veil covers the hand.

---

[1] Locman is the most celebrated of the Eastern sages, and is supposed by some to be the same as Æsop. The title usually given to a doctor in Persia is *Locman al zeman*, the Locman of his day.

To which the Frank replied, 'In order to judge of my patient's case I must not only feel the pulse, but see the tongue also.'

'Looking at the tongue is totally new in Persia,' said I; 'and I am sure you could never be indulged with such a sight in the seraglio, without a special order from the king himself; a eunuch would rather cut out his own tongue first.'

'Well, then,' said the doctor, 'recollect, that if I deliver my medicine to you, I do so without taking any responsibility upon myself for its effects; for if it does not cure it may perhaps kill.'

When I had assured him that no harm or prejudice could possibly accrue to him, he opened a large chest, which appeared to be full of drugs, and taking therefrom the smallest quantity of a certain white powder, he mixed it up, with some bread, into the form of a pill, and putting it into paper gave it me, with proper directions how it should be administered. Seeing that he made no mystery of his knowledge, I began to question him upon the nature and properties of this particular medicine, and upon his practice in general. He answered me without any reserve; not like our Persian doctors, who only make a parade of fine words, and who adjust every ailment that comes before them to what they read in their Galen, their Hippocrates, and their Abou Avicenna.

When I had learned all I could, I left him with great demonstration of friendship and thankfulness, and immediately returned to Mirza Ahmak, who doubtless was waiting for me with great impatience. Having divested myself of my borrowed cloak and resumed my own dress, I appeared before him with a face made up for the occasion, for I wished to make him believe that the lettuce and cucumbers had done their duty. At every word I pretended to receive a violent twitch, and acted my part so true to life, that the stern and inflexible nature of Mirza Ahmak himself was moved into somewhat like pity for me.

'There! there,' said I, as I entered his apartment, 'in the name of Allah take your prize:' and then pretending to be bent double, I made the most horrid grimaces, and uttered deep groans: 'there! I have followed your orders, and now throw myself upon your generosity.' He endeavoured to take the object of his search from me, but I kept it fast; and whilst I gave him to understand that I expected prompt reward, I made indications of an intention to swallow it, unless he actually gave me something in hand. So fearful was he of not being able to answer the king's interrogatories concerning the pill, so anxious to get it into his possession, that he actually pressed a gold piece upon me. No lover could sue his mistress with more earnestness to grant him a favour than the doctor did me for my pill. I should very probably have continued the deceit a little longer, and have endeavoured to extract another piece from him; but when I saw him preparing a dose of his own mixture to ease my pain, I thought it high time to finish, and pretending all of a sudden to have received relief, I gave up my prize.

When once he had got possession, he looked at it with intense eagerness, and turned it over and over on his palm, without appearing one whit more advanced in his knowledge than before. At length, after permitting him fully to exhaust his conjectures, I told him that the Frank doctor had made no secret in saying that it was composed of *jivch*, or mercury. 'Mercury, indeed!' exclaimed Mirza Ahmak—'just as if I did not know that. And so, because this infidel, this dog of an *Isauvi*,[1] chooses to poison us with mercury, I am to lose my reputation, and my prescriptions (such as his father never even saw in a dream) are to be turned into ridicule. Whoever heard of mercury as a medicine? Mercury is cold, and lettuce and cucumber are cold also. You would not apply ice to dissolve ice? The ass does not know the first rudiments of his profession. No, Hajjî, this will never do; we must not permit our beards to be laughed at in this manner.'

He continued to inveigh for a considerable time against his rival; and would, no doubt, have continued to do so much longer, but he was stopped by a message from the king, who ordered him to repair forthwith to his presence. In the greatest trepidation he immediately put himself into his court dress, exchanged his common black lamb's skin cap for one wound about with a shawl, huddled on his red cloth stockings, called for his horse, and, taking the pill with him, went off in great hurry, and full of the greatest apprehension at what might be the result of the audience.

---

[1] *Isauvi*, a follower of Jesus.

CHAPTER XXI: HE DESCRIBES THE MANNER
IN WHICH THE SHAH OF PERSIA TAKES MEDICINE

HE doctor's visit to the king had taken place late in the evening; and as soon as he returned from it he called for me. I found him apparently in great agitation, and full of anxiety. 'Hajjî,' said he, when I appeared, 'come close to me;' and having sent every one else out of the room, he said in a whisper, 'this infidel doctor must be disposed of somehow or other. What do you think has happened? The Shah has consulted him; he had him in private conference for an hour this morning, without my being apprised of it. His majesty sent for me to tell me its result; and I perceive that the Frank has already gained great influence. It seems that the king gave him the history of his complaints—of his debility, of his old asthma, and of his imperfect digestion, but talked in raptures of the wretch's sagacity and penetration; for merely by looking at the tongue and feeling the pulse before the infidel was told what was the state of the case, he asked whether his majesty did not use the hot-baths[1] very frequently; whether, when he smoked, he did

[1] This is the most approved form of speech among well-educated Persians, whenever any allusion to the mysteries of the harem is intended.

not immediately bring on a fit of coughing; and whether, in his food, he was not particularly addicted to pickles, sweetmeats, and rice swimming in butter? The king has given him three days to consider his case, to consult his books, and to gather the opinions of the Frank sages on subjects so important to the state of Persia, and to compose such a medicine as will entirely restore and renovate his constitution. The Centre of the Universe then asked my opinion, and requested me to speak boldly upon the natures and properties of Franks in general, and of their medicines. I did not lose this opportunity of giving utterance to my sentiments; so, after the usual preface to my speech, I said, "that as to their natures, the Shah, in his profound wisdom, must know, that they were an unbelieving and an unclean race; for that they treated our Prophet as a cheat, and ate pork and drank wine without any scruple; that they were women in looks, and in manners bears; that they ought to be held in the greatest suspicion, for their ultimate object (see what they had done in India) was to take kingdoms, and to make Shahs and Nabobs their humble servants. As to their medicines," I exclaimed, "Heaven preserve your majesty from them! they are just as treacherous in their effects as the Franks are in their politics: with what we give to procure death, they pretend to work their cures. Their principal ingredient is mercury (and here I produced my pill); and they use their instruments and knives so freely, that I have heard it said they will cut off a man's limbs to save his life." I then drew such a picture of the fatal effects likely to proceed from the foreign prescription, that I made the Shah promise that he would not take it without using every precaution that his prudence and wisdom might suggest. To this he consented; and as soon as the Frank shall have sent in the medicine which he is preparing, I shall be summoned to another interview. Now, Hajjî,' added the doctor, 'the Shah must not touch the infidel's physic; for if perchance it were to do good, I am a lost man. Who will ever consult Mirza Ahmak again? No, we must avert the occurrence of such an event, even if I were obliged to take all his drugs myself.'

We parted with mutual promises of doing everything in our power to thwart the infidel doctor; and three days after Mirza Ahmak was again called before the king in order to inspect the promised ordonnance, and which consisted of a box of pills. He, of course, created all sorts of suspicions against their efficacy, threw out some dark hints about the danger

of receiving any drug from the agent of a foreign power, and, finally, left
the Shah in the determination of referring the case to his ministers. The
next day, at the usual public audience, when the Shah was seated on his
throne, and surrounded by his prime vizier, his lord high treasurer, his
minister for the interior, his principal secretary of state, his lord chamber-
lain, his master of the horse, his principal master of the ceremonies, his
doctor in chief, and many other of the great officers of his household, addressing himself to his grand vizier, he stated the negotiations which he
had entered into with the foreign physician, now resident at his court, for
the restoration and the renovation of the royal person; that at the first conference, the said foreign physician, after a due inspection of the royal person, had reported that there existed several symptoms of debility. That at
the second, after assuring the Shah that he had for three whole days employed himself in consulting his books and records, and gathering from
them the opinions of his own country sages on the subject, he had combined the properties of various drugs into one whole, which, if taken in-
teriorly, would produce effects so wonderful, that no talisman could come
in competition with it. His majesty then said, that he had called into his
councils his Hakîm Bashi, or head physician, who, in his anxiety for the
weal of the Persian monarchy, had deeply pondered over the ordonnances
of the foreigner, and had set his face against them, owing to certain doubts
and apprehensions that had crept into his mind, which consisted, first,
whether it were politic to deliver over the internal administration of the
royal person to foreign regulations and ordonnances; and, second, whether,
in the remedy prescribed, there might not exist such latent and destructive
effects, as would endanger, undermine, and, finally, overthrow that royal
person and constitution, which it was supposed to be intended to restore
and renovate. 'Under these circumstances,' said the Centre of the Universe,
raising his voice at the time, 'I have thought it advisable to pause before I
proceeded in this business; and have resolved to lay the case before you,
in order that you may, in your united wisdoms, frame such an opinion as
may be fitting to be placed before the king: and in order that you may go
into the subject with a complete knowledge of the case, I have resolved, as
a preparatory act, that each of you, in your own persons, shall partake of
this medicine, in order that both you and I may judge of its various effects.'

To this most gracious speech the grand vizier and all the courtiers made exclamations, 'May the king live for ever! May the royal shadow never be less! We are happy not only to take physic, but to lay down our lives in your majesty's service! We are your sacrifice, your slaves! May God give the Shah health, and a victory over all his enemies!' Upon which the chief of the valets was ordered to bring the foreign physician's box of pills from the harem, and delivered it to the Shah in a golden salver. His majesty then ordered the Hakîm Bashi to approach, and delivering the box to him, ordered him to go round to all present, beginning with the prime vizier, and then to every man according to his rank, administering to each a pill.

This being done, the whole assembly took the prescribed gulp; after which ensued a general pause, during which the king looked carefully into each man's face to mark the first effects of the medicine. When the wry faces had subsided, the conversation took a turn upon the affairs of Europe; upon which his majesty asked a variety of questions, which were answered by the different persons present in the best manner they were able.

The medicine now gradually began to show its effects. The lord high treasurer first, a large coarse man, who, to this moment had stood immovable, merely saying *belli*, *belli*, yes, yes, whenever his majesty opened his mouth to speak, now appeared uneasy, for what he had swallowed had brought into action a store of old complaints which were before lying dormant. The eyes of all had been directed towards him, which had much increased his perturbed state; when the chief secretary of state, a tall, thin, lathy man, turned deadly pale, and began to stream from every pore. He was followed by the minister for the interior, whose unhappy looks seemed to supplicate a permission from his majesty to quit his august presence. All the rest in succession were moved in various ways, except the prime vizier, a little old man, famous for a hard and unyielding nature, and who appeared to be laughing in his sleeve at the misery which his compeers in office were undergoing.

When the Shah perceived that the medicine had taken effect, he dismissed the assembly, ordering Mirza Ahmak, as soon as he could ascertain the history of each pill, to give him an official report of the whole transaction, and then retired into his harem.

The crafty old doctor had now his rival within his power; of course, he set the matter in such a light before the king, that his majesty was deterred from making the experiment of the foreign physician's ordonnance, and it was forthwith consigned to oblivion. When he next saw me, and after he had made me acquainted with the preceding narrative, he could not restrain his joy and exultation. 'We have conquered, friend Hajjî,' would he say to me. 'The infidel thought that we were fools; but we will teach him what Persians are. Whose dog is he, that he should aspire to so high an honour as prescribing for a king of kings? No, that is left to such men as I. What do we care about his new discoveries? As our fathers did, so are we contented to do. The prescription that cured our ancestors shall cure us; and what Locman and Abou Avicenna ordained we may be satisfied to ordain after them.' He then dismissed me, to make fresh plans for destroying any influence or credit that the new physician might acquire, and for preserving his own consequence and reputation at court.

CHAPTER XXII: HAJJI BABA ASKS THE DOCTOR FOR A SALARY, AND OF THE SUCCESS OF HIS DEMAND

I HAD thus far lived with the doctor more as a friend than as a servant; for he permitted me to sit in his presence, to eat with him, and even to smoke his pipe, whilst at the same time I associated with his servants, ate, drank, and smoked with them also; but I found that this sort of life in nowise suited my views and expectations. The only money which I had received from him was the gold coin aforementioned, for which I was indebted to my own ingenuity; and, as things went, it appeared that it would be the last. I was therefore resolved to come to an explanation with him, and accordingly seized the opportunity when he was elated with his success over the European doctor, to open the subject of my grievances.

He had just returned from the imperial gate, after having seen the Shah; who, by his account, had been very gracious to him, having kept him standing without his shoes only two hours, by the side of a stone fountain, instead of six, which he generally does. 'What a good king he is!' he exclaimed, 'how affable, how considerate! It is impossible to say how much kindness he shows to me. He gave abuse to the European doctor, all out of compliment to my abilities, and said that he is not fit to hold my shoes. He then ordered his favourite running footman to bring me a present of two partridges, which were caught by the royal hawks.'

I observed, 'Yes, the king says true. Who is your equal nowadays in Persia? Happy Shah! to possess such a treasure. What are the Franks, that they should talk of medicine? If they want learning, science, and skill, let them look to Mirza Ahmak.'

Upon this, with a smile of self-complacency, he took the pipe from his mouth and gave it to me, pulled up his moustaches, and stroked his beard.

'*Inshallah!* may it please God,' I continued to say, 'that I also may share in the glory of your reputation; but I am like a dog, I am nothing, I am not even like the piece of clay, which was scented by the company of the rose.'

'How!' said the doctor; 'why are you out of spirits?'

'I will leave you to judge, and relate a story,' said I. 'Once upon a time there was a dog, who in looks and manners was so like a wolf, that the wolves used to admit him into their society. He ate, drank, and killed sheep with them, and, in short, was everything that a wolf ought to be; at the same time, he lived with his fellow dogs like a dog, and was admitted to all their parties. But, little by little, the dogs perceived that he associated with wolves, and became shy of him; and it also happened that the wolves discovered that he was in fact a dog, and did not like to admit him any longer into their circles; so between both, the poor dog became neglected and miserable; and, unable to bear his undefined state any longer, he determined to make a decided effort to become either a dog or a wolf. I am that dog!' exclaimed I: 'you permit me to sit and smoke with you, who are so much my superior; you talk to and consult me, and I am even admitted to the society of your friends; but what does that benefit me? I am still a servant, without enjoying any of the advantages of one: I get nothing. I pray you therefore to appoint me to the situation you wish me to hold in your service, and to fix a salary upon me.'

'A salary indeed!' exclaimed the doctor: 'I never give salaries. My servants get what they can from my patients, and you may do the same; they eat the remains of my dinner, and they receive a coat at the festival of the *No Rûz*[1]—what can they want more?' At this moment entered the Shah's running footman, bearing in his hands a silver tray, upon which were placed the two partridges that his majesty had presented to the

---

[1] *No Rûz* (the new day,) is the great Persian festival, which takes place in spring, when the Sun enters Aries. It is not Mohammedan and dates from very remote antiquity.

doctor, and which in great form he gave into his hands, who, rising from his seat, carried the tray to his head, and exclaimed, 'May the king's kindness never be less!—may his wealth increase, and may he live for ever!'

He then was called upon to make the bearer a present. He sent first five piastres, which the servant returned with great indignation. He then sent one tomaun: this also was sent back, until at length in despair he sent five tomauns, which, it was intimated, was the sum proper to be given. This disagreeable circumstance dissipated all the pleasure which such a present had produced, and the Hakim, in his rage, permitted himself to use such expressions, which, if reported to the king, would have brought him into considerable trouble. 'A present, indeed!' said he; 'I wish such presents were in the other world! 'Tis thus we pay the wages of the king's servants—a set of rapacious rascals, without either shame or conscience! And the worst of it is, we must pay them handsomely, or else whenever it happens that I get the bastinado on the soles of my feet, which come it will, they, who perform the operation, will show me no mercy. Let me not forget what Saadi says, that you can no more depend upon the friendship of a king than you can upon the voice of a child; the former changes on the slightest suspicion, the latter in the course of a night.'

Upon this reflection the doctor began to be alarmed at what he had said at the outset of his speech; and, with all the terrors of the *felek* before him, he seemed quite reconciled to the loss of his five tomauns.

I found that this would not be the best moment to resume the subject of my expectations, and therefore reserved it for some future opportunity; but I had heard enough to settle in my own mind, that I would leave the 'Locman of the age,' whenever an opportunity should offer, and for the present to content myself with being neither dog nor wolf.

CHAPTER XXIII: HAJJI BABA FALLS IN LOVE

DISCONTENTED with my present lot, and uncertain as to my future prospects, my days passed on in total idleness; and, as I had no inclination to pursue the profession of physic, which many before me had done on quite as slender a foundation as the one I had acquired, I cared little for those pursuits which engaged Mirza Ahmak. I should very probably have left him instantly, if a circumstance had not occurred, arising from the very state of unprofitableness in which I lived, which detained me in his house. The feelings to which it gave rise so entirely absorbed every other consideration, that I became their slave; and so violent were the emotions which they created, that I verily believe that Majnoun, in the height of his frenzy, could not have been madder than I. After this, it is needless to mention that I was in love.

The spring had passed over, and the first heats of summer, which now began to make themselves felt, had driven most of the inhabitants of the city to spread their beds and sleep on the house-tops. As I did not like to pass my night in company of the servants, the carpet-spreaders and the cook, who generally herded together in a room below, I extended my bed in a corner of the terrace, which overlooked the inner court of the doctor's house, in which were situated the apartments of the women. This court was a square, into which the windows of the different chambers looked, and was planted in the centre with rose-bushes, jessamines, and poplar-trees. A square wooden platform was erected in the middle, upon which mattresses were spread, where the inhabitants reposed during the great heats. I had seen several women seated in different parts of the court, but had never been particularly struck by the appearance of any one of them; and indeed had I been so, perhaps I should never have thought of looking at them again; for as soon as I was discovered, shouts of abuse were levelled at me, and I was called by every odious name that they could devise.

One night, however, soon after the sun had set, as I was preparing my bed, I perchance looked over a part of the wall that was a little broken down, and on a slip of terrace that was close under it I discovered a female, who was employed in assorting and spreading out tobacco-leaves. Her blue veil was negligently thrown over her head, and as she stooped, the two long tresses which flowed from her forehead hung down in so tantalizing a manner as nearly to screen all her face, but still left so much of it visible, that it created an intense desire in me to see the remainder. Everything that I saw in her announced beauty. Her hands were small, and dyed with *khena*;[1] her feet were equally small; and her whole air and form bespoke loveliness and grace. I gazed upon her until I could no

[1] This dye is used throughout all Asia, and produces a strong orange or auburn colour. The Persians dye the whole of their hands as far as the wrist with it, and also the soles of their feet. The Turks more commonly only tinge the nails: both use it for the hair.

longer contain my passion; I made a slight noise, which immediately
caused her to look up, and before she could cover herself with her veil, I
had had time to see the most enchanting features that the imagination can
conceive, and to receive a look from eyes so bewitching, that I immediately felt my heart in a blaze. With apparent displeasure she covered herself; but still I could perceive that she had managed her veil with so much
art, that there was room for a certain dark and sparkling eye to look at me,
and to enjoy my agitation. As I continued
to gaze upon her, she at length said,
though still going on with her work,
'Why do you look at me? It is criminal.'

'For the sake of the sainted Hosein,'
I exclaimed, 'do not turn from me; it is
no crime to love: your eyes have made
roast meat of my heart: by the mother
that bore you, let me look upon your
face again.'

In a more subdued voice she answered me, 'Why do you ask me? You
know it is a crime for a woman to let her
face be seen; and you are neither my
father, my brother, nor my husband; I
do not even know who you are. Have
you no shame, to talk thus to a maid?'

At this moment she let her veil fall, as if by chance, and I had time to
look again upon her face, which was even more beautiful than I had imagined. Her eyes were large and peculiarly black, and fringed by long
lashes, which, aided by the collyrium with which they were tinged, formed
a sort of ambuscade, from which she levelled her shafts. Her eyebrows
were finely arched, and nature had brought them together just over her
nose, in so strong a line, that there was no need of art to join them together. Her nose was aquiline, her mouth small, and full of sweet expression; and in the centre of her chin was a dimple which she kept carefully marked with a blue puncture. Nothing could equal the beauty of her
hair; it was black as jet, and fell in long tresses down her back. In short,
I was wrapped in amazement at her beauty. The sight of her explained to

me many things which I had read in our poets, of cypress forms, tender fawns, and sugar-eating parrots. It seemed to me that I could gaze at her for ever, and not be tired; but still I felt a great desire to leap over the wall and touch her. My passion was increasing, and I was on the point of approaching her, when I heard the name of *Zeenab* repeated several times, with great impatience, by a loud shrill voice; upon which my fair one left the terrace in haste, and I remained riveted to the place where I had first seen her. I continued there for a long time, in the hope that she might return, but to no purpose. I lent my ear to every noise, but nothing was to be heard below but the same angry voice, which, by turns, appeared to attack everything, and everybody, and which could belong to no one but the doctor's wife; a lady, who, as report would have it, was none of the mildest of her sex, and who kept her good man in great subjection.

The day had now entirely closed in, and I was about retiring to my bed in despair, when the voice was heard again, exclaiming, 'Zeenab, where are you going to? Why do you not retire to bed?'

I indistinctly heard the answer of my charmer, but soon guessed what it had been, when I saw her appear on the terrace again. My heart beat violently, and I was about to leap over the wall, which separated us, when I was stopped by seeing her taking up a basket, in which she had gathered her tobacco, and make a hasty retreat; but just as she was disappearing, she said to me, in a low tone of voice, 'Be here to-morrow night.' These words thrilled through my whole frame, in a manner that I had never before felt, and I did not cease to repeat them, and ponder over them, until, through exhaustion, I fell into a feverish doze, and I did not awaken on the following morning until the beams of the sun shone bright in my face.

CHAPTER XXIV: THE FAIR ZEENAB RELATES
HOW SHE PASSES HER TIME IN THE DOCTOR'S HAREM

SO,' said I, when I had well rubbed my eyes: 'so, now I am in love? Well! we shall see what will come of it. Who and what she is we shall know to-night, so please it; and if she is anything which belongs to the doctor, may his house be ruined if I do not teach him how to keep a better watch over his property. As for marriage, that is out of the question. Who would give a wife to me; I who have not even enough to buy myself a pair of trousers, much less to defray the expenses of a wedding? *Inshallah*, please God, that will take place one of these days, whenever I shall have got together some money; but now I will make play with love, and let the doctor pay for it.'

With that intention I forthwith got up and dressed myself; but it was with more care than usual. I combed my curls a great deal more than ordinary; I studied the tie of my girdle, and put my cap on one side. Then having rolled up my bed, and carried it into the servants' hall, I issued from home, with the intention of bathing, and making my person sweet, preparatory to my evening's assignation. I went to the bath, where I passed a great part of my morning in singing, and spent the remainder of the time, until the hour of meeting, in rambling about the town without any precise object in view.

At length the day drew towards its close, my impatience had reached its height, and I only waited for the termination of the *sham*, or the evening's meal, to feign a headache, and to retire to rest. My ill luck would have it, that the doctor was detained longer than usual in his attendance upon the Shah, and as the servants dined after him, and ate his leavings, it was late before I was at liberty. When that moment arrived, I was in a fever of expectation: the last glimmering of day tinged the western sky with a light shade of red, and the moon was just rising, when I appeared on the terrace with my bed under my arm. I threw it down and unfolded it in haste, and then, with a beating heart, flew to the broken wall. I looked over it with great precaution; but, to my utter disappointment, I saw nothing but the tobacco spread about in confused heaps, with baskets here and there, as if some work had been left unfinished. I looked all around, but saw no Zeenab. I coughed once or twice; no answer. The only sound which reached my ears was the voice of the doctor's wife, exerting itself upon some one within the house; although its shrillness pierced even the walls, yet I could not make out what was the cause of its being so excited, until of a sudden it burst into the open air with increasing violence.

'You talk of work to me, you daughter of the devil! Who told you to go to the bath? What business had you at the tombs? I suppose I am to be your slave, and you are to take your pleasure. Why is not your work done? You shall neither eat, drink, nor sleep, until it is done, so go to it immediately; and if you come away until it be finished, *wallah! billah!* by the prophet, I will beat you till your nails drop off.' Upon this I heard some pushing and scuffing, and immediately perceived my fair one proceeding with apparent reluctance to the spot, which not a moment before I had despaired of seeing blessed with her presence. Oh what a wonderful thing

is love! thought I to myself: how it sharpens the wits, and how fertile it is in expedients! I perceived at a glance how ingeniously my charmer had contrived everything for our interview, and for a continuance of it without the fear of interruption. She saw, but took no notice of me until the storm below had ceased; and then, when everything had relapsed into silence, she came towards me, and, as the reader may well suppose, I was at her side in an instant. Ye, who know what love is, may, perhaps, conceive our raptures, for they are not to be expressed.

I learnt from my fair friend that she was the daughter of a Cûrdish chief, who, with his whole family, including his flocks and herds, had been made prisoner when she was quite a child; and that, from circumstances which she promised hereafter to relate to me, she had fallen into the hands of the doctor, whose slave she now was.

After the first burst of the sentiments which we felt towards each other had subsided, she gave way to the feelings of anger, which she felt for the treatment that she had just experienced. 'Ah!' she exclaimed, 'did you hear what that woman called me! woman, without faith, without religion! 'Tis thus she always treats me; she constantly gives me abuse; I am become less than a dog. Everybody rails at me; no one comes near me; my liver is become water, and my soul is withered up. Why should I be called a child of the devil? I am a Cûrd; I am a Yezeedi.[1] 'Tis true that we fear the devil, and who does not? but I am no child of his. Oh! that I could

[1] The Yezeedis are a tribe of the Cûrds, who are said to worship the devil.

meet her in our mountains: she would then see what a Cûrdish girl can do.' I endeavoured to console her as well as I could, and persuaded her to smother her resentment until she could find a good opportunity of revenging herself. She despaired at that ever coming to pass; because all her actions were so strictly watched, that she could scarcely go from one room to another without her mistress being aware of it. The fact was, so she informed me, that the doctor, who was a man of low family, had, by orders of the king, married one of his majesty's slaves, who, from some misconduct, had been expelled from the harem. She brought the doctor no other dowry than an ill-temper, and a great share of pride, which always kept her in mind of her former influence at court; and she therefore holds her present husband as cheap as the dust under her feet, and keeps him in a most pitiful state of subjection. He dares not sit down before her, unless she permits him, which she very seldom does; and she is moreover so jealous, that there is no slave in her harem who does not excite her suspicions. The doctor, on the other hand, who is very ambitious, and pleased with his exaltation, is also subject to the frailties of human nature, and is by no means insensible to the charms of the fair creatures, his slaves. Zeenab herself, so she informed me, is the peculiar object of his attentions, and consequently that of the jealousy of his wife, who permits no look, word, or sign to pass unnoticed. Much intrigue and espionage is carried on in the harem; and when the lady herself goes to the bath or the mosque, as many precautions are taken about the distribution of the female slaves, with respect to time, place, and opportunity, as there would be in the arrangement of a wedding.

Having never seen more of the interior of an *anderûn* than what I recollected as a boy in my own family, I became surprised, and my curiosity was greatly excited in proportion as the fair Zeenab proceeded in her narrative of the history of her life in the doctor's house. 'We are five in the harem, besides our mistress,' said she: 'there is Shireen, the Georgian slave; then Nûr Jehan,[1] the Ethiopian slave girl; Fatmeh, the cook; and old Leilah, the duenna. My situation is that of handmaid to the *khanum*,[2] so my mistress is called: I attend her pipe, I hand her her coffee, bring in the meals, go with her to the bath, dress and undress her, make her clothes,

[1] The Persians give most magnificent names to their Negro slaves. *Nûr Jehan* means light of the world. [2] *Khanum* is the title given a Persian lady, and is equivalent to madam.

spread, sift, and pound tobacco, and stand before her. Shireen, the Georgian, is the *sandukdar*, or housekeeper; she has the care of the clothes of both my master and mistress, and indeed of the clothes of all the house; she superintends the expenses, lays in the corn for the house, as well as all the other provisions: she takes charge of all the porcelain, the silver, and other ware; and, in short, has the care of whatever is either precious or of consequence in the family. Nûr Jehan, the black slave, acts as *ferash*, or carpet-spreader: she does all the dirty work, spreads the carpets, sweeps the rooms, sprinkles the water over the courtyard, helps the cook, carries parcels and messages, and, in short, is at the call of every one. As for old Leilah, she is a sort of duenna over the young slaves: she is employed in the out-of-door service, carries on any little affair that the khanum may have with other harems, and is also supposed to be a spy upon the actions of the doctor. Such as we are, our days are passed in peevish disputes; whilst, at the same time, some two of us are usually leagued in strict friendship, to the exclusion of the others. At this present moment I am at open war with the Georgian, who, some time ago, found that her good luck in life had forsaken her, and she in consequence contrived to procure a talisman from a dervish. She had no sooner obtained it, than on the very next day the khanum presented her with a new jacket; this so excited my jealousy, that I also made interest with the dervish to supply me with a talisman that should secure me a good husband. On that very same evening I saw you on the terrace. Conceive my happiness! But this has established a rivality between myself and Shireen, which has ended in hatred, and we are now mortal enemies: perhaps we may as suddenly be friends again. I am now on the most intimate terms with Nûr Jehan, and at my persuasion she reports to the khanum every story unfavorable to my rival. Some rare sweetmeats, with *baklava* (sweet cake) made in the royal seraglio, were sent a few days ago from one of the Shah's ladies, as a present to our mistress; the rats ate a great part of them, and we gave out that the Georgian was the culprit, for which she received blows on the feet, which Nûr Jehan administered. I broke my mistress's favourite drinking-cup; Shireen incurred the blame, and was obliged to supply another. I know that she is plotting against me, for she is eternally closeted with Leilah, who is at present the confidant of our mistress. I take care not to eat or drink anything which has passed through her hands to me, for fear

of poison, and she returns me the same compliment. It is not, that our hatred amounts to poison yet, but such precautions are constantly in use in
all harems. We have as yet only once come to blows: she excited me to
violent anger by spitting and saying, '*lahnet be Sheitan*,' curse be on the
devil, which you know to the Yezeedies is a gross insult; when I fell upon
her, calling her by every wicked name that I had learnt in Persian, and
fastening upon her hair, of which I pulled out whole tresses by the roots.
We were parted by Leilah, who came in for her share of abuse, and we
continued railing at each other until our throats were quite dried up with
rage and exhaustion. Our violence has much abated since this conflict; but
her enmity is undiminished, for she continues to show her spite against me
in every manner she can devise.'

Zeenab continued to entertain me in this manner until the first dawn
of the morning, and when we heard the *muezzin*[1] call the morning prayers
from the mosque, we thought it prudent to retire; but not until we had
made mutual promises of seeing each other as often as prudence would allow. We agreed, that whenever she had by her stratagems secured an opportunity for meeting, she should hang her veil upon the bough of a tree
in the court, which could be seen from my terrace; and that if it were not
there, I was to conclude that our interview on that night was impossible.

CHAPTER XXV: THE LOVERS MEET AGAIN AND ARE VERY HAPPY. HAJJI BABA SINGS

ON the following evening, I ascended the terrace in the hope of seeing the signal of meeting; but in vain; no veil was visible; and I sat
myself down in despair. The tobacco, and all the apparatus for cleaning it,
had disappeared, and all was hushed below. Even the unceasing voice of
the doctor's wife, which I now began to look upon as the most agreeable
sound in nature, was wanting; and the occasional drag of a slipper, which
I guessed might proceed from the crawl of old Leilah, was the only sign of
an inhabitant. I had in succession watched the distant din of the king's
band, the crash of the drums, and the swell of the trumpets, announcing
sunset. I had listened to the various tones of the muezzins, announcing the

---

[1] The priest is so called who invites the Mohamedans to prayers from the minaret, or
from the roof of the mosque.

evening prayer; as well as to the small drum of the police, ordering the people to shut their shops, and retire to their homes. The cry of the sentinels on the watch-towers of the king's palace was heard at distant intervals; night had completely closed in upon me, and still the same silence prevailed in the doctor's harem.

'What can be the reason of this?' said I to myself. 'If they have been to the bath, they cannot have remained thus late: besides, the baths are open for the women in the mornings only. Some one must be sick, or there is a marriage, or a birth, or perhaps a burial; or the doctor may have received the bastinado'; in short, I was killing myself with conjecture, when of a sudden a great beating at the door took place, and, as it opened, the clatter of slippers was heard, attended by the mingled sounds of many female voices, amongst which the well-known querulous tone of the khanum was prominent. Several lanterns passed to and fro, which showed me the forms of the women, amongst whom, as they threw off their veils, I recognized that of my Zeenab. I determined to watch, in the hope that I might still be blessed with an interview; and, in fact, it was not long before she appeared. She stole to me with great precaution, to say that circumstances would prevent our meeting on this occasion, as she should not fail being missed; but that, certainly, ere long, she would contrive to secure an interview. In few words, she informed me that her mistress had been called upon to attend her sister (one of the ladies in the Shah's seraglio), who being taken suddenly ill, had expired almost immediately (it was supposed by poison administered by a rival), and that she had taken all her women with her, in order to increase the clamour of lamentation which was always made on such occasions; that they had been there since noon, rending the air with every proper exclamation, until they were all hoarse; that her mistress had already torn her clothes, an etiquette which she had performed however with great care, considering that she wore a favourite jacket, having permitted only one or two seams of it to be ripped open. As the burial would take place the next day, it was necessary that they should be at their post early in the morning to continue the lamentations, a service for which she expected to receive a black handkerchief, and to eat sweetmeats. My fair one then left me, promising that she would do her utmost to secure a meeting on the following evening, and telling me not to forget the signal.

On getting up the next morning, I was much surprised to see it already made, and to perceive Zeenab below, beckoning me to go to her. I did not hesitate immediately to descend from the terrace by the same flight of steps which she used to ascend it, and then of a sudden I found myself in the very centre of the harem. An involuntary tremor seized me, when I reflected that I was in a place into which no man with impunity is permitted to enter; but, fortified by the smiles and the unconstrained manner of my enchantress, I proceeded.

'Come, Hajjî,' said she, 'banish all fear; no one is here but Zeenab, and, if our luck is good, we may have the whole day to ourselves.'

'By what miracle,' exclaimed I, 'have you done this? Where is the Khanum? where are the women? and, if they are not here, how shall I escape the doctor?'

'Do not fear,' she repeated again; 'I have barred all the doors; and should any one come, you will have time to escape before I open them: but there is no fear of that; all the women are gone to the funeral; and as for Mirza Ahmak, my mistress has taken care to dispose of him in such a manner, now that I am left by myself, that he will not dare to come within a parasang of his own house. You must know then,' said she, 'for I see you are all astonishment, that our destinies are on the rise, and that it was a lucky hour when we first saw each other. Everything plays into our hands.

My rival, the Georgian, put it into the khanum's head, that Leilah, who is a professed weeper at burials, having learned the art, in all its branches since a child, was a personage absolutely necessary on the present occasion, and that she ought to go in preference to me, who am a Cûrd, and can know but little of Persian customs: all this, of course, to deprive me of my black handkerchief, and other advantages. Accordingly, I have been left at home; and the whole party went off an hour ago to the house of the deceased. I pretended to be very angry, and opposed Leilah's taking my place with apparent warmth; but, thank Heaven, here we are, and so let us make the most of our time.'

Upon which she went into the kitchen to prepare a tray, containing a breakfast for me, whilst she left me to explore that which is hidden from all bachelors, namely, the interior of the harem.

I first went into the apartments of the khanum herself. It opened upon the garden by an immense sash-window, composed of stained glass; and in the corner was the accustomed seat of the lady, marked by a thick felt carpet, folded double, and a large down cushion, covered with cloth of gold, with two tassels at the extremities, and veiled by a thin outer covering of muslin. Near this seat was a looking-glass, prettily painted, and a box containing all sorts of curiosities; the *surmeh* (collyrium) for the eyes, with its small instrument for applying it; some Chinese rouge; a pair of armlets, containing talismans; a *toû zoulfeh*, or an ornament to hitch into the hair, and hang on the forehead; a knife, scissors, and other things. A guitar and a tambourine lay close at hand. Her bed, rolled up in a distant corner, was enclosed in a large wrapper of blue and white cloth. Several pictures, without frames, were hung against the walls, and the shelf which occupied the top of the room was covered with different sorts of glasses, basins, &c. In a corner were seen several bottles of Shiraz wine, one of which, just stopped with a flower, appeared to have been used by the good lady that very morning; most likely in order to keep up her spirits during the melancholy ceremony she was about to attend.

'So,' said I to myself, 'the Prophet is not much heeded in this house. I shall know another time how to appreciate a sanctified and mortified look. Our doctor, who calls himself a staunch Mussulman, I see makes up for his large potations of cold water and sherbet abroad, by his good stock of wine at home.'

By the time I had satisfied my curiosity here, and had inspected the other rooms, which belonged to the servants, Zeenab had prepared our breakfast, which she placed before us in the khanum's room. We sat down next to each other, and reposed upon the very cushion of which I have just given the description. Nothing could be more delicious than the meal which she had prepared: there was a dish of rice, white as snow, and near it a plate of roast meat, cut into small bits, wrapped up in a large flap of bread; then a beautiful Ispahan melon, in long slices; some pears and apricots; an omelette warmed from a preceding meal; cheese, onions, and leeks; a basin of sour curds, and two different sorts of sherbet: added to this, we had some delicious sweetmeats, and a basin full of new honey.

'How, in the name of your mother,' exclaimed I, as I pulled up my whiskers, and surveyed the good things before me, 'how have you managed to collect all this so soon? This is a breakfast fit for the Shah.'

'Oh, as to that,' she replied, 'do not trouble yourself, but fall to. My mistress ordered her breakfast to be prepared overnight, but on second thoughts this morning she determined to make her meal at the house of the deceased, and has left me, as you see, but little to do. Come, let us eat and be merry.'

Accordingly, we did honour to the breakfast, and left but little for those who might come after us. After we had washed our hands, we placed the wine before us, and having each broken the commandment by taking a cup, we congratulated ourselves upon being two of the happiest of human beings.

Such was my delight, that taking up the guitar which was near me, and putting aside all apprehension for the present, and all care for the future, I tuned it to my voice, and sang the following ode of Hafiz, which I had learnt in my youth, when I used to charm my hearers in the bath.

> *What bliss is like to whisp'ring love,*
> *Or dalliance in the bowers of spring?*
> *Why then delay my bliss t'improve?*
> *Haste, haste, my love, the goblet bring.*

> *Each hour that joy and mirth bestow*
> *Call it treasure, count it gain;*
> *Fool is the man who seeks to know*
> *His pleasure will it end in pain!*

The links which our existence bind
  Hang not by one weak thread alone;
Of man's distress why tease the mind?
  Sufficient 'tis—we know our own.

The double charms of love and wine
  Alike from one sweet source arise:
Are we to blame, shall we repine,
  When unconstrain'd the passions rise?

If, innocent in heart and mind,
  I sin unconscious of offence,
What use, O casuist, shall I find
  In absolution's recompense?

Hermits the flowing spring approve;
  Poets the sparkling bowl enjoy:
And, till he's judged by powers above,
  Hafiz will drink, and sing, and toy.

Zeenab was quite in ecstasy: she had never heard anything so delightful in her life, and forgetting that both of us were but wretched individuals—she a slave, I the most destitute of beings—we did and felt as if all that surrounded us was our own, and that the wine and our love would last for ever.

Having sang several more songs, and emptied several cups of wine, I found that my poetry was exhausted as well as our bottle.

It was still quite early, and we had much time before us. 'Zeenab,' said I, 'you have long promised to tell me the history of your life, and now is a good opportunity; we are not likely to be interrupted for a long while, and, as our meetings at night are very uncertain, an hour cannot be better filled up than by the recital of your adventures.' She assented to my proposal with much good humour, and began as follows.

CHAPTER XXVI: THE HISTORY OF
THE BEAUTIFUL ZEENAB, THE CURDISH SLAVE

I AM the daughter of a chief, well known in the Cûrdistan by the name of Okous Aga. Who my mother was I do not precisely know. I have heard that I am the produce of one of the secret meetings at Kerrund; but as such mysterious doings are hushed up among the Cûrds, I have never dared to question anybody concerning them, and cannot, therefore, ascertain whether the reports about my birth be true or not. It is very certain that I never looked up to any one as my mother; but was brought up at hazard among our women, and that my earliest friend was a foal, that lived as an inmate with us. It was born in the very tent which my father's wives occupied; and its dam, of the purest Arabian blood, was treated more like one of the family than a quadruped: in fact, it received much more attention than any of the wives; it enjoyed the warmest place in the tent, was beautifully clothed, and in all our journeys was the first object of our cares. When the mare died, a universal lamentation ensued throughout the encampment. The foal lived to be my father's war-horse, and is to this day the pride of the Cûrdistan. But would to Heaven that we had felt less affection for these animals! then I might still have been a free woman; for, in truth, the many vicissitudes which we have undergone originated in the possession of a mare, of which you shall hear more hereafter.

'You must know that although the Cûrds do not allow that they are subject to any power, yet our ancestors (and so did my father to a certain time) grazed their flocks and pitched their tents in that part of the Cûrdistan mountains belonging to Turkey, which are situated in the government of the Pasha of Bagdad. Whenever that chief had any war on his hands, he frequently called upon our tribes to afford him supplies of horsemen, who, being celebrated throughout Asia, were always foremost in the battle. My father, from his strength, his courage, and his horsemanship, was a great favourite with the Pasha, and in high request on such occasions. He was a majestic figure on horseback; and when his countenance was shaded by the back part of his cap thrown over his brow, his look inspired terror. He had killed several men, and was consequently honoured with the distinction of bearing a tuft of hair on his spear. But it was when clad in armour that he was most to be admired. I shall never forget the grandeur of his appearance, when, with his horse curvetting under him, I saw him in the midst of a thousand cavaliers, all dressed in shining cuirasses, peacock's feathers streaming from their helmets, and their spears glittering in the sun, preparing themselves to join the Pasha. From the result of this expedition we date part of our misfortunes. The Wahabi had advanced into the territory of Bagdad, and even threatened that city, when the Pasha thought it high time to call the Cûrds to his assistance. He took the field with a considerable number of troops, and immediately marched against the enemy. In a night attack my father happened to fall in with and slay the son of the Arab Sheikh himself, who commanded the Wahabi; and, having despoiled him of his arms, he led away with him the mare which his antagonist had mounted. He too well knew the value of such a prize not immediately to take the utmost care of it; and, in order to keep his good fortune from the knowledge of the Turkish chieftain, who would do everything in his power to get it from him, he sent the beast to his encampment, with orders that it should be carefully concealed, and lodged in the tent which his harem occupied. His precautions were useless, because the feat which he had performed, and the circumstances attending it, were soon known to every one; but as the Pasha had a great esteem for him, and there being no reason to suppose that the mare was more than an ordinary one, he made no inquiries about her. However, not very long after the war had ceased, the Wahabi having been driven back into the desert, and the Cûrds having retired to their mountains, we were surprised one morning by a visit from one of the Pasha's chief officers, viz. the *Mirakhor*, or master of the horse, who came escorted by a handsome train of ten men, well mounted and armed. Everybody was immediately on the alert to do them honour. Their horses were taken to the nearest pasture, and picketed with plenty of grass before them: the horsemen were led into the men's tent with much ceremony, where they were treated with coffee and pipes; and a large cauldron of rice was set on the fire to make a *pilau*. Two lambs were immediately killed, and cooked into a savoury dish by the women, who also baked piles of bread on the occasion. In short, we did all in our power to put into practice those obligations of hospitality which are binding upon the wandering tribes.

'As soon as my father was apprised of the approach of his visitors, even when they were first espied at a distance, it immediately occurred to him what might be their object, and he ordered his eldest son to mount the mare without a moment's delay, to take her into a neighbouring dell until he should hear further from him. Our tents were pitched in a line, on the brink of a mountain torrent; and it was therefore easy to steal away unperceived in the deep bed through which it flowed; and the high mountains in our neighbourhood, with the intricacies of which we were well acquainted, afforded good shelter to us in case of disturbance.

'I recollect the whole circumstance just as if it were yesterday; for we women could peep into the place where the men were assembled, and our curiosity led us to listen to what they said. The Mirakhor and two other Turks were seated; the others stood at the entrance of the tent, resting on their arms. My father placed himself at some distance, on the carpet, with his hands before him, and his feet tucked under him, looking very humble, but at the same time casting his eyes very sharply around him.

'"You are welcome, and you have brought happiness with you," exclaimed my father.

'"Happily met," answered the Mirakhor; "it is long since we have seen each other"; and when they had repeated these and similar sorts of compliments over and over again, they relapsed into silence; their pipes, which they smoked until the place was darkened with the fume, holding them in lieu of conversation.

'"Our master, the Pasha," said the Mirakhor, "sends you health and peace; he loves you, and says that you are one of his best and oldest friends. *Mashallah!* praise be to God! You are a good man; all Cûrds are good; their friends are our friends, and their enemies our enemies."

'An old Turk, who was standing, the foremost of the attendants, applauded this speech by a sort of low growl; and then my father, shrugging up his shoulders, and pressing his hands on his knees, answered: "I am the Pasha's slave; I am your slave; you do me much honour. *Il hem dillah*, thanks to heaven, we eat our bread in peace under the Pasha's shade, and put our caps on one side without fear. God give him plenty."

'After a short pause: "The business of our coming, Okous Aga," said the Mirakhor, "is this: The Wahabi (curses be on their beards!) have sent a deputation to our chief, requiring from him the mare upon which the son of their Sheikh was mounted at the time that he was killed. Although they say that his blood is on our heads, and that nothing but the Pasha's life, or that of his son, can ever redeem it; yet that subject they will for the present waive, in order to regain possession of her. They say, she has the most perfect pedigree of any in Arabia; that from generation to generation her descent is to be traced to the mare which the Prophet rode on his flight from Medina; and, in order to regain her, they offer to throw money on the board until the Pasha shall say stop. Now all the world knows that you are the brave he, who overcame and slew the Sheikh's son, and that yours is the spoil of the mare. My master, after consulting with the nobles and the chief men of Bagdad, has determined to take the offer of the Wahabi into consideration; and since it is become a business of government, has sent me to request you to deliver her up into my hands. This is my errand, and I have said it."

'"*Wallah! billah!* By the Pasha's salt which I have eat, by your soul, by the mother who bore you, by the stars and the heavens, I swear that all the Wahabi say is false. Where is the mare they pretend to have lost, and where the miserable jade that fell to my lot? I got a mare, 'tis true, but so lean, so wretched, that I sold her to an Arab the day after the battle. You may have the bridle and saddle, if you please; but as for the beast, I have her not."

and all the party, consisting of the Mirakhor, his ten followers, my father and three of his attendants, settling themselves round the dish, with their right shoulders advanced forwards, partook of the soup with wooden spoons. A lamb roasted whole succeeded the mess, which was pulled to pieces in a short time, each man getting as large a portion of it for himself as he could. The feast was closed by an immense dish of rice, which was dived into by the hands and fingers of all present. As fast as they were satisfied, each man got up and washed, saying *Shukur Allah*, thanks to God; and *Allah bereket versin*, may God restore you plenty. The remains were then rolled up in the leathern cloth, and taken outside the tents, where my father's shepherds soon made an end of them.

'The Mirakhor being anxious to sleep at a village in the plain, expressed a wish to depart, and his suite went to prepare their horses, leaving him and my father in the tent. I, who had narrowly watched the whole of the proceedings, was determined to see what should take place between them, and lent an ear to what they said.

'My father said, "Indeed ten ducats is all I can give—we are poor—where shall I find more?" To which the Mirakhor replied, "It is impossible: you know perfectly what will happen if I do not receive double that sum: the Pasha, when he finds that we have not brought the mare, will order me back again to seize you, and will take possession of all your property. I am indeed ordered to do that now, in case you refuse his request, but shall not touch you, if you come to my terms, which are twenty gold pieces. So, my friend, decide." Upon which, my father took the handkerchief from his bosom, and taking out the money from it, counted twenty ducats into the Mirakhor's hand, who, when satisfied that they were all good, untied the white muslin that was wound round his turban, and placing them in the folds of it, twisted it round his head again. "Now," said he to my father, "we have ate salt together; we are friends; and should the Pasha attempt anything, I will interfere. But you must send him a present, or otherwise it will be impossible to prevent him from molesting you."

'"*Bashem ustun*, upon my head be it!" answered my father. "I possess a famous greyhound, celebrated throughout the whole of the Cûrdistan, which can seize an antelope at full speed; a creature the like of which the Shah of Persia's father never even saw in a dream. Will that do?"

'"Perfectly well for one thing; but that is not enough. Consider of what consequence it is that my master should be pleased with you."

'"I tell you what," said he: "a thought has struck me; I have a daughter, more beautiful than the moon, round, large hipped, and greatly inclined to corpulency. You must say to him, that although the Yezeedies are infidels in his eyes, and as the dust under his feet, yet still he may perhaps be anxious to possess a beauty, which even the houris of Mohamed's Paradise would be jealous of, and I am ready to send her to him."

'The Mirakhor clapped his hands in ecstasy, and said, *"Aferin! Aferin!* well said! this is excellent! I will make the offer, and no doubt he will accept it; and thus you will have a powerful friend in his harem, who will get you out of this scrape, and protect you for the future." Upon this they seemed agreed. I, who it appears was to be the victim, left my watching-place to ruminate upon what was likely to be my future destiny. At first I was inclined to weep, and to lament over my fate; but after a little consideration, I exclaimed, "O my soul! am I to be a Pasha's lady? am I to wear fine clothes?  am I to be borne in a litter? Oh! the delight of a litter will be too great! How all the girls of the mountains will envy me!"

'After some time had elapsed, looking from the tents into the open country, I saw the Mirakhor and his party, who had not failed to take the greyhound with him, duly dressed out in its gayest trappings, making their way along the side of the chain of hills which bordered our camp. I then heard my father expressing his thankfulness and gratitude for having so well got rid of such unwelcome visitors.

'As soon as they were fairly out of sight, he dispatched one of his shepherd's boys to his son in the mountains, ordering him to bring back the mare; and when the animal was safely lodged in the women's tent, he called together the elders of his tribe, consisting of his own and his wives' relations, who were encamped in our vicinity. He explained to them the situation in which he was placed; showing that his and their destruction was inevitable should they continue any longer in the territory of the Pasha, who would not fail to seize this opportunity of levying fines and exactions, and reducing them to want and beggary. They were assembled in the men's tent, to the number of ten persons; the place of honour, the corner, being given to my father's uncle, the elder of the tribe, an old man, whose beard, as white as snow, descended to his girdle.

'"You know," said my father, "that we are Yezeedies; and you also know the hatred which all Mussulmans bear to us: the Pasha has hitherto pretended friendship to me individually, because I have fought his battles, because I am a lion in the fight, and drink the blood of his enemies; but his love of money is so great that nothing can satisfy it; and rather than lose this opportunity, he would see me, my father, my grandfather, my great-grandfather, and all my race grilling in eternal fires. We are too few to resist him, although, by that great Power whom we all worship, if we had not wives and children to protect, I, with a spear in my hand, my sword by my side, and mounted on my mare—I would not fear to encounter the whole host of his dastardly ragamuffins, and I should like to see the *cherkaji*[1] that would face me. I propose, therefore, that, without a moment's delay, we abandon the Turkish territory, and migrate into Persia, where we shall not fail to meet with welcome and protection."

'"Okous Aga," said his uncle to him, whilst every one seemed to listen with great respect to what he would say, "Okous Aga, you are my brother's son; you are my child; you are the head of our tribe, and our best support and protection. If I were to advise you to give up the mare to the Pasha, you would think me unworthy of being a Cûrd and a Yezeedi; and even were he now to get possession of her, we should not be spared; for such is the experience I have of Turkish governors, that when once they have a pretext in hand for oppression, they never fail to make use of it. Therefore, I am of your opinion—we cannot remain here. Old as I am, and accustomed as I have been from my earliest infancy to graze our flocks and herds upon these mountains—to see the sun rise over yonder hill and

---

[1] The *cherkajis* (literally *wheelers about*) in oriental armies are skirmishers, who are thrown out from the main body to engage in the fight, and are generally esteemed the most expert horsemen and the best soldiers.

"Your eyes have made roast meat of my heart"

set in that distant plain—much as I love these spots upon which our ancestors have been bred and born; yet it shall not be said that I have been the cause of the ruin of our tribe. I am, therefore, for immediate departure: delay now would be dangerous. In two more days we shall be visited by the Pasha's troops, who will take from us hostages, and then here shall we be fixed, and here will ruin overwhelm us. Let us go, my children; God is great and merciful. The time may come when you will be restored to your ancient seats, and when you may again range from your summer pastures to your winter quarters, and from your winter quarters to your pastures, without fear and apprehension."

'When he had done speaking, an old shepherd, who had great experience in all that related to the seasons, and considerable knowledge of the country between our mountains and those of Persia, spoke as follows: "If we go, we must go immediately, for a day's delay might stop us. The snows on the mountains are already beginning to melt, and the torrents will be so swollen in another week, that we shall not be able to get the sheep across them. Besides, it is now about three weeks to the day when the sun enters the sign of the Ram, at which time our ewes will, *inshallah*, please God, bring forth in plenty; and they ought to have performed their journey and be at rest long before that time. We ought to settle beforehand in what tract of country we shall fix ourselves, because the Persian wandering tribes are very tenacious of their rights of pasturage; and should we trespass upon them, without proper authority from the government, our shepherds and theirs would not fail to come to blows, and God only knows the consequences."

'"He speaks true," exclaimed my father: then turning to the shepherd, he exclaimed, "Well said, Karabeg; well done! you are a good servant, and you have given good advice. Before we think of establishing ourselves in Persia, one of us must go to Kermanshah, and ask leave of the Prince to appoint us to a good country; and when once we have got out of the Pasha's reach, I will perform that service, and return to you in time to prevent strife with the other wandering tribes."

'The assembly being unanimous for immediate departure, my father gave his orders, that the cattle should be called in, the tents broken up, and the oxen in readiness to receive their loads; that the camels should have their pack-saddles put upon them, and that everything should be in

readiness to depart by midnight, in order that we might reach our first
stage about an hour after sunrise. His mare, which was now become an object of the first consequence, was to be mounted by my father, in person,
whilst his chief wife, with her children, were to travel in the *cajaveh* or
panniers; the camel which was to carry them being ornamented with trappings inlaid with beads, set off by red cloth trimmings, and a thick profusion of tassels.

'As soon as this was known by the women, they set up shouts of wailing and lamentation. The evil appeared to them greater than it really was;
for they expected nothing less than the immediate approach of the Pasha's
troops to seize upon the tribe, and carry them all into slavery.

'As for me,' said Zeenab, 'my misery arose from another cause; for
ever since I had overheard the conversation between my father and the
Mirakhor, I could think of nothing else than of the charms of being a
Pasha's lady. My dream was now over, and instead of the rich dresses, the
sumptuous palaces, the gilded litters, and the luxury of state, which I had
flattered myself was to be my future lot, I had now nothing before me but

my old drudgeries—the loading of beasts, the packing up of baggage, the churning of milk, and the making of butter.

'Our whole camp was now in motion: and, as far as the eye could reach, the mountains were swarming with the flocks and herds of our tribe, which were driven by the shepherds towards their different encampments. The tents were taken to pieces, and prepared for loading. The women, who took the greatest share in the labour of departure, were seen everywhere actively bestirring themselves to pack up the furniture and utensils. The carpets were rolled up; the camel-trunks filled; all the materials for making butter collected; and the pack-saddles of the mules, oxen, and camels, laid out for immediate use. The cattle being arrived, the camels were made to kneel down in a ring, and were covered with their pack-saddles; the oxen had their pads put upon them; and the mules were tied into strings of five or seven each, and ornamented with their bells and thick felt coverings. The sheep and goats, in the meanwhile, at the close of day, had already began their march, guarded by their watch-dogs, and accompanied by their shepherds, one of whom walked in front, whilst the whole train followed.

'At midnight the whole camp had cleared the ground; and, as the day dawned, our line of march was to be seen to a great distance, winding along the mountains. We kept a track little followed, in order not to meet any one, who might give information of our movements to the Pasha; and, after several days' march, we reached the frontier of Persia, with much fewer accidents, and much less difficulties, than might have been expected. During the journey, my father, in conjunction with the principal men of his tribe, kept a constant look out in the rear, determined, should any of the Pasha's people approach us with an intention of impeding our progress, they would, without hesitation, make every resistance in their power. But fortune favoured us, and we saw none but shepherds, belonging to Cûrdish tribes, who occupied part of the country that we travelled over.

'When we had reached a place of safety, my father rode forwards to Kermanshah, the seat of government of a powerful Prince, one of the king of Persia's sons, in order to claim his protection, and to receive his permission to occupy one of the pasturages situated within the Persian territory. We waited for his return with great anxiety, for in the meanwhile we were liable to an attack from both Turks and Persians; but as it is the policy of both countries to entice the wandering tribes into their territory, we met with no molestation from the chief of the Persian town which happened to be the nearest to us.

'At length my father returned, and with him an officer belonging to the prince, who assigned us a tract of country, about ten parasangs within the Persian frontier. Our winter residence was situated in a sheltered nook of the mountains, not far from a copious spring of water; and our summer quarters, about three days' journey off, were described as situated in the coolest spot of the adjacent mountains, abounding in grass and water, and distant from any chance of molestation from the Turks.

'My father was well known at Kermanshah, and when his arrival and the object of his mission were known, the Prince expressed great pleasure, treated him with much consideration, and dismissed him invested with a dress of honour. No stipulations were made as to the terms upon which he was to be received, and unlimited promises of protection were held out to him. "If the Pasha," said the Prince, "claims you and your tribe, as the property of his government, and sends me a request that I should not admit you into mine, I will burn his father, and laugh at his beard. The face of God's world is open to every one, and if man is ill-treated in one spot, he will take himself where better treatment is to be found." In short, we settled, and returned to our former habits and occupations.

'As the Prince had expected, so it happened. A very short time after our arrival an officer from the Pasha appeared at Kermanshah, bearing a letter, making a formal demand, that my father, with the whole of his tribe, should be sent back to his territory; and stating all the circumstances relative to our flight. My father was called a thief, and accused of having stolen a mare of immense value, which was described as the Pasha's property. The animal was demanded to be instantly restored; and in case it were not, threats were made that immediate reprisals on Persian property should ensue. The whole of these circumstances were made known to my father, and he was summoned forthwith to appear before the Prince.

'Consternation seized us as soon as this intelligence was known amongst us. It was evident that the Pasha was determined to leave nothing undone to regain possession of the mare, and to ruin my father; nor could it be supposed that a weak and poor tribe like ours was likely to withstand the intrigues, bribes, and machinations of so powerful a chief: besides, the possession of such a treasure would of itself be a crime in the eyes of the Persians, and they would certainly endeavour to get her from us, if not now, yet at some more favourable opportunity. It would soon be known that many of us were Yezeedies, a circumstance of itself sufficient to excite the hatred and execration of every good sectary of Ali; and every probability existed, even supposing the mare to be out of the question, that we should be a prey to every sort of persecution as soon as time enough should have passed over our heads for intrigue to have worked its effects.

'Before my father left us to attend the Prince's summons, he had given secret orders that the mare should be put into some place of safety, in case he should be obliged to deny that he possessed her; but on his return we found that such a precaution was unnecessary. He had been kindly received by the Prince, who had assured him that he was resolved not to accede to the Pasha's demands in any one case; that my father might enjoy the possession of his mare, and depend upon protection and security as long as he remained in his territory. His words were something to this purpose: "Set your mind at ease, Okous Aga. As long as you remain under our shade you may lay your head on your pillow in full security. What does the Pasha mean by claiming you and your tribe as the subjects of his government? The gates of the palace of my father, the Centre of the Universe and King of Kings, are open to every one, and as soon as the stranger has touched the skirt of his robe he is safe. You have sought our protection, and we should not be Mussulmans if we refused it. Go, return to your tents, be happy, and leave the Pasha to us."

'This produced great rejoicings amongst us; and my father, to celebrate his success, gave a feast to the chiefs and elders of the tribe, where our present situation was fully discussed, and our plans for the future taken into consideration. Every one present was elated with the success that had attended our flight excepting one, and that was the old man, my father's uncle. He had seen much of the Persians, having served under Nadir Shah when a youth, and nothing could induce him to put any faith in the promises and fair words of the Prince. "You do not know the Persians," said he, addressing himself to the assembly. "You have never had any dealings with them, and therefore you permit yourselves to be lulled into security by their flattering expressions and their winning and amiable manners. But I have lived long with them, and have learned the value of

what they say. Their weapons are not such as you have been accustomed
to meet in the bold encounter, and the open attack: instead of the sword
and spear, theirs are treachery, deceit, falsehood; and when you are the
least prepared, you find yourselves caught as in a net; ruin and desolation
surround when you think that you are seated on a bed of roses. Lying is
their great, their national vice. Do not you remark that they confirm every
word by an oath? What is the use of oaths to men who speak the truth? One
man swears by your soul, and by his own head, by your child, by the
Prophet, by his relations and ancestors; another swears by the *Kebleh*,[1] by
the king, and by his beard; a third by your death, by the salt he eats, by
the death of Imâm Hosein. Do they care for any one of these things? No,
they feel all the time that they lie, and then out comes the oath. Now in
our case, is it to be supposed that we shall be left unmolested, in the quiet
possession of this mare, which has brought so much misfortune already on
our heads? The Persians are more wild, if possible, on the subject of horses
than the Turks, and an Arabian mare in their sight is of greater value than
diamonds and rubies. Should the Shah hear of the one we possess, he will
instantly send for it, and what are we to do then? Shall we continue in arms
against all the world? No, my friends. You may think what you please;
but, for my part, I look upon your situation as precarious, and advise you,
as a general rule, not to put your trust in Persians, be they who or what
they may."

'The event proved to be precisely what the old man had predicted, and
was the cause of placing me where you now see me.

'One morning, about an hour before the dawn of day, we heard an unusual stir among the dogs of the camp; they did not cease to bark and
make a most furious noise. As we were accustomed to the attacks of wolves,
who were kept at bay by our dogs, we did not at first pay attention to the
disturbance; but at length my father and his sons arose, and, taking their
guns with them, went to see what could have happened. They had not
proceeded twenty steps before they saw a horseman, and then a second,
and shortly after several more; in short, they discovered that their tents
were surrounded. My father immediately gave the alarm, and instantly
all the camp was in motion. The horsemen rushed on my father, and attempted to seize him; but he shot the first dead at his feet, and with his

[1] The point towards which the Mohammedans turn in prayer.

sword wounded the second. The report of the gun, and the noise of the fray, was a signal to the invaders for a general attack, and in a short time our camp was entered at every corner. Their principal object was evidently the mare; for the women's tent was attacked first, and there they instantly seized the object of their search.

'As the day dawned, we observed that our invaders were Persians, and we also soon discovered that they were acting from authority. My father had unluckily killed their chief, and that was a sufficient reason for our our being made prisoners. Conceive our situation: it was a scene of misery that I shall never forget. My father was treated with every indignity before our eyes; our property was pillaged, and—'

Zeenab was proceeding to relate to me how she became the property of Mirza Ahmak, when a loud knocking at the gate of the house was heard. We both got up in great alarm. My fair one entreated me to take my departure by the terrace, while she went to see who it might be. By the voice, that was ordering the door to be opened, she recognized the doctor himself, and trusting to her own ingenuity for giving good reasons for the appearance of breakfast and good cheer, which he would perceive, she forthwith unbarred the gate and admitted him.

From the terrace I could watch all that was going on. The doctor appeared quite delighted to find Zeenab alone, and made her some speeches so full of tenderness, that there was no mistaking how his affections were placed. Looking into the window of his wife's apartment, he perceived the remains of the breakfast, and every appearance of the room having been occupied. He was asking some questions concerning what he saw, when in came the khanum herself, followed by her women. She entered the house so unexpectedly, that she appeared before them ere they could separate. I shall never forget her look and attitude at this sight.

'*Selam aleikum!* peace be unto ye!' said she, with mock respect, 'I am your very humble servant. I hope that the health of both your excellencies is good, and that you have passed your time agreeably. I have arrived too soon, I fear.' Then the blood creeping into her face, she very soon relinquished her raillery, and fell tooth and nail upon the unhappy culprits.

'And breakfast too—and in my room. *Mashallah! Mashallah!* It is understood, then, that I am become less than a dog; now that in my own house, on my own carpet, on my very pillow, my slaves give up their hearts to joy. *La Allah il Allah!* There is but one God! I am all astonishment! I am fallen from the heavens to the ground!'

Then addressing herself to her husband, she said, 'As for you, Mirza Ahmak, look at me, and tell me, by my soul, are you to be counted a man amongst men? A doctor too, the Locman of his day, a sage, with that monkey's face, with that goat's beard, with that humped back, to be playing the lover, the swain! Curses attend such a beard!' then putting up her five fingers to his face, she said, '*Poof!* I spit on such a face. Who am I, then, that you prefer an unclean slave to me? What have I done, that you should treat me with such indignity? When you had nothing but your prescriptions and your medicines in the world, I came, and made a man of you. You are become something, thanks to me! You now stand before a king: men bow the head to you. You wear a Cashmerian shawl: you are become a person of substance. Say, then, oh, you less than man! what is the meaning of all this?'

The doctor, during this attack upon him, was swearing abundance of oaths, and making ten thousands of exclamations, in proof of his innocence. Nothing, however, could stop the volubility of his wife, or calm her rage. By this time she had worked her passion up to such a pitch, that oath succeeded oath; and blasphemy blasphemy, in one raging, unceasing torrent. From her husband she fell on Zeenab, and from Zeenab she returned again to her husband, until she foamed at the mouth. She was not satisfied with words alone, but seizing the wretched girl by one of the long tresses which hung down her back, she pulled it till she roared with pain; then, with the assistance of the other slaves, she was thrown into the reservoir, where they beat and soused her until both parties were nearly exhausted. Oh, how I burned to fly to her rescue! My body was become like glowing fire. I could have drunk the blood of the unfeeling wretches. But what could I do? Had I rushed into the harem, death would have been my lot; for most probably they would have impaled me on the spot; and what good would that have done to Zeenab? She would have been even more cruelly treated than before, and the doctor's wife would not have been the less jealous. So when the storm had subsided, I quietly stepped down from my hiding-place on the terrace, and walked into the open country without the town, to consider upon the course which I ought to pursue. To remain with the doctor was out of the question; and to expect to enjoy Zeenab's company again was folly. My heart bled, when I reflected what might be the fate of that poor girl; for I had heard horrid stories of the iniquities performed in harems, and there was no length to which such a demon as the khanum might not go, with one so entirely in her power.

CHAPTER XXVII: OF THE PREPARATIONS MADE BY THE CHIEF PHYSICIAN TO RECEIVE THE SHAH AS HIS GUEST, AND OF THE GREAT EXPENSE WHICH THREATENED HIM

IN my walk I had almost determined to quit the doctor's house immediately, and abandon Tehran, such was the desperate view I took of my situation; but my love for Zeenab overcame this resolution; and in the hope of seeing her again, I continued to drag on a miserable existence as a dependent on Mirza Ahmak. He had no suspicion that I was his rival, and that I had been the cause of the late confusion in his harem; but he was aware that some one must have had access to it, and therefore took such precautions for the future, that I found great difficulty in discovering how it fared with my love, or what had been the consequences of the anger of the khanum. I daily watched the door of the *anderûn*, in the hope of seeing Zeenab in the suite of her mistress when she went out, but in vain: there was no indication of her, and my imagination made me apprehend either that she was kept in close confinement, or that she had fallen a victim of the violence of her enemies in the harem. My impatience had risen to the utmost, when I, one day, perceived that Nûr Jehan,[1] the black slave, had issued from the house by herself, and was making her way to the bazaar. I followed her, and trusting to the friendship that she formerly entertained for the mistress of my heart, I ventured to accost her.

'Peace be with you, Nûr Jehan!' said I; 'where are you going in such haste by yourself?'—'May your kindness never be less, Aga[2] Hajjî,' answered she; 'I am bound to the druggist's for our Cûrdish slave.'

'What! Zeenab?' exclaimed I, in great agitation. 'What has befallen her? Is she sick?'

'Ah, poor thing,' replied the good negro girl, 'she has been sick and sorry too. You Persians are a wicked nation. We who are black, and slaves, have twice the heart that you have. You may talk of your hospitality, and of your kindness to strangers; but was there ever an animal, not to say a human creature, treated in the way that this poor stranger has been?'

'What have they done to her? For God's sake tell me, Nûr Jehan!' said I; 'by my soul, tell me!'

Softened by my manner, and by the interest which I took in what she said, she informed me, that in consequence of the jealousy of her mistress, Zeenab had been confined to a small back room, whence she was prohibited stirring; that the treatment which she had received had occasioned a violent fever, which had brought her to the brink of the grave, but that her youth and strength had enabled her to overcome it: and now that she was quite recovered, her mistress began to relent, and had permitted her to use the *khena* and the *surmeh*,[3] which she was about to procure from the druggist. But she was sure that this indulgence would never have been granted, if the report had not been spread, that it was the Shah's intention to pay Mirza Ahmak a visit; and as it is his privilege to enter every man's harem at pleasure, and to inspect his women unveiled; her mistress, who wanted to make as great a display of slaves and attendants as possible, had released Zeenab from the confinement of her room, in order that she should wait upon her: but she was still restricted to the walls of the secret chamber.

[1] Light of the world. The Persians are apt to give high-sounding names to their slaves, and particularly to the guardians of their women.
[2] *Aga* is used in the sense of *master*. [3] The *surmeh* is a collyrium.

I was relieved by this intelligence, and began to turn in my mind how I could manage to obtain an interview; but such insurmountable obstacles did I foresee, that, fearful of entailing fresh miseries upon her, I determined to remain quiet for the present, and to follow the poet's advice— 'to fold up the carpet of my desires, and not to prowl round and round my inclination.'

In the meanwhile, the day of the Shah's departure for his usual summer campaign approached; and, according to custom, he passed the intermediate time in visiting the noblemen of his court, and thereby reaping for himself and his suite a harvest of presents, which every one who is distinguished by so great an honour is obliged to make.

Nûr Jehan's intelligence to me was true: the king had selected Mirza Ahmak as one of those to whom he intended the honour of a visit; for the doctor had the reputation of being rich, and he had long been marked as prey fit for the royal grasp. Accordingly, he was informed of the day when this new and special proof of favour would be conferred upon him; and as a most distinguishing mark of it, he was told, that it should not be an ordinary visit, but that the doctor should enjoy the satisfaction of entertaining his majesty: in short, the king would take his _shâm_,[1] or dinner, at his house.

The doctor, half elated with the greatness of the distinction, half trembling at the ruin that awaited his finances, set to work to make all the necessary preparations. The first thing to be settled was the value and nature of the _Pah-endaz_.[2] This he knew would be talked of throughout the country; and this was to be the standard of the favour in which he stood with his sovereign. His vanity was roused on the one hand, and his avarice alarmed on the other. If he exhibited too much wealth, he would remain a mark for future exactions; and if he made no display, his rivals in consequence would treat him with contempt. He had not deigned to consult me for a long time, and I had dwindled into a mere hanger-on; but recollecting the success which had attended my negotiation with the European doctor, he called me again into his councils.

'Hajjî,' said he, 'what is to be done in this difficult case? I have received

---

[1] The _shâm_ is, in truth, the evening meal, and is served up at sunset.
[2] The ceremony of the _pah-endaz_ consists in spreading rich stuffs for the king to walk upon.

a hint, that the king expects from me a considerable *pah-endaz*, and this from the lord high treasurer himself, whose magnificence on such occasions is the theme of wonder throughout the whole of Persia. Now, it is impossible that I can rival him. He insisted, that I ought to spread broad cloth from the entrance of the street to where the king alights from his horse; that there he should tread upon cloth of gold, until he reached the entrance of the garden; and from thence, the whole length of the court to his seat, a carpet of Cashmerian shawls was to be extended, each shawl increasing in value, until the one upon the *musnud*, or carpet of state, which should be of an extraordinary price. Now, you know I am not the man to make such display: I am a *hakîm*, one of the learned: I make no profession of riches. Besides, 'tis plain that the lord high treasurer only says this, because he has cloth, brocades, and shawls to dispose of, which he wishes me to take off his hands. No, it is impossible that I can listen to his extravagant proposals. What then is to be done?'

I answered, ''Tis true that you are a hakîm; but then you are the royal physician; you hold a situation of great consequence: besides, for the sake of the lady, your wife, you are bound to do something worthy of such an alliance. The king will be displeased if you do not receive him in a manner that will show your sense of the confidence he reposes in you.'

'Yes,' said the Mirza, 'and that may all be very true, friend Hajjî; still I am but a doctor, and cannot be supposed to have all these shawls, brocades, and stuffs by me whenever I want them.'

'But what can you do otherwise?' replied I; 'you would not strew the road with jalap, and spread his majesty's seat with a blister plaster?'

'No,' said he; 'but we might strew flowers, which, you know, are cheap; and perhaps we might sacrifice an ox, and break plenty of bottles full of sweetmeats under his horse's feet.[1]—Would not that answer?'

'It is impossible,' exclaimed I; 'if you act thus, the Shah, and your enemies, will devise means to strip you as naked as my hand. Perhaps there is no necessity to do all the lord high treasurer advises; but you might spread chintz in the street, velvet at the alighting spot, brocade in the courtyard, and shawls in the room; that will not be very expensive.'

'You do not say ill,' said the doctor: 'I might perhaps manage that.

[1] This is an ancient Persian custom, and is supposed to secure good fortune—sweetness, and consequently sugar, being an emblem of felicity.

We have chintz in the house, which was intended for the women's trousers; that will probably do. A patient gave me a piece of Ispahan velvet the other day; I can sell my last dress of honour for some brocade; and two or three of my wife's shawls will suffice for the room.—By the blessing of Ali, that is settled.'

'Ah, but the harem!' exclaimed I; 'the Shah must go there. You know it brings good luck to be looked at by the king, and your women must appear well-dressed on the occasion.'

'Oh, as for that,' said the doctor, 'they can borrow; they can borrow anything they like from their friends—jewels, trousers, jackets, shawls—they can get whatever they want.'

Not so, said my lady the khanum. As soon as this arrangement was mentioned to her, she protested against it; she called her husband a low born, niggardly carle; one unfit for the honour of possessing her for a wife; and insisted upon his conducting himself on this occasion in a manner worthy of the high distinction that was about to be conferred upon him. It was in vain to contend against her; and therefore the preparations were made upon a scale far exceeding what the doctor had intended; and every individual of his house appeared to be actuated by only one feeling, that of making him refund all that money which he so long and so unpitifully had extorted from others.

CHAPTER XXVIII: CONCERNING THE MANNER OF THE SHAH'S RECEPTION: OF THE PRESENT MADE HIM, AND THE CONVERSATION WHICH ENSUED

ON the morning of the day upon which this great event was to happen (a day which had been duly settled as auspicious by the astrologers) the note of preparation was heard throughout the whole of Mirza Ahmak's dwelling. The king's tent-pitchers had taken possession of the saloon of audience in which he was to hold his court, where they spread fresh carpets and prepared the royal musnud,[1] covering it with a magnificent shawl. They threw water over the courtyard, set the fountains play-

---

[1] The *musnud*, in Eastern acceptation, is, in fact, the throne; but on occasions such as the one here described the mode of making a musnud is to double up a thick carpet, by which means there is only room for one person to be seated upon it.

ing, and fitted on a new curtain to the front of the building. The king's gardeners also came and decked the premises with flowers. On the surface of the pool of water, immediately facing the spot where his majesty was to be seated, they spread rose leaves in curious devices. Around the marble basin they placed rows of oranges, and a general appearance of freshness and cheerfulness was given to the whole scene.

Then the cooks, a numerous and most despotic band, arrived with such accompaniments of pots, pans, braziers, and boilers, that the doctor, out of all patience, inquired of the head of the kitchen, 'what this meant; whether it was intended that he should feed all the city, as well as the king,' 'Not quite all,' was his answer; 'but perhaps you will recollect the words of Saadi:

> *"If from the peasant's tree, the king an apple craves,*
> *Down with it root and branch, exclaim his ready slaves;*
> *And should he, in dainty mood, one single egg require,*
> *Lo! thousand spitted birds revolve before the fire."* '

They took possession of the kitchen, which did not contain one-quarter of the space required for their operations, and consequently it was necessary to erect temporary fire-places in the adjoining court, where the braziers were placed, and in which was boiled the rice that is distributed on such occasions to all present. Besides the cooks, a body of confectioners established themselves in one of the apartments, where the sweetmeats, the sherbets, the ices, and the fruits were prepared; and they called for so many ingredients, that the doctor had nearly expired when the list was presented to him. In addition to all these, arrived the king's band of singers and musicians, and the *Lûti Bashi* (jester in chief) accompanied by twenty Lûtis, each with a drum hanging over his shoulder.

The time appointed for the visit was after the evening's prayer, which is made at sunset. At that hour, when the heat of the day had partly subsided, and the inhabitants of Tehran were about to enjoy the cool of the evening, the Shah left his palace, and proceeded to the doctor's house. The streets had been swept and watered; and as the royal cortege approached, flowers were strewn on the path. Mirza Ahmak himself had proceeded to the royal presence to announce that all was ready, and walked close to the king's stirrup during the cavalcade.

The procession was opened by the heralds, who, with the distinguishing club of office in their hands, and ornament on the head, proclaimed the king's approach, and marshalled every one on the road. The tops of the walls were occupied by women in their white veils, and in the better houses they were seen to be peeping through the holes made in the screens which surround their terraces. Then followed a great body of tent-pitchers and carpet-spreaders, with long slender sticks in their hands, keeping the road clear from intruders. After this, walked a crowd of well-dressed officers of the stable, bearing rich embroidered saddle housings over their shoulders; then servants in the gayest attire, with gold pipes in their hands, the king's shoe bearer, the king's ewer and basin bearer, the carrier of his cloak, the comptroller of the opium box, and a number of other domestics. As this was only a private procession, his majesty was preceded by no led horses, which usually form so splendid a part of his grand displays. To these succeeded a train of running footmen, two and two, fantastically dressed, some with gold coins embroidered on their black velvet coats, others dressed in brocades, and others in silks: they immediately preceded the Shah in person, who was attended by the chief of the running footmen, a man of considerable consequence, known by the enamelled handled whip stuck in his girdle. The king rode a quiet ambling horse, richly caparisoned; but his own dress was plain, and only distinguished by the beauty of the shawls and other materials of which it was composed. After him, at an interval of fifty paces, followed three of the king's sons, then the noble of nobles, the great master of the ceremonies, the master of the horse, the court poet, and many others, all attended by their servants: and at length when the whole party were collected together, who were to partake of Mirza Ahmak's substance, five hundred would probably be called a moderate number.

The king alighted at the gate, the entrance being too narrow to ride through; and proceeded up the centre walk of the court to the seat prepared for him in the great saloon. Every one, except the princes, stood without, and the doctor himself did the duties of a menial.

After his majesty had been seated some little time, the master of ceremonies, accompanied by the master of the house, walking barefooted, appeared near the reservoir, the latter holding up breast high a silver salver, in which were spread one hundred tomauns of new coinage. The master of ceremonies then exclaimed, in a loud voice, 'The meanest of your majesty's slaves makes a humble representation to the Centre of the Universe, the King of Kings, the Shadow of God upon earth, that Mirza Ahmak, the king's chief physician, dares to approach the sacred dust of your majesty's feet, and to bring by way of an offering one hundred gold tomauns.'

To which the king answered, 'You are welcome, Mirza Ahmak. Praise be to God, you are a good servant. The Shah has a particular share of condescension for you; your face is whitened, your consequence has increased, Go, give praises to God, that the king has come to your house, and has accepted your present.'

Upon which the doctor knelt down and kissed the ground.

Then his majesty, turning to his noble of nobles, exclaimed, 'By the head of the Shah, Mirza Ahmak is a good man. There is no one like him now in Persia—he is wiser by far than Locman—more learned than Galen.'

'Yes, yes,' answered the noble of nobles; 'Locman indeed! whose dog was he, or Galen? This also comes from the happy star of the King of Kings. Such a king Persia before never saw, and such a doctor for such a king! Men may praise the doctors of Europe and of India, but where is science to be found, if it be not in Persia?—Who shall dare to claim a superiority, as long as the land of Persia is enlightened by the presence of its Shah without compare?'

'That's all true,' said the king. 'Persia is the country which, from the beginning of the world to the present day, has always been famous for the genius of its inhabitants, and the wisdom and splendour of its monarchs. From Kaiumars, the first king of the world, to me who am the present Shah, what list is so perfect, so glorious? India also had her sovereigns, Arabia her caliphs, Turkey her *Khon Khors* (lit. blood drinkers), Tartary her khans, and China her emperors; but as for the Franks, who come into my dominions from God knows where, to buy and sell, and to bring me tribute of presents;—they, poor infidels! have a parcel of kings, of whose countries even the names have not reached our ears.'

'*Belli, belli,* Yes, yes!' said the nobleman, 'I am your sacrifice. Except the English and the French nations, which by all accounts are something in the world, all others are but little better than nothing. As for Moscovites, they are not Europeans—they are less than the dogs of Europe.'

'Ha! ha! ha! you say true, answered the king, laughing. 'They had their *Khûrshîd Colah*, their 'Head of Glory' as they called her, who for a woman was a wonderful person,[1] 'tis true—and we all know that when a woman meddles with anything, *pena be khoda*, it is then time to put one's trust in God; but after her, they had a Paul, who was a pure madman; who, to give you an instance of what his folly was, wanted to march an army to India; just as if the *Kizzil Bashes*[2] would ever have allowed it. A Russian puts on a hat, a tight coat, and tight breeches, shaves his beard, and then calls himself a European. You might just as well tie the wings of a goose to your back and call yourself an angel.'

'Wonderful, wonderful,' exclaimed the head of the nobles; 'the *Shah-in-Shah* speaks like an angel. Show us a king in Europe that would speak like him.'

'Yes, yes,' was chorused by all the bystanders. 'May he live a thousand years,' said one. 'May his shadow never be less,' said another.

'But it is of their women,' continued the king, 'of whom we hear the most extraordinary accounts. In the first place, they have no *anderûn*[3] in their houses; men and women all live together—then the women never wear veils—they show their faces to whoever chooses to look at them, like those of our wandering tribes. Tell me, Mirza Ahmak, you that are a doctor and a philosopher, by what extraordinary arrangement of Providence does it happen, that we Mussulmans should be the only people on earth who can depend upon our wives, and who can keep them in subjection. You,' said his majesty, smiling ironically, 'you I hear are blessed above all men in an obedient and dutiful wife.'

'Possessed of the kindness and protection of the King of Kings,' answered the doctor, 'I am blessed with everything that can make life happy. I, my wife, my family, are your humble slaves, and everything we have your property. If your slave possesses any merit, it is none of his; it all emanates from the asylum of the world: even my failings become virtues, when the king commands me. "But what lamp can shine in the face of the sun, or what minaret can be called high at the foot of the mountain of Alwend?" With respect to what your majesty has been pleased to say concerning women, it appears to the meanest of your slaves, that there must be a great affinity between beasts and Europeans, and which accounts for the inferiority of the latter to Mussulmans. Male and female beasts herd

[1] Catherine II is so styled by the Persians. [2] *Kizzil Bash*, or Red Head, is a sort of nickname given from old times to the Persians. [3] The *inner*, or women's apartment.

'"*Allah, Allah!*" exclaimed the Mirakhor, "this is a business of much consequence. Okous Aga, you are an upright man, and so am I. Do not laugh at our beards, and send us away without caps on our heads. If we do not bring back the mare, our faces will be black to all eternity, and the doors of friendship between you and the Pasha will be shut. By my soul, tell me; where is the beast?"

'"Friend," answered my father, "what shall I say? what can I do? The mare is not here—the Wahabi are liars—and I speak the truth." Then with a softened tone, he approached the Mirakhor, and spoke to him for a long time in a whisper, with much animation and apparent persuasion; for, at the end of their conversation, they appeared to be well agreed.

'The Mirakhor then said aloud: "Well, if such is the case, and the beast is not in your possession, *Allah kerim*, God is merciful, and there is no combating against fate. We must return to Bagdad."

'My father then rose from his seat, and came into the women's tent, leaving his guests to smoke their pipes and drink coffee, preparatory to the meal which was making ready for them. He ordered his wife, who was the depository of his money, to bring him a bag of gold, that was carefully wrapped in many a piece of old cloth, and deposited in a trunk, which, with his rich horse furniture, the parade pack-saddle, and other things of value, were placed in a corner of the tent. He took out twenty *Bajoglis* (ducats), which he tied into the corner of a handkerchief, and thrust them into his bosom; and then giving his orders that the victuals should forthwith be served up, he returned to his guests. Little was said until the hour of eating came, and the few words that were uttered turned on horses, dogs, and arms. The Mirakhor drew from his girdle a long pistol, mounted in silver, which was shown around to all the company as a real English pistol. Another man exhibited his scimitar, which was assured to be a black *Khorassani* blade of the first water; and my father produced a long straight sword, sharp on both edges, which he had taken from the son of the Arab Sheikh whom he had slain.

'The dinner being ready, the round leathern cloth was placed before the Mirakhor, upon which many flaps of bread, just baked, were thrown, and water was handed about for washing the right hand. A mess of *chorba*, or soup, was served up in a large wooden dish, and placed in the centre of the cloth. My father then said aloud, "*Bismillah*," in the name of God;

promiscuously together; so do the Europeans. The female beasts do not
hide their faces; neither do the Europeans. They wash not, nor do they
pray five times a day; neither do the Europeans. They live in friendship
with swine; so do the Europeans; for
instead of exterminating the unclean
beast, as we do, I hear that every house
in Europe has an apartment fitted up
for its hog. Then as for their women
indeed!—What dog seeing its female
in the streets does not go and make
himself agreeable?—so doubtless does
the European. Wife in those unclean
countries must be a word without a
meaning, since every man's wife is
every man's property.'

'Well said, doctor,' exclaimed the king; ''tis plain, then, that all are
beasts but us. Our holy Prophet (upon whom be blessing and peace!) has
told us as much. The infidel will never cease roasting, whilst the true believer will be eternally seated next to his houri in the seventh heaven! But
we hear, doctor, that your Paradise has begun here on earth, and that you
have got your houris already:—hah! how is that?'

Upon which Mirza Ahmak made a low prostration, and said, 'Whatever the monarch permits his slave to possess is the monarch's. The hour
will be fortunate, and Mirza Ahmak's head will reach the skies, when the
propitious step of the King of Kings shall pass the threshold of his unworthy *anderûn*.'

'We shall see with our own eyes,' rejoined the king; 'a look from the
king brings good luck. Go, give notice to your harem that the Shah will
visit it; and if there be any one sick—any one whose desires are unaccom-
plished—any maiden who sighs for her lover, or any wife who wishes to
get rid of her husband—let them come forward, let them look at the king,
and good fortune will attend them.'

Upon this the poet, who had hitherto remained silent, his mind apparently absorbed in thought, exclaimed, 'Whatever the king hath ordained
is only an additional proof of his beneficence and condescension;' and then
in very good verse he sung—

'*The firmament possesses but one sun, and the land of Irâk but one king.*

'*Life, light, joy, and prosperity attend them both wherever they appear.*

'*The doctor may boast of his medicine; but what medicine is equal to a glance from the king's eye?*

'*What is spikenard? what* mumiai[1]*? what* pahzer*? compared even to the twinkle of a royal eyelash!*

'*Oh! Mirza Ahmak, happiest of men, and most blessed of doctors!*

'*Now, indeed, you possess within your walls an antidote to every disorder, a specific against every evil.*

'*Shut up your Galen, burn your Hippocrates, and put Avicenna in a corner: the father of them all is here in person.*

'*Who will take cassia when an eye is to be had, or will writhe under a blister when a look will relieve him?*

'*Oh! Mirza Ahmak, happiest of men, and most blessed of doctors!*'

Every one present had kept the strictest silence when this was repeating, when the king exclaimed, '*Aferîn*, this is well; you are indeed a poet, and worthy of our reign. Who was Ferdousi when compared to you? As for Mahmoud, the Ghaznevi, *hâk bûd* (he was dirt). Go to him,' said he to the noble of nobles, 'go, kiss him on the mouth, and, when that is done, fill it with sugar-candy. Every pleasure should attend such a mouth, from whence such good things proceed.'

Upon which the noble of nobles, who was endowed with a large and bushy beard, approached the poet, and inflicted a kiss upon his mouth, which also was protected by an appropriate quantity of hair; and then from a plate of sugar-candy, which was handed to him, he took as many lumps as would quite fill his jaws, and inserted them therein with his fingers with all due form.

Though evidently distressed with his felicity, the poet did his utmost to appear at the summit of all happiness, and grinned with such rare contortions, that involuntary tears flowed from his eyes as fast as the sugar-candy distilled through his lips.

The king then dismissed his courtiers and attendants, and preparations were made for serving up the royal dinner.

[1] *Mumiai* and *Pahzer* are antidotes in which the Persians have great faith. Our Bezoar is evidently a corruption of *Pahzer*.

CHAPTER XXIX: A DESCRIPTION OF THE
ENTERTAINMENT, WHICH IS FOLLOWED BY AN EVENT
DESTRUCTIVE TO HAJJI BABA'S HAPPINESS

THE only persons, besides servants, admitted into the saloon where the Shah dined, were the three princes, his sons, who had accompanied him; and they stood at the farthest end, with their backs against the wall, attired in dresses of ceremony, with swords by their sides. Mirza Ahmak remained in attendance without. A cloth, of the finest Cashmerian shawl fringed with gold, was then spread on the carpet before the king, by the chief of the valets, and a gold ewer and basin were presented for washing hands. The dinner was then brought in trays, which, as a precaution against poison, had been sealed with the signet of the head steward before they left the kitchen, and were broken open by him again in the presence of the Shah. Here were displayed all the refinements of cookery: rice, in various shapes, smoked upon the board; first, the *chilau*, as white as snow; then the *pilau*, with a piece of boiled lamb, smothered in the rice; then another *pilau*, with a baked fowl in it; a fourth, coloured with saffron, mixed up with dried peas; and at length, the king of Persian dishes, the *narinj pilau*, made with slips of orange-peel, spices

of all sorts, almonds, and sugar: salmon and herring, from the Caspian Sea, were seen among the dishes; and trout from the river Zengî, near Erivan; then in china basins and bowls of different sizes were the ragouts, which consisted of hash made of a fowl boiled to rags, stewed up with rice, sweet herbs, and onions; a stew, in which was a lamb's marrow-bone, with some loose flesh about it, and boiled in its own juice; small gourds, crammed with force-meat, and done in butter; a fowl stewed to rags, with a brown sauce of prunes; a large omelette, about two inches thick; a cup full of the essence of meat, mixed up with rags of lamb, almonds, prunes, and tamarinds, which was poured upon the top of the chilau; a plate of poached eggs, fried in sugar and butter; a dish of *badenjáns*, slit in the middle and boiled in grease; a stew of venison; and a great variety of other messes too numerous to mention. After these came the roasts. A lamb was served up hot from the spit, the tail of which, like marrow, was curled up over its back. Partridges, and what is looked upon as the rarest delicacy in Persia, two *capk dereh*, partridges of the valley, were procured on the occasion. Pheasants from Mazanderan were there also, as well as some of the choicest bits of the wild ass and antelope. The display and the abundance of delicacies surprised every one; and they were piled up in such profusion around the king, that he seemed almost to form a part of the heap. I do not mention the innumerable little accessories of preserves, pickles, cheese, butter, onions, celery, salt, pepper, sweets, and sours, which were to be found in different parts of the tray, for that would be tedious: but the sherbets were worthy of notice, from their peculiar delicacy: these were contained in immense bowls of the most costly china, and drank by the help of spoons of the most exquisite workmanship, made of the pear-tree. They consisted of the common lemonade, made with superior art; of the *sekenjebîn*, or vinegar, sugar, and water, so mixed that the sour and the sweet were as equally balanced as the blessings and miseries of life; the sherbet of sugar and water, with rose-water to give it a perfume, and sweet seeds to increase its flavour; and that made of the pomegranate; all highly cooled by lumps of floating ice.

The king then, doubling himself down with his head reclining towards his food, buried his hand in the pilaus and other dishes before him, and ate in silence, whilst the princes and the servants in waiting, in attitudes of respect, remained immovable. When he had finished he got up, and walked into an adjoining room, where he washed his hands, drank his coffee, and smoked his water-pipe.

In the course of his eating he ordered one of the pilaus, of which he had partaken, to be carried to Mirza Ahmak, his host, by a servant in waiting. As this is considered a mark of peculiar honour, the mirza was obliged to give a present in money to the bearer. A similar distinction was conferred upon the poet for his impromptu, and he also made a suitable present. His majesty also sent one of the messes, of which he had freely partaken, to the doctor's wife, who liberally rewarded the bearer. And in this manner he contrived to reward two persons, the one who received the present, and the other who bore it.

The princes then sat down, and when they had eat their fill they rose, and the dishes were served up in another room, where the noble of nobles, the court poet, the master of the horse, and all the officers of state and courtiers who had attended his majesty, were seated, and who continued the feast which the king and his sons had begun. After this, the dinner was taken in succession to the different servants, until the dishes were cleared by the tent-pitchers and scullions.

In the meanwhile the Shah had been introduced into the harem by the doctor in person; and as immediate death would have been inflicted upon any one who might have been caught peeping, I waited in the greatest suspense until I could learn what might have taken place there; but what was my horror! what my consternation! on hearing (as soon as the king had returned to the great saloon) that the doctor had made a present of his Cûrdish slave to his majesty! At this intelligence I grew sick with apprehension; and, although there was every reason to rejoice at her leaving her present situation, yet there were consequences which I anticipated— consequences which might even ultimately affect her life, at the very thought of which my blood ran cold. We had been too much enamoured to listen to the dictates of prudence, and now the future opened a prospect to me, the background of which was darkened by images the most horrible that the imagination can conceive.

'I will endeavour,' thought I, 'to gain some certain intelligence of what has happened; perhaps in the confusion, I may chance to get a sight of Zeenab herself.' I lost no time, therefore, in resorting to our old place of meeting on the terrace. Much noise and clatter were heard below amongst the women, a large number having come as visitors, in addition to those which composed the doctor's harem; but I could perceive no one amongst them that looked at all like her I sought; indeed, the night had closed in, and I despaired of making any sign which might be recognized; but, trusting to the sympathies of love, I thought it certain that she would hit upon precisely the same plan which I had devised to see her. Part of the terrace where our first interview had taken place was situated near the street, and upon this the women of the harem were accustomed to take their station whenever anything remarkable was to be seen abroad. Here I hoped Zeenab would not fail to come at the moment of the Shah's departure, which was now close at hand. The clatter of the horses, the shouts of men, the passing to and fro of lanterns, all announced the close of the scene; and to my delight I heard a corresponding shuffling of women's slippers and voices making for the steps of the terrace. I had placed myself behind the wall, so as to be seen by those only who had a knowledge of the premises, and I flattered myself that Zeenab, by a natural impulse, would turn her eyes towards me. I was not mistaken. She was among the women who had ascended the terrace, and she recognized me. That was all I wanted, and I left it to her ingenuity to devise a mode of conversing with me.

The cry of *Gitchin!* Begone! made by the heralds whenever the king rises to depart, was now heard, and every one arranged himself in the procession. With the exception of the numerous lanterns, which by their size announced the dignity of the different personages whose steps they lighted, the ceremony of the king's return to his palace was the same as on his leaving it, and with his majesty departed all that had a moment before given life and animation to the place.

The women, satisfied that nothing more was to be seen, also left the terrace. Their conversation, during the time of their stay, had consisted almost entirely of disputes of who had been most seen and admired by the Shah; and, as they were descending, I overheard great expressions of envy and jealousy at the good fortune which, in their eyes, had fallen to the share of Zeenab.

'I can't conceive,' said one, 'what the Shah could have seen so attractive in her. After all, she has no beauty. Did you ever see so large a mouth? She has no salt[1] in her complexion.'

[1] This is a Persian idiom, and is intended to denote the fascinations of a brunette.

'She is crooked,' said another.

'As for her waist,' said a third, ''tis like that of an elephant; and then her feet—a camel has smaller.'

'And then,' said a fourth, 'she is a Yezeedi. She must have got a charm from the *shaitan* himself, to make herself remarked.' 'That is the truth,' they all exclaimed. 'Yes, that's it—she and the devil are in partnership to make the king eat dirt.' Upon this they all seemed satisfied, and I heard no more of them.

But one woman still remained behind on the terrace, apparently engrossed with what was passing on in the street; she immediately rose when the others had left it, and came towards me. It was Zeenab.

CHAPTER XXX: HAJJI BABA MEETS WITH A RIVAL IN THE SHAH HIMSELF, AND LOSES THE FAIR OBJECT OF HIS AFFECTIONS

THE wall behind which I had taken post was not long a barrier between us, and I had scarcely made known to her the unhappy state of my mind, before she apprised me of the danger that we incurred in such an interview. She soon gave me to understand that this must be our last meeting; for, as she now belonged to the royal harem, death would be our fate if we were found together. I was anxious to hear in what manner the king had gained possession of her, and what was to be her future destiny; but sobs stifled everything I had to say. She, on the other hand, did not appear to take our separation quite so much to heart; for, whether dazzled by the prospect of her future destinies, or subdued by the miseries she had already endured on my account, certainly I did not meet that return to my affection which I had so warmly anticipated.

She informed me, that when the Shah entered the *anderûn*, he was received by a band of female singers, who went before, singing his praises, to the accompaniment of tambourines; and, as soon as he had seated himself in the open saloon, the khanum was permitted to enjoy the privilege of kissing his knee. A *pahendaz*, composed of embroidered silks, had been spread for him, which, as soon as the royal footsteps had passed over, was snapped up by the eunuchs, who shared it as their perquisite. The king's female master of the ceremonies was in attendance, and she made an offering of the khanum's present, which was laid out on a silver tray, and consisted of six *arac gîrs*, or skull caps, embroidered by that lady's own hands; six *sineh gîrs*, or breast covers, made of padded shawl, worn in cold weather over the shirt; two pairs of trousers of Cashmerian shawl; three silk shirts, and six pairs of stockings, knitted by the women of the doctor's house. His majesty having accepted this, with many encomiums on the khanum's industry and skill, the women were marshalled in two lines on each side of him; 'and I,' said Zeenab, 'in order that every mortification possible might be heaped upon me, was placed the last in the row, even below Nûr Jehan, the black slave. You ought to have seen the pains which all of us, even old Leilah, took to attract the Shah's attention: some were bashful, others stole wicked looks and glanced sideways; others, again, were bold, and kept their eyes fixed on the king's face. Having inspected each in turn, he paused, and keeping his eyes riveted upon me, turned to the doctor, and said, "What sort of thing is this? she is no indifferent commodity. By the king's *Jika*,[1] the animal is fine! Doctor, *mashallah!* you have a good taste— the moon face, the stag eye, the cypress waist, everything is here."

'Upon which the doctor, making the lowest obeisance, said, "May I be your sacrifice, notwithstanding the slave is totally unworthy of notice; yet, since I and everything that belongs to me is the property of the King of Kings, may I venture to place her as an offering at the foot of your majesty's throne?"

'"*Caboul!* I accept her," said the Shah; and then calling the chief eunuch to him, he ordered that I should be educated for a *baziger* (dancer or singer), that all my clothes, &c., should be made suited to my future profession, and that I should be ready accomplished to appear before him upon his return from his summer campaign.

'Oh! I shall never forget,' exclaimed Zeenab, 'the looks of the doctor's wife when this conversation was passing; she turned towards the Shah in great humility, acquiescing in all that was said, and then cast glances upon me, which spoke the thousand angry passions by which her breast was agitated. As for the Georgian, she looked daggers and arsenic, whilst Nûr Jehan's good-humoured face was lightened up with every expression of happiness at my good fortune. I, in the meanwhile, prostrated myself to the ground before the king, who still kept surveying me with a kind aspect.

[1] The *jika* is an upright ornament worn in front of the crown, and is an insignia of royalty.

'As soon as his majesty was gone, you ought to have seen the immediate change which took place in the khanum's conduct towards me. I was no longer "a child of the devil", "a maiden accursed"; but it was "my love, my soul, light of my eyes, my child". I, who had never smoked before her, was now invited to partake of her own pipe; and whether I would or not, she thrust bits of sweetmeat into my mouth with her own fingers. As for the Georgian, she could not stand the sight, but withdrew to another place, to digest her envy as she might. I received the congratulations of the other women, who did not cease repeating a long list of delights that were preparing for me. Love, wine, music, jewels, fine clothes, bathing, and standing before the king, were to be my future occupations. Some talked to me of the best spells to secure love, and to destroy the influence of rivals; others gave me the best advice how to get presents of finery; and many again began to teach me the forms of speech and compliment which I must use in case the Shah spoke to me. In short, poor Zeenab, the most miserable and neglected of human beings, all of a sudden found herself the object of universal attention and admiration.'

Zeenab here finished talking, and the joy which she seemed to feel for the change which was about to take place in her situation was so natural, that I could not find in my heart to destroy it by communicating to her my forebodings of the danger which awaited her. She little knew the horrible penalty she would incur, in case, when called upon to attend the Shah, she should be found unworthy of his attentions; for it was upon record, under such circumstances, that death, a horrid, cruel death, had been inflicted, and that without appeal to any tribunal upon earth. I therefore seemed to partake her happiness, and although we felt we must be separated, yet we were consoled with the hope that opportunities of mutual intelligence would not be wanting.

She told me that one of the king's eunuchs was to call on the following morning, to conduct her to the seraglio, and, when bathed and newly dressed, she was to be delivered over to the department of the Bazigers, when her education was immediately to commence.

Hearing her name repeatedly called, she was afraid of risking herself longer with me, and after ten thousands and thousands protestations of mutual love, we parted, perhaps to meet no more.

CHAPTER XXXI: HIS REFLECTIONS ON
THE LOSS OF ZEENAB. HE IS SUDDENLY CALLED UPON TO
EXERT HIS SKILL AS A DOCTOR

AS soon as she was gone I sat down on the same spot where we had been standing, and gave myself up to thought. 'So,' said I to myself, 'so, this is being two kernels in one almond? Well, if such be the world, then what I have been taken up with for these two last months is only a dream. I thought myself a Majnoun, and she a Leilah, and as long as the sun and moon endured we should go on loving, and getting thin, and burning like charcoal, and making *kabob*[1] of our hearts. But 'tis clear that my beard has been laughed at. The Shah came, looked, said two words, and all was over. Hajjî was forgotten in an instant, and Zeenab took upon herself the airs of royalty.'

I passed a feverish night, and rose early in the morning, full of new projects. In order to reflect more at my ease, I determined to take a walk without the city walls, but just as I had stepped from the house, I met Zeenab mounted on a horse, finely caparisoned, conducted by one of the royal eunuchs, and escorted by servants making way for her to pass. I expected, that at the sight of me she would have lifted up the flap of her veil; but no, she did not even move from her perpendicular on the saddle, and I walked on, more determined than ever to drive her from my recollection. But somehow or other, instead of taking my path to the gate of the city, I followed her, and was led on imperceptibly towards the king's palace.

Entering the great square, which is situated immediately before the

[1] Roast meat.

principal gate, I found it filled with cavalry, passing muster, or the *soum*, as it is called, before the Shah in person, who was seated in the upper room over the porch. I lost Zeenab and her conductor in the crowd, who were permitted to pass, whilst I was kept back by the guards. The current of my thoughts was soon arrested by the scene carrying on before me. The troops now under examination consisted of a body of cavalry under the command of Namerd Khan, the chief executioner, who was present, dressed in cloth of gold, with the enamelled ornament on his head glittering in the sun, and mounted upon a superb charger. The review was quite new to me; and as I gazed upon the horses and the horsemen, the spears and the muskets, the days which I had passed among the Turcomans came again to my mind, and I longed once more to be engaged in active life. The troops to be reviewed were stationed on one side of the square. The secretary at war with his six scribes were placed in the middle, taken up with their different registers: two criers were also present, the one who, with a loud voice, called out the name of the soldier, and the other answering *hazir* (present) as soon as he had passed muster. Whenever a name was called, a cavalier, completely equipped, dashed from the condensed body, and crossed the square at the full speed of his horse, making a low obeisance as he passed the Shah; and this ceremony was performed by each man until the whole were reviewed. Many and various were the appearance of the horsemen. Some came forwards in fine style, looking like Rustams, whilst others, who had perhaps borrowed a beast for the occasion, went hobbling through as if the day of battle had already taken place. I recognized many of my acquaintance as they galloped by, and was admiring the animated manner of a young man, who had urged his horse forwards, when, by some fatal accident, the beast fell just as they were about passing the high pole which is erected in the middle of the course, and its rider was thrown with great violence against the foot of it. He was immediately taken up and carried through the crowd. Some one, recognizing me to belong to the Shah's physician, invited me to take charge of him, and, without the least apprehension from my ignorance, I did not hesitate to put on the airs of a doctor. I found the unfortunate man stretched on the ground, apparently without life. Those who surrounded him had already prescribed largely. One was pouring water down his throat, 'in the name of the blessed Hossien'; another was smoking a pipe up his nose in order to awaken him; and a third was kneading his body and limbs, to promote circulation. As soon as I appeared, these different operations were suspended, and, room being made, I felt his pulse with great solemnity, and as the surrounding uplifted faces seemed to solicit a decision, I declared, with emphasis, that he had been struck by fate, and that life and death were now wrestling with each other who should have him. Thus (according to the practice of my master) having prepared my hearers for the worst, I ordered, as a preliminary to other remedies, that the patient should be well shaken, in order to discover if life was in him or no. No prescription was ever better administered, for the crowd almost shook him to dislocation. This had no effect. I was about prescribing again, when a cry was heard in the crowd, *Rah bedeh*, give way: *Ser hisab*, heads, heads! and the Frank doctor (of whose skill I have before given some account) made his appearance, having been sent by his ambassador, who had witnessed the catastrophe. Without having seen the patient, he cried out, 'Take blood instantly! you must not lose a moment.'

I, who now felt myself called upon to assert the dignity of the Persian faculty, and give proofs of my superior wisdom, said, 'Take blood! what doctrine is this? Do not you know that death is cold, and that blood is hot, and that the first principle of the art is to apply warm remedies to cold diseases? Pocrat,[1] who is the father of all doctors, has thus ordained, and surely you cannot say that he eats his own soil. If you take blood from that body, it dies; and go tell the world that I say so.'

'As for that,' said the Frank, who had now examined it, 'we may save ourselves any further trouble: it is dead already, and hot and cold are now all one.' Upon this he took his leave, and left me and my Pocrat with our noses in the air.

'Then death', said I, 'has had the best of it; the wisdom of man is unavailing, when opposed to the decrees of God. We doctors can no more contend with destiny, than the waters of an aqueduct can overcome those of a river.'

A Mollah, who was present, ordered his feet to be turned towards the Kebleh, his two great toes to be tied together, a handkerchief wrapped under his chin, and fastened over his head, and then all the bystanders after him repeated aloud the profession of the true faith. By this time some

[1] So Hippocrates is called in Persia.

of his relatives had gathered round him, and had begun the usual lamentations, when the bier was brought, and the dead body conveyed to his family. Upon inquiry I found that the deceased had been a *Nasakchi*, i.e. one of the officers attached to the chief executioner, who has one hundred and fifty such under his command, and whose duties consist in preceding the Shah in his marches, dispersing crowds, maintaining order, taking charge of state prisoners, and, in short, acting as police officers throughout the country. It immediately struck me, how agreeable and how convenient it would be to step into the dead man's shoes, and how much better my temper and disposition were suited to filling such an office than mixing drugs and visiting the sick. In turning over in my mind the possibility of acquiring this situation, I recollected that the chief executioner was a great friend of Mirza Ahmak, and under considerable obligations to him; for, but a few days since, he had persuaded the doctor to swear to the Shah, that wine, which is strictly prohibited at court, was absolutely necessary for his health, and that in consequence he had received a dispensation from the head of the law to drink it—a privilege, in which he indulged to the greatest excess. I therefore determined to interest the Mirza in my favour, and if possible, to turn the waters of bitterness, which the fountain of fate had been pouring into the cup of the deceased, into streams of sweet sherbet for myself.

CHAPTER XXXII: HAJJI IS APPOINTED TO A SITUATION UNDER GOVERNMENT: HE BECOMES AN EXECUTIONER

I WATCHED an opportunity before the doctor set out the next morning for the *Der-Khoneh*,[1] to speak upon my future plans, and to request him to lose no time in asking for me the place of the deceased Nasakchi from the chief executioner. I urged the necessity of acting immediately; for as the Shah would leave the capital for his camp at Sultanieh, in the course of a few days, and as the doctor would be called upon to accompany him, it was plain, if he did not in some manner provide for me, I should be left upon his hands.

The doctor, who was still calculating the expenses of his entertainment to the Shah, and had resolved upon adopting a system of more rigid

---

[1] The gate of the palace, where public business is transacted.

economy in his household, was not sorry to lose a hungry hanger-on, and without hesitation he promised to assist me. It was agreed between us, that he would forthwith call upon the chief executioner, and appointed me to meet him at court, after the morning's *Selam* (levee) was over. As soon, therefore, as the mid-day prayer had been announced from the mosque, I went to the palace, and took my station without the room which is appropriated for the use of the head executioner, and which is situated with its large window immediately facing the principal gate. Several persons were collected there. He himself was taken up with saying his prayers in a corner, and apparently completely abstracted from a conversation that was carrying on between my friend the poet laureate and the under-master of ceremonies.

The latter was describing to the former the death of the unfortunate Nasakchi, and was mixing a considerable portion of the marvellous in his narrative, when the chief executioner, from the middle of his devotions, cried out, '*Een derough est*,'—'that's a lie—have patience, and I will tell you how it was,' and then went on with his holy invocations. As soon as they were over, and almost before he had finished his last prostration, he began his story, relating the fact with infinitely more exaggeration than the master of the ceremonies had done, and finishing by a round assertion, that the Frank had bled the poor man to death, after the Persian doctor had brought him to life only by shaking him.

During the chief executioner's narration, Mirza Ahmak entered the room, and far from denying what was asserted of the two doctors, he confirmed it the more by new and stronger circumstances, and then finished by pointing to me, and said, 'This is he who would have saved the Nasakchi's life, if he had not been prevented.' Upon this, the eyes of all present were turned upon me, and I was called upon to relate the whole circumstance as it had happened, which I did, making my version coincide as nearly as possible with what had been already related; but giving all the merit of the science which I had displayed to the tuition of the chief physician. Mirza Ahmak, elated by my praise, was full of zeal to serve me, and he then introduced me to the chief executioner as a man fit and willing to undertake the office of the deceased Nasakchi.

'How!' said the head of the Nasakchies, 'a doctor become an executioner! how can that be?'

'There is no harm in that,' said the poet (looking at the doctor through the corner of his eye)—'they are both in the same line—the one does his business with more certainty than the other, that's true; but after all, it signifies little whether a man dies gradually by a pill, or at once by a stroke of the scimitar.'

'As for that,' retorted Mirza Ahmak, 'to judge of others by you, poets are in the same line too; for they murder men's reputations; and everybody will agree with me, that that is a worse sort of killing than the doctor's (as you were pleased to say), or the Nasakchi's.'

'That's all very well,' exclaimed the chief executioner; 'you may kill in any manner you choose, provided you leave me the soldier's manner. Give me good hard fighting—let me have my thrust with the lance, and my cut with the sabre, and I want nothing more—let me snuff up the smell of gunpowder, and I leave the scent of the rose to you, Mr. Poet—give me but the roar of cannon, and I shall never envy you the song of the nightingale.—We all have our weaknesses—these are mine.'

'Yes,' said the master of the ceremonies, addressing himself to the whole assembly: 'Everybody knows your several merits. The Shah particularly (who by the by has studied the art of killing as well as any of you) is frequently expressing his delight, that of all the monarchs which Persia ever had, he is the best served; and with that feeling he talks of carrying his arms into the very heart of Georgia. If the Russians once hear that you are going amongst them,' addressing himself to the chief executioner, 'they may begin to make their accounts clear in this world, and prepare for the next.'

'What are the Russians?' said the executioner, with half a shrug and half a shiver; 'they are dust—they are nothing—the possession of Georgia by the Russians is to Persia what a flea which has got into my shirt is to me: it teazes me now and then, but if I gave myself the least trouble, I would hunt it out in a minute. The Russians are nothing.' Then, as if he were anxious to waive the subject, he turned to me, and said: 'Well, I agree to take you into the service, provided you are as fond of the smell of powder as I am. A Nasakchi must have the strength of a Rustam, the heart of a lion, and the activity of a tiger.' Then looking at me from head to foot, he seemed pleased with my appearance, and forthwith ordered me to go to his *Naïb*, or lieutenant, who would equip me for my office, and give me instructions respecting all the duties I should have to perform. I found the *Naib* to be in the midst of preparations for the departure of the Shah, giving his orders, and receiving the reports of those under his command. As soon as he was informed that I was the man appointed to succeed the deceased officer, he put me in possession of his horse and its accoutrements, gave me strict injunctions to take the greatest care of it, and informed me that I could not be provided with another unless I brought back its tail and the mark peculiar to the royal horses, which is burnt on its flank. My stipend was fixed at thirty tomauns per annum, with food for myself and horse. I found myself in dress and arms, except a small hatchet, which indicated my office and was provided by the government.

But before I proceed further, it is necessary that I make my reader acquainted with the person and character of Namerd Khan,[1] my new master. He was a tall, square-shouldered, bony man, about forty-five years of age —young enough to be still called a *khûb jûan* (a fine youth). The features of his face were cast in a deep mould, and shaded by black and thick eyebrows, as well as by a jet black beard and moustachios. His hand was particularly large and muscular; and from the black hairs that curled out from the crevices of his shirt, it was evident that his fur was of the thickest quality. Altogether he was of a figure commanding, but coarse, and looked his office greatly to the advantage of the peace of the city, for the very sight of him was sufficient to awe the evil-minded. He was the most celebrated *khôsh guzerân* (sensualist) in Tehran. He drank wine without compunction, and freely cursed the mollahs, who promised him a seat in the regions below for holding the injunctions of the Prophet so cheap. His house was the seat of revelry; the noise of singing and tambours was heard there from night till morning. He kept men dancers and women dancers; and was the protector of every *Lûti*,[2] however impudent and obscene he might be. But with all this, he did not in the least relax in the severities of his office; and one might frequently hear, amid the sounds of revelry, the cries and groans of some unfortunate wretch who was writhing under the torture of the bastinado on his feet. He was an excellent horseman, and very dexterous at the spear exercise; and although there

[1] Perhaps the description of this personage will bring to the recollection of those who were in Persia in 1813 and 1814 the character of the nasakchi bashi of that day.
[2] *Lûti* here is used in the sense of *polisson*.

was everything in his appearance to make one believe that he was a soldier and a man of prowess, yet in fact he was a most arrant coward. He
endeavoured to conceal this defect of his nature by boasting and big words;
and succeeded in persuading those who did not know his real character,
that he was among the modern Persians, what Sâm and Afrasiâb[1] were
among the ancient.

His lieutenant, a man of stern aspect, was an active and intelligent
officer: he understood the management of his chief, whom he flattered into
a belief, that, besides the Shah and himself, no one was worthy to be called
a man in Persia. I soon discovered that his prevailing passion was avarice;
for when he found that I was to be installed in my office without making
him a present, there was no end to the difficulties which he threw in my
way. However, by dint of making use of that tongue which nature had
given me, and persuading him, in his turn, that he was the cream of lieu-
tenants, and the very best of materials for the future executioner in chief,
he relaxed in his dislike, and even flattered me so much as to say, that, by
the blessing of Allah, the benign and the merciful, he believed that I should
not fail to become in time an ornament to the profession.

I still kept my lodging at the doctor's house until the period of the
Shah's departure, and filled up my time in preparing for the journey. The
very circumstance of being a nasakchi gave me consequence in the bazaar,
and I found no difficulty in procuring everything I wanted upon credit.
During my stay with the doctor, I had managed to set myself up with a
small capital of necessaries, which I had procured either in presents from
patients, or by happy contrivances of my own. As for instance, I wanted a
bed, a quilt, and a pillow: a poor man happening to die under our charge,
I assured his relations, whom I knew to be the most bigoted of Mussulmans, that his death could be no fault of ours, for no one could doubt the
skill with which he had been treated, but that the bed upon which he lay
must be unfortunate; for in the first place, the quilt was of silk;[2] and in
the next, the foot of the bed had not been turned towards the kebleh,[3] as
it ought to have been: this was enough for the family to discard the bed,
and it became mine.

[1] Celebrated heroes in the *Shahnameh*, a book which is believed, by the present Persians,
to contain their ancient history.   [2] Strict Mussulmans hold silk unclean.
[3] In the direction of Mecca.

A looking-glass was necessary to my toilet: a mirza, sick of the jaundice, looked at himself in one which he possessed, and was horror-struck at his colour. I assured him that it only proceeded from a defect in the glass, for that in fact he was as fresh as a rose. He threw it away, and I took it home with me.

No one was stricter than Mirza Ahmak himself in all the exteriors of religion, and scrupulous to a fault about things forbidden as unclean. I was in want of a pair of *yakhdans*, or trunks, and a pair belonging to the doctor, which were lying idle in an unfrequented room, were frequently the objects of my contemplation. How shall I manage to become master of these? thought I: had I but half the invention of Dervish Sefer, I should already have been packing up my things in them. A thought struck me: one of the many curs, which range wild throughout Tehran, had just pupped under a ruined archway, close to our house. Unseen, I contrived to lodge the whole litter within one of the trunks, and to make a deposit of old bones in the other. When they came to be moved, preparatory to the doctor's journey (for he always accompanies the Shah), the puppies and their mother set up such a confusion of yells, that the servant who had disturbed them ran breathless with the information to the doctor, who, followed by his household, including myself, proceeded to the spot. As soon as the state of the case had been ascertained, many were struck by the singularity of the circumstance, as an omen portending no good to the doctor's house. One said, 'This comes of marrying the khanum; she will give him a houseful of *harem zadehs!*'[1] Another said, 'The puppies are yet blind: God grant that we and the doctor may not become so likewise!' The doctor himself was only vexed by the loss of his trunks; he pronounced them to be *nejes* (unclean) from that moment, and ordered them, puppies, bitch and all, immediately to be expelled. I was not long in appropriating them; and very soon assumed all the consequence of a man possessing trunks, which also implied things worthy to be put into them. Little by little, I scraped together a sufficient quantity of effects to be able to talk big about my baggage; and when preparations for our departure were making, I held myself entitled to the privilege of squabbling with the king's mule-drivers concerning the necessity of a mule for carrying it.

[1] Illegitimate born.

CHAPTER XXXIII: HE ACCOMPANIES THE SHAH TO
HIS CAMP AND GETS SOME INSIGHT INTO HIS PROFESSION

T length the day of departure for Sultanieh was fixed by the astrologers. The Shah left his palace just half an hour before sunrise, on the *21st Rebbi*[1] *el evel*, and travelled without drawing bridle, until he reached his palace of Sulimanieh, which is situated on the banks of the Caraj, at a distance of nine parasangs from Tehran. The different corps composing the army to be collected at Sultanieh were ordered to meet there at a given time, whilst the Shah's escort was to consist only of his body guard, his camel artillery, and a heavy squadron of cavalry. The great officers of the court, with the viziers, and those employed in the public offices, departed at about the same time, and thus the city was bereft, almost in one day, of nearly two-thirds of its population. Everything and everybody were in motion; and a stranger would have thought that all the inhabitants, like bees hiving, by one common consent had broken up housekeeping, and were about to settle in some other place. Strings of mules and camels, laden with beds, carpets, cooking utensils, tents, horse furniture and provisions of all sorts, were soon making their

[1] The third month in the Arabic calendar.

way through each avenue, raising an impenetrable dust, whilst their conductors mingled their cries with the various toned bells which decked their beasts.

On the morning of departure, I was stationed at the Casbîn gate to keep order, and to prevent any impediment to the Shah's passage. The peasants bringing provisions to the city, who are in waiting every day previously to opening the gates, were ordered to take another direction. The road was watered by all the sakas of the town, and every precaution taken to make the royal exit as propitious as possible. In particular, no old woman was permitted to be seen, lest the Shah might cast a look upon her, and thus get a stroke of the evil eye.

I found within myself an energy and a vigour in driving the people about, that I never thought appertained to my character; for I recollected well, when one of the mob, how entirely I abominated every man in office. I made use of my stick so freely upon the heads and backs of the crowd, that my brother executioners quite stared, and wondered what demon they had got amongst them. I was anxious to establish a reputation for courage, which I expected would in time promote me to a higher situation.

At length the procession began to move forwards. A detachment of camel artillery had proceeded on the evening before to receive the Shah when he should alight at Sulimanieh; and now was heard the salute which announced his leaving the palace at Tehran. All was hushed into anxiety and expectation. The chief executioner himself, mounted upon a superb charger, galloped through the streets in haste; and horsemen were seen running to and fro, all intent upon the one object of preparing the road. First came the heralds; then the led horses, magnificently caparisoned in jewellery, shawls, and cloth of gold; after them the running footmen; then the Shah in person; the princes succeeded, followed by the viziers; and last of all an immense body of cavalry.

When it is mentioned that every man of any consequence was accompanied by his train of attendants, most of whom had also their trains; and when the sum total of mirzas, of servants, of pipe-bearers, of cooks and scullions, of carpet-spreaders, of running-footmen, of grooms and horses, of mule drivers and camel drivers, and of ten thousand other camp followers is reckoned up, the imagination may perhaps conceive what was the crowd which passed before me in succession, as I stood at the Casbîn gate.

When the Shah approached, his long beard floating to his girdle, with all the terrors of despotism concentrated in his person, I could not help feeling an odd sort of sensation about my neck; and I made my lowest prostration to that power, which by a single nod might have ordered my head to take leave of my shoulders, even before I could make an objection.

The whole procession having cleared the city gates, I lingered behind to smoke with the guards who are there stationed; and at that time the women of one of the viziers who were permitted to accompany him to camp passing by, brought Zeenab once again to my recollection. I sighed profoundly, when I reflected on the probable miserable fate which awaited her. She had been sent (so I heard from Nûr Jehan the day before our departure) to a small summer-house belonging to the Shah, situated at the foot of the high mountains which surround Tehran, where, with many other of the bazigers, she was to receive her education of dancing, music, and tumbling. The Shah had ordered that she was to be mistress of these accomplishments previously to his return in the autumn; when she would be honoured by the permission of exhibiting before him. As I rode away, I could not help turning my head towards the spot where she was now confined, and which I could just discern a speck at the foot of the mountain. Perhaps at any other time I should have left every duty to endeavour to obtain a glimpse of her; but I was called up to head the procession again, and to be in readiness at Sulimanieh when the king should alight from his horse.

The day's march, and the attendance at my post being at an end, I proceeded to the quarters of the chief executioner, where I found a small tent prepared for me and five other nasakchies, who were destined to be my companions for the remainder of the journey. I had already made their acquaintance in the city; but now we were brought into closer contact, for our tent was not more than six *ghez*[1] long and four broad, and we were thus thrown almost one upon the other. I, as the junior, fared of course the worst; but I determined to put the best face possible upon any present inconveniences, anticipating many future advantages, which a certain confidence in my own pretty self whispered to me I should not fail to secure.

In addition to the chief executioner's naib, there was also a sub-lieutenant, who must have a place in my narrative, because, in fact, it was

[1] A ghez is not quite a yard.

through him that I ultimately became noticed by the higher powers. His name was Shîr Ali, in rank a *Beg*, and a Shirazi by birth. Although natives of the two rival cities of Persia, yet without any particular previous cause, and by a combination of those nothings which give rise to most friendships, we became inseparable companions. He had given me a piece of watermelon one hot day when I was thirsty; I had lighted his pipe for him on another occasion: he had bled me with his penknife when I had overloaded my stomach with too much rice; and I had cured his horse of the colic by administering an injection of tobacco-water: in short, one thing led on to another, until a very close intimacy was established between us. He was three years older than I, tall, handsome, broad-shouldered, narrow-waisted, with the prettiest oval beard possible, just long enough to fringe round his chin, and with two large curls, twisting beautifully behind his ear, like a vine curling over the garden wall.

He had been long enough in the service to acquire all the tricks of his profession; for when we came to converse upon the subject, it was surprising what a vast field for the exercise of genius he threw open to my view.

He said, 'Do not suppose that the salary which the Shah gives his servants is a matter of much consideration with them: no, the value of their places depends upon the range of extortion which circumstances may afford, and upon their ingenuity in taking advantage of it. As, for instance, take our chief: his salary is 1,000 tomauns per annum, which may or may not be regularly paid; that signifies little to him. He spends at least five or six times that sum; and how is he to get it, if it flows not from the contributions of those who come under his cognizance? A khan has incurred the Shah's displeasure; he is to be beaten and fined: the chief executioner beats and mulcts in the inverse proportion of the present which the sufferer makes him. A rebel's eyes are to be put out; it depends upon what he receives, whether the punishment is done rudely with a dagger, or neatly with a penknife. He is sent on an expedition at the head of an army; wherever he goes presents are sent him from the towns and villages on his road to induce him not to quarter his troops upon them; and he uses his discretion, according to the value of what he receives, in choosing his halting stations. Most of those in high offices, even the viziers, make him annual gifts, in case the day of the Shah's displeasure should come, and then they would hope to be dealt with gently by him. In short, wherever a stick is to be brandished, wherever punishment is to be inflicted, there the chief executioner levies his dues; and they descend in a gradual measure from him to the lowest of his officers. Before I was a naib, and when I was called upon to lay the bastinado on some wretched culprit, many is the time that my compassion has been moved by a direct appeal to my purse; and then, instead of beating the sufferer's feet, I struck the *felek* upon which they rested. It was but last year that the principal secretary of state incurred the wrath of the Shah. He was ordered to receive the bastinado, and, by way of distinction, a small carpet was spread for him to lie upon: I and another were the operators, whilst two more held the felek. When we were taking the shawl and cap from his head, his girdle and outer coat (which became our lawful perquisites), he whispered to us, low enough not to be heard by the Shah (for this was all done in his presence), "By the mothers that bore you, do not beat me much! I'll give you each ten tomauns if you will not strike me." His heels were tripped up, his feet placed in the noose, whilst his back reposed on the carpet; and then we set to work. For our own sakes, we were obliged to start fair, and we laid on until he roared sufficiently; and then, having ably made him increase his offer until he had bid up to any price we wished, we gradually ceased beating his feet, and only broke our sticks over the felek. Much ingenuity was displayed on both sides, in order that the Shah might not discover that there was any understanding between us. His bidding was interwoven with his groans, something after this manner:—"*Ahi amân! amân!* For pity's sake, by the soul of the Prophet! twelve tomauns.—By the love of your fathers and mothers! fifteen tomauns.—By the king's beard! twenty tomauns.—By all the Imâms! by all the prophets! thirty, forty, fifty, sixty, hundred, thousand,—anything you want." When it was over, we soon found that his generosity had diminished quite as rapidly as it had before increased, and we were satisfied to receive what he first offered to us, which he was obliged to give, fearing if a similar misfortune again overtook him, we should then show him no mercy.'

Shîr Ali, holding this sort of language, gave me such an insight into the advantages of my situation that I could dream of nothing but bastinadoing, and getting money. I went about all day flourishing a stick over my head, practising upon any object that had the least resemblance to human feet, and to such perfection did I bring my hand, that I verily believe I could have hit each toe separately, had I been so ordered. The first impulse of my nature was not cruelty, that I knew: I was neither fierce nor brave, that I also knew: I therefore marvelled greatly how of a sudden I had become such an unsainted lion.[1] The fact is, the example of others always had the strongest influence over my mind and actions; and I now lived in such an atmosphere of violence and cruelty, I heard of nothing but of slitting noses, cutting off ears, putting out eyes, blowing up in mortars, chopping men in two, and baking them in ovens, that, in truth, I am persuaded, with a proper example before me, I could almost have impaled my own father.

CHAPTER XXXIV: EMPLOYED IN HIS OFFICIAL CAPACITY HAJJI BABA GIVES A SPECIMEN OF PERSIAN DESPOTISM

THE Shah moved slowly towards Sultanieh, and at length, after fourteen days' march, when a fortunate hour had been selected for his arrival, he took possession of the summer palace, which has of late days been erected there for his residence. Situated on a hill, not far from the remains of the ancient city, it commands a view of the whole plain, which now, to an immense extent, was covered with the white tents of the camp. It was a magnificent sight, and I felt all the importance of the nasakchi rising in my breast, as I contrasted my present situation with my wretched and forlorn condition when an inmate in the tents of the Turcomans. 'In short, I am somebody now,' said I to myself; 'formerly I was one of the beaten, now I am one of the beaters. I should just do for an example of the active and passive participle, with which my old master, the mollah at Ispahan, used to puzzle me, when endeavouring to instil a little Arabic into my mind. Please Heaven that my good dispositions towards my fellow-creatures may soon have an opportunity of being displayed.'

Scarcely I had made these reflections, when Shîr Ali came up to me, and said, 'Our fortune has taken a flight upwards: you are to accompany me, and *Inshallah!* please Allah! we shall make clean work of it. You must know, that the provisions for the king's camp are supplied, in great meas-

[1] *Shîr bi pîr*—a lion without a saint, is a favourite Persian epithet, when applied to a desperado, a fellow without compassion.

ure, by the surrounding villages. It seems that the village of Kadj Sawar, situated between this and Hamadan, has not sent its quota, upon a pretext that one of the princes, with his suite, not long ago, on a hunting excursion, had there settled himself for several days, and eaten the inhabitants out of house and home. I am ordered to proceed thither, to investigate the business, and to conduct the *ked khoda* (the head man), with the elders of the village, before our chief. Since you are my friend, I have received permission to take you with me, although the other nasakchies complain that they have lost their turn. You must be ready to join me after the evening prayer, for I intend to be there to-morrow morning.'

I was overjoyed to find myself so soon brought into action; and, although I did not know precisely the plan of operations which Shîr Ali would adopt, yet I had wit enough to perceive that a great field was open to the ingenuity of fellows like us, who are always guided by the state of the weather.[1] 'Our star will be an evil one, indeed,' said I, 'if that destructive prince has left us nothing to glean. Some poet once said "no melon is so bad but hath its rind, and although a tyrant may pluck out a beard by the roots, yet still the chin is left upon which it grew."' With these thoughts in my head I went to my horse, which, with the other nasakchies' horses, was picketed near our tents, and prepared him for the journey. Casting off his head and heel ropes, I could not help comparing him to myself.— 'Now,' said I, 'beast! you are free to kick and plunge, and do what mischief you can'; and so, thought I, is the Persian when absolved from the fear of his master.

Shîr Ali and I quitted the camp at sunset, accompanied by a lad, seated on the top of a loaded mule, that carried our beds; and the coverings, ropes, &c. for our horses. Since I had become a soldier, I also had attached the title of Beg to my name: and, to add to my importance in this expedition, I borrowed a silver chain for my horse's head, and a handsome silver mounted pistol for my girdle, from one of my comrades, and promised to bring him a *soghat*, or present, in case the harvest proved abundant.

We travelled all night, and, having slept for two hours at a village on the road, reached Kadj Sawar just as the women were driving the cattle from their stables, and the men smoking their pipes, previously to going

[1] The expression is *'hawa been'*, which answers to our 'time-servers', but which literally signifies what has been given in the text.

to their work in the field. As soon as we were perceived making for the village, it was evident that a great stir was produced. The women ceased from their cries, and hid their faces, and the men arose from their seats. I wish my reader could have seen the air and countenance which Shîr Ali Beg put on as we approached. He swelled himself out at least into the size of the chief executioner himself, and with a tone of authority, which sufficiently indicated who and what he was, inquired for the chief of the village. A plain man, with a grey beard, humble mien, and still humbler clothing, stepped forward, and said, 'Peace be with you, Aga! I am he; I am your servant. May your footsteps be fortunate, and your shadow never be less!'

And then saying '*Bismillah!* in the name of God!' we were helped off our horses with all due respect. One held the horse's head, another the stirrup, whilst a third put his hand under the arm-pit, and thus we alighted, giving ourselves as much weight as we could, and making up our backs like men of consequence. A small carpet was spread at the door of the ked khoda's house, to which we had been conducted, followed by almost all the male population of the village, and there we seated ourselves until a room within was prepared. The ked khoda himself pulled off our boots, and otherwise performed all the acts of politeness and attention which are shown to guests on their arrival. Shîr Ali having received this with the dignity of one who thought it his due, and having let off several long whiffs from his pipe, said, with great emphasis, to our host, 'You, that are the ked khoda of Kadj Sawar, know, that I am come on the part of Shah—on the part of the Shah, again I say—that I am come to know why this village has not sent its quota of provisions for the use of the royal camp at Sultanieh, according to the order issued in the firman two months ago, signified to you by the governor of Hamadan? Give me an answer, and make your face white if you can.'

The ked khoda answered, 'Yes, by my eyes! what I have said before I will say now. All these men present' (pointing to his fellow villagers) 'know it to be the truth; and if I lie, may I become stone blind! *Arz mi kunum*, I beg leave to state, O nasakchi! that you, by the blessing of God, you, in fine, are a man—you are a wise, a clever, and a sharp-sighted man —you are also a Mussulman, and you fear God. I shall not say more than the truth, nor less; I shall explain what has happened, and then leave you to decide.'

'Well, well, say on,' said Ali; 'I am the king's servant: whatever the Shah will decide, that you must look to.'

'You are the master,' replied the ked khoda; 'but pray give ear to my tale. About three months ago, when the wheat was nearly a *gez* high, and lambs were bleating all over the country, a servant belonging to the Prince Kharab Cûli Mirza announced to us, that his master would take up his quarters in the village the next day, in order to hunt in the surrounding country, which abounds in antelopes, wild asses, partridges, bustards, and game of all descriptions. He ordered the best houses to be in readiness for him and his suite, turned out their inhabitants, and made demands for provisions of all sorts. As soon as this intelligence was known, alarm was spread throughout the village, and seeing that nothing was to be done with the Prince's servant, either by bribe or persuasion, to evade the disaster, we determined to abandon our houses and take to the mountains until the evil day had gone by. Had you seen the state of these peasants, when forced to abandon everything they had in the world, your heart would have turned upside down, and your liver would have become water.'

'What do you mean?' exclaimed Shîr Ali: 'the Shah's villages are left desolate, and I am to pity the fugitives? No, they would have all been put to death had the Shah known it.'

'For pity's sake,' continued the old villager, 'hear the end of my story, and allow yourself to be softened. We loaded our cattle at nightfall with everything we could carry away, and took to the mountains, where we settled in a dell, close to a stream of running water. There only remained behind three sick old women and the village cats.'

'Do you hear that, Hajjî?' said my companion, addressing himself to me: 'they carried away everything valuable, and left the bare walls, and their old women to the Prince. Well,' said he to the ked khoda, 'proceed.'

'We sent spies from time to time,' continued the old man, 'to bring intelligence of what was doing, and took up our abode among the rocks and cliffs of the mountains. About noon the next day the party appeared, and when they discovered that we had fled, their rage and disappointment were great. The servants of the Prince went from house to house, and drove in the doors with violence. The only object which at all restrained them was one of the old women, who having acquired sufficient strength to rise from her bed, attacked them with such reproaches, that none was bold enough to face her. The Prince sent for provisions from a neighbouring town, and took up his abode in my house. Wherever they found corn, they seized upon it; they burnt our implements of husbandry for firewood, and when they were expended had recourse to doors and windows, and even to the beams and rafters of our houses. Their horses were picketed in the new wheat, and they even cut down a great extent of it to carry away. In short, we are entirely ruined; we have neither money, clothes, cattle, houses, nor provisions; and, except in God and you,' addressing himself to Shîr Ali and me, 'we have no other refuge.'

Upon this Shîr Ali Beg jumped up from his seat, took the old man vigorously by the beard, and said, 'Are not you ashamed, old man, with these grey hairs, to utter such lies? But a moment ago you told us that you had carried into the mountains all that was most valuable, and now pretend that you are ruined. This can never be! We have not travelled all this way to eat your dirt. If you think that we have brought our beards to market to be laughed at, you are mistaken. You don't yet know Shîr Ali: we are men who sleep with one eye open and the other shut; no fox steals from its hole without our knowledge: if you think yourself a cat, we are the fathers of cats. Your beard must be a great deal longer, you must have seen much more country, before you can expect to take us in.'

'No, God forgive me!' said the ked khoda, 'if I have thought to deceive you. Who am I, that I should dare to think so? We are the Shah's *rayats*, peasantry; whatever we have is his; but we have been stripped, we have been skinned; go, see with your own eyes—look at our fields—look into our store-rooms—we have neither corn abroad nor corn at home.'

'Well,' said Shîr Ali, 'skinned or unskinned, with corn or without it, we have only one course to pursue, and one word to say—the Shah's orders must be executed. Either you deliver in kind or in money your prescribed quota of provisions, or you and your elders must proceed with us to Sultanieh, where you will be consigned over to the proper authorities.'

After these words, much whispering and consultation took place between the ked khoda and the village elders, who, having huddled themselves into a corner, left us wrapt up in our own dignity, smoking our pipes, with apparently the greatest indifference.

At length the result of their conference was made known, and they changed their order of attack; for the chief of the village now undertook to soften me, and another old man Shîr Ali Beg. The former approached me with every manifestation of great friendship, and began, as usual, by flattery. According to him, I was the most perfect of God's creatures. He then swore that I had excited feelings of love both in his breast, and in that of all the villagers, and that I alone was the person to extricate them from their difficulties. As long as this lasted, I merely kept a steady countenance, and made play with my pipe; but when he had a little more entered into particulars, and talked of what we were likely to get, I must own that I became considerably more interested. He said that they had consulted upon what was to be done; and were unanimous, that to send what they had not was impossible, and therefore out of the question; but perhaps if something could be offered to us to protect their interests, they were ready to satisfy us on that head.

'All this is very well,' said I, 'but I am not the only person to be considered. We here are only two, but recollect that our chief must be also satisfied, and if you do not begin by him, your labour and expense will be in vain: and I can tell you, if you grease his palm, you must measure your *roghun* (grease) by the *maun*,[1] and not by the *miscal*.'

'Whatever we possess,' said the ked khoda, 'we will give; but of late taxation has been so heavy, that, excepting our wives and children, we have in fact nothing to offer.'

'I tell you what, friend,' said I, 'unless you have money, ready downright cash, to give, any other offer is useless: with money in your hand, you may buy the Shah's crown from his head; but without it, I can only promise you a harvest of bastinadoes.'

'Ah!' said the ked khoda, 'money, money! where are we to procure money? Our women, when they get a piece, bore a hole through it, and

[1] A maun is seven pounds and a half; a miscal, twenty-four grains.

hang it about their necks by way of ornament; and if we, after a life of hard toil, can scrape up some fifty tomauns, we bury them in the earth, and they give us more anxiety than if we possessed the mountain[1] of light.' Then approaching to put his mouth to my ear, he whispered with great earnestness, 'You are a Mussulman, in fine, and no ass. You do not conceive that we will go into the lion's mouth if it can be avoided; tell me (pointing to my companion) how much will he be contented with?—can I offer him five tomauns, and a pair of crimson *shalwars* (trousers)?'

'What do I know,' said I, 'what will satisfy him? all I can say is, that he possesses not a grain of commiseration: make the tomauns ten, and the trousers a coat, and I will endeavour to make him accept them.'

'Oh, that is too much,' said the old man; 'our whole village is not worth that sum. Satisfy him with the five and the trousers, and our gratitude will be shown, by a present for yourself that will astonish you.'

Upon this our conference broke off, and I was as anxious to hear what had taken up my companion, as he was impatient to learn the result of my whisperings with the ked khoda. Comparing notes, we found that both the old villagers had been endeavouring to ascertain what might be our respective prices. I assured Shîr Ali that I had given him out for the veriest crucible in Persia, saying, that he could digest more gold than an ostrich could iron, and was withal so proud, that he rejected units as totally unworthy of notice, and never took less than tens.

'Well said,' answered Shîr Ali; 'and I told my old negotiator, that unless you were handsomely paid, you were equal to any violence, notwithstanding your silence and quiet looks.'

At length, after some delay, the whole party came forward again, headed by the ked khoda, who, bringing an ostensible present of apples, pears, a pot of honey, and some new cheese, begged my companion to accept it, in terms usually made on such occasions. When it had been spread before us, in an undertone of voice the ked khoda made his offer of five tomauns and the trousers, and talked of his misery and that of his village in a manner which would have melted any breast but that of Shîr Ali.

We agreed at once to reject the present, and ordered it to be taken from before us. This produced considerable dismay among the poor peo-

[1] The Shah's great diamond, which he wears in one of his armlets, is called the *koh nûr*, or the mountain of light.

ple, and they walked off with their trays of fruit, &c., on their heads, with slow and sorrowful steps.

In about half an hour they appeared again, the ked khoda having previously ascertained that if he came with the ten tomauns and a coat, the present would be accepted. When we had eaten thereof, Shîr Ali Beg having pocketed his gold and secured his coat, I began to look for that something for myself which was to astonish me: nothing, however, was produced, notwithstanding certain significant winks and blinks with which the ked khoda ever and anon kept me in play.

'Where is it?' said I to him at last, quite out of patience. 'What is it? how much?'

'It is coming,' said he; 'have a little patience; it is not yet quite prepared.'

At length, after some waiting, with great parade, the pair of trousers, which had been rejected by Shîr Ali, were placed before me on a tray, and offered for my acceptance, accompanied by a profusion of fine words.

'What news is this?' exclaimed I: 'do you know, ye men without shame!' addressing myself to those who stood before me, 'that I am an executioner,—one who can burn your fathers, and can give you more grief to devour than you have ever yet experienced? What mean ye by bringing me this pair of frouzy *shalwars*? That which has passed through many generations of your ignoble ancestors, do ye now pretend to put off upon me? Fools indeed you must be, to suppose that I will espouse your interests, and set forth your grievances, merely for the sake of this dirty rag! Away with it, or you will see what a nasakchi can do!'

Upon this they were about complying with my orders, when Shîr Ali Beg stopped them, and said, 'Let me look at the trousers. Ah,' said he, holding them up at the same time between his eyes and the sun, and examining them with all the care of an old clothes' broker, 'they will do; they have no defect: be it so, they are my property, and many thanks for them. May your family prosper!'

Every one looked astonished; no one dared make an objection; and thus I, who had been anticipating such great advantages, lost even the miserable perquisite which I might have had, and only gained sufficient experience to know another time how to deal with my countrymen, and, moreover, how to trust one who called himself my friend.

"What bliss is like to whisp'ring love?"

CHAPTER XXXV: FORTUNE, WHICH PRETENDED TO FROWN, IN FACT SMILES UPON HAJJI BABA, AND PROMOTES HIM TO BE SUB-LIEUTENANT TO THE CHIEF EXECUTIONER

TWO fat lambs, which were tied on our baggage mule, were the only present we brought with us for our chief. As soon as we reached the camp, we immediately presented ourselves to the Naib, who forthwith carried us before the executioner, who was seated in his tent, in conversation with one or two of his friends.

'Well,' said he to Shîr Ali, 'what have you done? Have you brought the corn, or the ked khoda, which?'

'I beg leave to state for your service,' said Shîr Ali, 'neither. The ked khoda and the elders of Kadj Sawar have sent two lambs to be laid at your feet; and they have convinced us with our own eyes, that excepting them, not a thing have they left, not even their own souls, so entirely and completely have they been pillaged: on the contrary, if food be not sent to them, they will eat up one another.'

'Do you say so, indeed!' exclaimed the khan: 'if they have lambs, they must also have sheep. By what account do you reckon?'

'That's true,' said Shîr Ali, 'and everything that you say is equally so;
but we were talking of corn, and not of sheep.'

'But why did not you follow your orders, and bring the ked khoda and
the elders?' said our chief. 'If I had been there, the rogues, I would have
roasted them alive. I would have tied them with the camel tie,[1] until they
confessed that they had something. Tell me, why did you not bring them?'

'We wished much to bring them,' said Shîr Ali, looking at me to help
him out. 'Yes, we had bound them all together, and we wanted very much
to bring them: we also beat and abused them. Hajjî Baba knows it all; for
Hajjî Baba told them if they had not money to give, they would certainly
meet with no mercy. Mercy was a thing totally out of our way; for if they
knew anything, they must be aware that our khan, our lord and master,
the Nasakchi Bashi, was a man of such invincible courage, of a resolution
so great, and of bowels so immovable, that if once they got within his
grasp, it was all over with them. Yes, we told them all that, and they
almost sunk into the earth.'

'What does he say, Hajjî Baba?' said the khan, turning round to me:
'I have not quite understood why these men were not brought to me?'

I answered in great humility, 'Indeed, O khan, I also do not understand. Shîr Ali Beg, who is your deputy-lieutenant, had the whole business
in his hands. I went in his service; I am nobody.'

Upon this the khan got into a violent rage, and branded us by every
odious name of contempt and reproach that he could think of. 'It is plain,'
said he to his friends, 'that these villains have been playing tricks. Tell
me,' said he to Shîr Ali, 'by my soul, by the king's salt, tell me, how much
have you got for yourself? And you, Aga Hajjî,' addressing himself to me,
'you, who have scarcely been a month in service, how much have you
secured?'

In vain we both protested our innocence; in vain we swore that there
was nothing to gain; nobody would believe us; and the scene ended by our
being driven out of the tent in custody of the Naib, who was ordered to
confine us until the chiefs of the village should have been actually brought
to the camp, and confronted with us.

[1] The camel tie is made by fastening the lower and upper limb of one of the forelegs
together, which is done to prevent an unruly animal from straying from the pasture
ground and becoming lost.

When Shîr Ali and I were left to ourselves, he immediately endeavoured to make me a partaker of the spoil, and offered to give me up half of it.

'Not so, my friend,' said I; 'it is now too late. If you have drank and enjoyed the forbidden wine, and have got a headache by it, it is no reason that you should endeavour to make me sick too. I have had a lesson, in which you have acted as master, which will satisfy me for this time.'

He then endeavoured to make me promise to stand by him, when we should be confronted with the ked khoda, and to swear through thick and thin to everything that he intended to advance; but I was too much alive to the consequences to make any such promise. He said that if once he were brought to the felek to receive the bastinado, he knew that he could not survive it; for so universal a terrorist had he been when operating upon the feet of others, that now he felt he should be treated without the least mercy; and he therefore swore upon the Korân, that he would undergo every misery rather than be tied to the stake.

When the time came for being called up again before our chief, Shîr Ali was nowhere to be found. He had absconded, and when I was interrogated, all that I could say amounted to this,—that I knew he dreaded the idea of being bastinadoed, and that I supposed he had made off to escape it.

As soon as I appeared before my judge, the men of Kadj Sawar, who were already standing before him, declared one and all, that I had neither exacted nor received anything from them; but, on the contrary, that I had urged them to make a considerable present to the khan. They poured out the whole of their complaints against Shîr Ali, who they declared had put the finishing stroke to their misery, and had even torn off the new skin that had began to cover their old wounds.

All this was slowly working for my advantage, and paving the road to my promotion. The story had got abroad, and was in every one's mouth. I was looked upon as a paragon of moderation.

'This comes from having been a doctor,' says one; 'wisdom is better than riches.' 'He knows the doctrine of consequences,' says another; 'his feet will never be where his head should be.' In short, I had acquired the reputation of being a clever and a cautious fellow, merely owing to events playing fortunately into my hands; and I lost nothing from being looked upon as a man whose *taleh* (luck) was good, and one whose star was fortunate.

The result of this part of my history was, that I was installed in the situation of the fugitive, and became the sub-lieutenant to the chief executioner of Persia—a character, whatever my readers may think of it, of no small consequence, as they will hereafter discover.

CHAPTER XXXVI: ALTHOUGH BY TRADE AN EXECUTIONER
HE SHOWS A FEELING HEART. HE MEETS WITH A YOUNG MAN
AND WOMAN IN DISTRESS

THE Shah was at this time engaged in a war with the Moscovites, who had established themselves in Georgia, and were threatening the frontier provinces of Persia situated between the rivers Kûr and Arras. The governor of Erivan, known by the title of *Serdar* or general, and one of the Shah's most favourite officers, had long ago opened the campaign by desultory attacks upon the advanced posts of the enemy, and by laying waste the villages and country in the track they were likely to keep in advancing towards Persia. An army, under the command of the heir apparent and governor of the great province of Aderbijân, had also been collected near Tabrîz; and it was intended that he should immediately proceed to the seat of war, in order if possible to drive the enemy back to Teflis, and, according to the language of the court, carry its arms even to the walls of Moscow.

Intelligence was daily expected at the royal camp of Sultanieh, from the Serdar, concerning an attack which he had announced it his intention to make upon the Russian post of Gavmishlû; and orders were issued for giving a suitable reception to the heads of the enemy, which it is always the etiquette to send upon announcing a victory, for such no doubt was expected to be the result of the attack. A *chapper*, or courier, was at length seen riding towards the camp in great haste. He was the conductor of five horse-loads of heads, 'tis true, and they were heaped up with great pomp and parade before the principal entrance of the royal tents; but it became evident that something had taken place which required a reinforcement; for on the very next morning our chief, Namerd Khan, was appointed to the command of a body of ten thousand cavalry, which were ordered to march immediately to the banks of the Arras.

The *Min Bashies*, the heads of thousands; the *Yûz bashies*, the heads of hundreds, the *On bashies*, the heads of tens; and all the officers commanding the troops, were seen hurrying over the camp in various directions, attending upon their khans, and receiving their orders. The tent of Namerd Khan was filled with the chiefs of the expedition, to whom he distributed his directions, giving them the order of march, and allotting to each division its station in halting at the villages on the route. My duty was to precede the troops by a day, accompanied by a detachment of nasakchies, to make arrangements for billeting the men in the villages. This was a duty requiring activity and exertion; but at the same time accompanied by great advantages, which, had I chosen to avail myself of, might have increased the weight of my purse. However, the recent example of Shîr Ali Beg was too strong before my eyes not to repress any desire I might have of levying contributions, so I determined for the present to keep my hands pure, and to quench the flame of covetousness by the waters of prudence.

I set off with my detachment, and reached Erivan several days before the troops could arrive. We here found the Serdar, who, after his attack upon Gavmishlû, had retreated, to wait the reinforcement of the cavalry under our chief. The army under the prince royal had proceeded to another part of the frontier, with the intention of attacking the fortress of Ganja, of which the enemy had recently acquired possession, and unable to spare any of his troops, the Serdar had solicited assistance from the Shah.

As soon as Namerd Khan and the Serdar had met and consulted, it was determined that spies should immediately be sent forwards in order to ascertain the position, and the movements of the Russians; and I was fixed upon to head a detachment of twenty men on the part of the chief executioner, whilst a similar number was sent by the Serdar, who at the same time were to be our guides through such parts of the country as were unknown to me.

We assembled at the close of day, and began our march just as the muezzins called the evening prayer. Proceeding at once to the village of Ashtarek, we passed Etchmiazin, the seat of the Armenian patriarch, on our left. It was scarcely dawn of day when we reached the bridge of Ashtarek, still obscured by the deepest shade, owing to the very high and rocky banks of the river, forming, as it were, two abrupt walls on either side. The village itself, situated on the brink of these banks, was just sufficiently lighted up to be distinguished from the rocks among which it was built; whilst the ruins of a large structure, of heavy architecture, rose conspicuous on the darkest side, and gave a character of solemnity and grandeur to the whole scenery. This, my companions informed me, was the remains of the many Armenian churches so frequently seen in this part of Persia. The river dashed along through its dark bed, and we could perceive the foam of its waters as we began to cross the bridge. The rattle of our horses' hoofs over its pavement had alarmed the village dogs, whose bark we could just distinguish; the shrill crow of a cock was also heard, and most of our eyes were directed towards the houses, when one of our men, stopping his horse, exclaimed, 'Ya, Ali! what is that?' pointing with his hand to the church: 'do not you see, there, something white?'

'Yes, yes,' said another, 'I see it; it's a *ghôl*: without doubt it's a ghôl! This is the true hour: it is in search of a corpse. I dare say it is devouring one now.'

I also could see that something was there, but it was impossible to make it out.

We halted upon the bridge, looking up with all our eyes, every one being satisfied that it was a supernatural being. One called upon Ali, another upon Hossein, and a third invoked the Prophet and the twelve Imâms. None seemed inclined to approach it, but every one suggested some new mode of exorcism. 'Untie the string of your trousers,' said an old Irâki, 'that's the way we treat our ghôls, in the desert near Ispahan, and they depart instantly.'

'What good will that do?' answered a *delikhan* (a hare-brained youth); 'I'd rather keep the beast out than let it in.'

In short, what with joking, and what with serious talk, the morning broke sufficiently to convince us that the apparition must have been an illusion of our senses, for nothing now was to be seen. However, having passed the bridge, the said delikhan, shivering in his stirrups, and anxious to gallop his horse, exclaimed, 'I'll go and find the ghôl,' drove his horse up a steep bank, and made towards the ruined church. We saw him return very speedily, with intelligence, that what we had taken for a ghôl was a woman, whose white veil had attracted our notice, and that she, with a man, were apparently hiding themselves among the deep shades of the broken walls.

Full of anxiety for what might throw a light upon the object of my duty, I lost no time in proceeding to the ruin, in order to ascertain why these people hid themselves so mysteriously, and ordering five men to follow me, I made the rest halt near the bridge.

We saw no one until turning the sharp angle of a wall we found, seated under an arch, the objects of our search. A woman, apparently sick, was extended on the ground, whilst a man, leaning over, supported her head, in an attitude of the greatest solicitude. Enough of daylight now shone upon them to discover that they were both young. The woman's face, partially hid by her veil, notwithstanding its deadly paleness, was surprisingly beautiful; and the youth was the finest specimen of strength, activity, and manliness that I had ever seen. He was dressed in the costume of Georgia, a long knife hung over his thigh, and a gun rested against the wall. Her veil, which was of the purest white, was here and there stained with blood, and torn in several places. Although I had been living amongst men inured to scenes of misery, utter strangers to feelings of pity or commiseration, yet in this instance I and my companions could not fail being much interested at what we saw, and paused with a sort of respect for the grief of these apparently unfriended strangers, before we ventured to break the silence of our meeting.

'What are you doing here?' said I. 'If you are strangers, and travellers, why do you not go into the village?'

'If you have the feelings of a man,' said the youth, 'give me help, for the love of God! Should you be sent to seize us by the Serdar, still help me to save this poor creature who is dying. I have no resistance to offer; but pray save her.'

'Who are you?' said I. 'The Serdar has given us no orders concerning you. Where do you come from? Whither going?'

'Our story is long and melancholy,' said the young man: 'if you will help me to convey this poor suffering girl where she may be taken care of, I will relate everything that has happened to us. She may recover with good and kind usage: she is wounded, but I trust not mortally, and with quiet may recover. Thanks to Heaven, you are not one of the Serdar's officers! I entreat you to befriend me, and my lamentable tale may perhaps induce you to take us under your protection.' This appeal to my feelings was unnecessary: the countenance and appearance of the youth had excited great interest in my breast, and I immediately lent myself to his wishes, telling him that we would, without delay, convey his sick friend to the village, and then, having heard his story, settle what to do for him.

She had to this moment said nothing, but gathered her veil round her with great precaution, now and then uttering low groans, which indicated pain, and venting the apparent misery of her mind by suppressed sighs. I ordered one of my followers to dismount from his horse; we placed her upon it, and immediately proceeded to the village, where, having inspected the interior of several houses, I pitched upon that which afforded the best accommodation, and whose owner appeared obliging and humane; there we deposited her, giving directions that she should be nursed with the greatest care. An old woman of the village, who had the reputation of skill in curing wounds and bruises, was sent for, and she undertook her cure. I learnt from the youth that he and his companion were Armenians; and as the inhabitants of Ashtarek were of the same persuasion, they very soon understood each other, and the poor sufferer felt that she could not have fallen into better hands.

CHAPTER XXXVII: THE HISTORY OF YUSUF, THE ARMENIAN, AND HIS WIFE MARIAM

T was my intention to have proceeded to the heights of Aberan, where we should have found a cool region and good pasturage for our horses, before halting for the day; but hearing that the wandering tribes, whom we had expected to find encamped in a certain spot, and upon whose tents and provisions I had reckoned, were removed far into the mountains, fearful of the war which had just broken out, I determined to halt at Ashtarek until the heat of the day should have subsided. Accordingly, my men were quartered in different parts of the village: some settled themselves under the arches of the bridge, picketing their horses among the long grass: one or two took possession of a mill, situated in the bed of the river, whose wheel was turned by water, made to flow in an elevated channel for the purpose; and I spread my carpet in an open room, built upon a shelf, on the highest part of the rocky bank, from whence I had a view of the whole scene, and also could discern any object that might be coming towards us from the Russian frontier.

Feeling refreshed by two hours' sound sleep, upon awaking I sent for the Armenian youth; and whilst the good people of the village served us a light breakfast, of which we were both much in need, I requested him to relate his adventures, and particularly what had brought him into the situation in which he had been discovered. Refreshed with rest and food, the morning sun enlightening the spot we occupied, the manly features of the youth exhibited all their beauty; and, as he spoke, their animation and earnestness helped wonderfully to convince me that all he said was the truth. He spoke as follows:

'I am an Armenian by birth, and a Christian; my name is Yûsûf. My father is chief of the village of Gavmishlû, inhabited entirely by Armenians, situated not far from the beautiful river of Pembaki, and about six agatch from this place. In the middle of a verdant country, full of the richest pasturage, and enjoying a climate celebrated for coolness and serenity, we are a healthy and a hardy race; and, nothwithstanding the numerous exactions of our governors, were happy in our poverty. We live so far within the mountains, that we are more distant from the tyranny usually exercised upon those who abide nearer great towns, the residences of governors; and, secluded from the world, our habits are simple, and our modes of life patriarchal. I had an uncle, my father's brother, a deacon, and an attendant upon the head of our church, the patriarch at Etchmiazin; and another uncle, by my mother's side, was the priest of our village: therefore my family, being well in the church, determined that I should follow the sacred profession. My father himself, who subsisted by tilling the ground, and by his own labour had cleared away a considerable tract near the village, having two sons besides me, expected to receive sufficient help from them in the field, and therefore agreed to spare me for the church. Accordingly, when about ten years old, I went to Etchmiazin to be educated, where I learned to read, write, and perform the church service. I derived great pleasure from instruction, and read every book that came in my way. A very extensive library of Armenian books exists at the convent, of which I managed now and then to get a few; and although mostly on religious subjects, yet it happened that I once got a history of Armenia, which riveted all my attention; for I learnt by it that we once were a nation, having kings, who made themselves respected in the world. Reflecting upon our degraded state at the present day, and considering who were our governors, I became full of energy to shake off the yoke, and these feelings turned my thoughts from the sacred profession to which I was destined. About this time war broke out between Persia and Russia, and our village lying in the track of the armies marching to the frontiers, I felt that my family would require every protection possible, and that I should be more usefully employed with them than in a cloister. Accordingly, but a short time before taking priest's orders, I left my friends at Etchmiazin, and returned to my father's house. I was welcomed by every one. Already had they felt the horrors of war; for marauding parties of both Persians and Russians (both equally to be feared) had made their appearance, and molested the peaceable and inoffensive inhabitants of ours and the neighbouring villages. This frontier warfare, in its general results, was of no great utility to either of the powers at war, yet to those who inhabited the seat of it, its consequences were dreadful. We were continually harassed either by the fears of the invading enemy, or by the exactions and molestations of the troops of our own government. Our harvests were destroyed, our cattle dispersed, and ourselves in constant danger of being carried away prisoners. Anxious to preserve our property, and our only resource to keep us from starvation, we continued to till our fields, but went to work with swords by our sides, and guns ready loaded slung at our backs; and when a stranger appeared, whoever he might be, we immediately assembled and made a show of defence. By this means, for several years, we managed, with great difficulty and perseverance, to get in our harvest, and, by the blessing of Providence, had enough to subsist upon. But here I must begin some of those particulars which relate to my individual history.

'About two years ago, when securing our harvest, I had gone out long before the dawn to reap the corn of one of our most distant fields, armed and prepared as usual. I perceived a Persian horseman, bearing a female behind him, and making great speed through a glen that wound nearly at the foot of a more elevated spot, upon which I was standing. The female evidently had been placed there against her will, for as soon as she perceived me she uttered loud shrieks, and extended her arms. I immediately flew down the craggy side of the mountain, and reached the lowermost part of the glen time enough to intercept the horseman's road. I called out to him to stop, and seconded my words by drawing my sword, and putting myself in an attitude to seize his bridle as he passed. Embarrassed by the burden behind him, he was unable either to use his sword or the gun slung at his back, so he excited his horse to an increased speed, hoping thus to ride over me; but I stood my ground, and as I made a cut with my sabre, the horse bounded from the road with so sudden a start that the frightened woman lost her hold and fell off. The horseman, free of his incumbrance, would now have used his gun; but, seeing mine already aimed at him, he thought it most prudent to continue his road, and I saw nothing more of him.

'I ran to the assistance of the fallen woman, whom by her dress I discovered to be an Armenian. She was stunned and severely bruised: her outward veil had already disengaged itself, and in order to give her air, I immediately pulled away the under veil, which hides the lower part of the face (common to the Armenians), and, to my extreme surprise, beheld the most beautiful features that imagination can conceive. The lovely creature whom I supported in my arms was about fifteen years of age. Oh! I shall never forget the thrill of love, delight, and apprehension, which I felt at gazing upon her. I hung over her with all the intenseness of a first passion; a feeling arose in my heart which was new to me, and, forgetting everything but the object immediately before me, I verily believe that I should have been for ever riveted to that spot had she not opened her eyes and began to show signs of life. The first words she spoke went to my very soul; but when she discovered where she was, and in the hands of an utter stranger, she began to cry and bewail herself in a manner that quite alarmed me. Little by little, however, she became more composed; and when she found that I was one of her own nation and religion, that I was, moreover, her deliverer, she began to look upon me with different feelings: my vanity made me hope that, perhaps, she was not displeased at the interest she had awakened in me. One thing, however, she did not cease to deplore, and to upbraid me with—I had withdrawn her veil; there was no forgiveness for me—that indulgence which even a husband scarcely ever enjoys, that distinguishing emblem of chastity and honour, so sacred in the eyes of an Armenian woman—every sense of decency had been disregarded by me, and I stood before her in the criminal character of one who had seen all her face. In vain I represented, that had I not relieved her mouth and nose from the pressure of the lower band, she must have suffocated; that her fall having deprived her of all sensation, had she not inhaled the fresh air, death would have been the consequence. Nothing would convince her that she was not a lost woman. However, the following argument had more effect upon her than any other; no one but myself was witness to her dishonour (if such she must call it); and I swore so fervently by the Holy Cross, and by St. Gregorio, that it should remain a profound secret in my heart as long as I had one to keep it in, that she permitted herself at length to be comforted. I then requested her to give me an account of her late adventure, and to tell me from whom it had been my good fortune to liberate her.

'"As for the man," said she, "all I know of him is, that he is a Persian. I never saw him before, and know of no object that he could have had in carrying me off, excepting to sell me for a slave. A few days ago a skirmish took place between a detachment of Persian cavalry and Georgians. The latter were driven back, and the Persians made some prisoners, whom they carried away in great triumph to Erivan. Our village had been occupied by the Persian troops some days before this affray, and I suppose then my ravisher laid his plan to carry me off, and make me pass for a Georgian prisoner. I had just got up in the morning, and had gone to the village-well with my pitcher to bring home water, when he darted from behind a broken wall, showed his knife, threatening to kill me if I did not follow him without noise, and made me mount behind him on his horse. We galloped away just as some other of the village maidens were proceeding to the well, and my only hope of being saved was from the alarm which I knew they would instantly spread. We were out of sight in a few minutes, for we rode furiously over hill and dale, and cut across parts of the country unfrequented by travellers. At length, seeing you on the brow of the hill, I took courage, and gave vent to my cries, notwithstanding the threats of the Persian. You know the rest."

'She had scarcely finished speaking when we discovered several persons, one on horseback, the rest on foot, making towards us in great haste, and as they approached and were recognized by my fair one, it was delightful to watch her emotions.

'"Oh! there is my father," exclaimed she, "and my brothers! there is Ovanes, and Agoop, and Aratoon! and my uncle too!"

'As they came up, she embraced them all with transports of delight. I was in agonies of apprehension lest some youth should appear, who might have excited other feelings in her heart; but no, none but relations were there. They explained to her that the alarm of her seizure had been spread throughout the village by her young friends; that luckily they had not yet gone to the fields, and the family horse was at home, upon which her father was instantly mounted. They had traced the fresh footsteps of her ravisher's horse as long as he kept the road, had marked the place where he turned from it, had seen them again in several places, had tracked him through a corn-field that led up a steep slope, and at length, from a high summit, Ovanes had seen them descending a glen, which must have been very near the spot where they had now found her.

'She said all this was true, and again thanked God and St. Gregory for her escape; and, after some hesitation, in a most embarrassed manner, pointed me out as her deliverer. The attention of the whole party was then directed to me. "Whose son are you?" said the old man, her father.

'"I am the son of Coja Petros," said I, "the chief of the village of Gavmishlû."

'"Ah! he is my friend and neighbour," answered he; "but I do not know you; perhaps you are the son who was educating at the Three Churches for a priest, and who came to the help of your family?"

'I answered in the affirmative, and then he said, "You are welcome.— May your house prosper!—You have saved our daughter, and we owe you eternal gratitude. You must come with us and be our guest. If ever it were necessary to kill a lamb, to eat and be merry, it is now. We, and all our families, will carry you upon our heads; we will kiss your feet, and smooth your brow, for having saved our Mariam, and preserved her from dragging out her existence the slave of the Mussulman."

'I then received the congratulations and kind speeches of her brothers and uncle, who all invited me to their village in so pressing a manner, that, unable to resist, and propelled by my anxiety to see Mariam, I accepted their offer, and we forthwith proceeded in a body.

'As we were winding down the side of one of the mountains, Mariam's village, for such I shall call it, was pointed out to me, situated among trees, snugly seated in a warm nook, protected from every wind but the east, which here coming from the *Kulzum*, or the Caspian Sea, is delightfully cool and serene. Beyond was the Pembaki river, winding its way through a beautiful valley, diversified by rich vegetation; and at a greater distance we could just discern the church of Kara Klisseh, or the Black Monastery,

the first station of the Russians on this part of their frontier, and situated
on a dark and precipitous rock, rising conspicuous among the verdure of
the surrounding scenery.

'When near the village we discovered that all its inhabitants, particularly the women and children, had been watching our steps down the slope,
anxious to know whether Mariam had been retaken; and when they saw
her safe, there was no end to their expressions of joy. The story of her
flight and of her rescue was soon told, and carried from one mouth to another with such rapidity and with such additional circumstances, that at
length it came out that she had been carried away by a giant, who had an
iron head, claws and feet of steel, and scales on his back, mounted upon a
beast that tore up the ground at every bound, and made noises in its rapid
course over the hills like the discharges of artillery. They added to this,
that of a sudden an angel, in the shape of a ploughboy, descended from the
top of a high mountain in a cloud, and as he wielded a sword of fire in his
hand, it frightened the horse, threw Mariam to the ground, and reduced
the giant and his steed to ashes: for when she recovered from her fright,
they were no longer to be seen. I was pointed out as the illustrious ploughboy, and immediately the attention of the whole village was turned towards me; but, unfortunately, when about receiving nearly divine honours,
a youth, whom I had frequently met tending cattle in the mountains, recognized me, and said, "He is no angel—he is Yûsûf, the son of Coja Petros,
of Gavmishlû"; and thus I was reduced to my mortality once more. However, I was treated with the greatest distinction by everybody, and Mariam's relations could not sufficiently testify their gratitude for the service
I had rendered. But, all this time, love was making deep inroads in my
heart. I no longer saw Mariam unveiled, that happy moment of my life
had gone by; but it had put the seal to my future fate. "No," said I to
myself, "nothing shall separate me from that beautiful maid; our destinies
forthwith are one; Heaven has miraculously brought us together, and nothing but the decrees of Providence shall disunite us, even though to gain
her I should be obliged to adopt the violence of the Persian, and carry
her away by force." We met now and then, Mariam and I; and although
our words were few, yet our eyes said much, and I knew that my passion
was returned. Oh, how I longed to have met and engaged another, aye,
twenty more Persians, to prove my love! but I recollected that I was noth-

ing but a poor Armenian, belonging to a degraded and despised nation, and that the greatest feat which I could ever expect to perform would be to keep the wolf from my father's flocks, or to drive the marauder from our fields.

'I remained the whole of that eventful day at Geuklû (the name of the village), where the promised lamb was killed, and a large cauldron of rice boiled. I returned on the following day to my parents, who had been alarmed at my absence, and who listened to the history of my adventures with all the earnestness and interest that I could wish.

'I was so entirely absorbed by my love, that I could think of nothing else; therefore I determined to inform them of the situation of my affections. "I am of an age now," said I to them, "to think and act for myself. Thanks to God, and to you, I have strong arms, and can work for my bread; I wish to marry, and Providence has prepared the way for me."

'I then requested them forthwith to demand Mariam from her parents, in order that I might make her my wife; and finished by kissing my father's hand, and embracing my mother.

'They said in answer, "That marriage was a serious consideration in these difficult times, and that the family was now too poor to incur the expense of a wedding. It was necessary to buy clothes, a ring, candles, sweetmeats, a crimson veil, bed and bed-covering, to pay the singers and musicians, and to make a feast; and where was money to be found to meet all this?"

'I said, "'Tis true that money is wanted, and that no marriage can take place without it, both for the honour of our family, and for the purpose of showing my love to my intended; but I can borrow; I have friends both at Erivan and at the Three Churches; and I think I could borrow enough from the one and the other to pay the expenses of my wedding; and as for repayment, I will work so laboriously, and live so frugally, that little by little I shall pay off my debt. Besides, I can become the servant of a merchant, who would give me a share in his adventures; and one journey to Constantinople or to Astrachan would yield me enough profit to repay every one with interest."

'In short, I said so much, that at length they were persuaded to make the necessary overtures to the parents of Mariam; and it was fixed, that in the course of a few days my father, my uncle the priest, and one of the elders of the village should proceed to Geuklû, and ask her in marriage for me. In the meanwhile, I myself had been there almost every day, upon one pretext or another, and I had had several opportunities of informing her of my intentions, in order that she and her family might not be taken unawares.

'My father and his colleagues were very well received by the parents of my intended. Having talked over the matter, and seizing this opportunity of drinking some more than usual glasses of arrack, they agreed that we should be united as soon as the marriage-articles should have been agreed upon, and the forms of the *nâm zed* (the ceremony of betrothing) should have been gone through.

'Three days after this, my mother, accompanied by two old women of our village, by my uncle the priest, and me, proceeded to Geuklû for the purpose of the nâm zed, and settling the terms of the marriage. They were received with more ceremony than my father and his colleagues had been, and the women of the other party having met ours, negotiations were opened.

'My mother offered, on my part, that I should give of clothes to my bride two full suits, consisting of two shifts, one of crimson silk, the other of blue cotton; two pairs of trousers, one of silk, the other of striped cotton; two *jubbehs*, or robes, fitting tight to the body, of chintz; two veils, one of white cotton, the other of chequered blue; two pair of slippers, one of green shagreen skin and high heels, the other of brown leather, with flat bone heels and shod with iron: and I was also to add a printed muslin handkerchief, and a set of bandages and kerchiefs for the head. She moreover offered fifty piastres in silver coin for minor expenses; and a chain for the neck, from which there should be suspended one gold tomaun of Persia.

'After some little consultation among the friends of my wife, this was agreed upon; but one of the old women, who had been a servant in a Persian family, started a demand which gave rise to some discussion; it was, that I ought to give something for *sheer baha*, or milk money, as is the custom throughout Persia. Our party said this was not usual among the Armenians; the adverse party contended it was; in short, words were running high, when I requested my mother not to make any difficulty, but to offer ten piastres more; which being agreed upon, the whole was amicably adjusted to the satisfaction of both parties.

'This had taken place among the women alone. I was then called in, with my uncle, to go through the ceremony, and strict injunctions were made me not to laugh, nor even to smile, while it lasted; for ill luck would attend the marriage if anything so indecorous took place at the first interview.

'I found my mother seated on the ground, flanked by her two old women, opposite to my bride's mother, supported by hers. Mariam entered at the same moment, and my mother then presented her with a ring (a brass one, alas!) from me, which she put on her finger, and then wine was administered to the priest; of which, when he had taken a copious draught, it was announced that we were betrothed man and wife, and we received the congratulations of all those around us. I was delighted, although prohibited from communicating with my intended; but went about kissing everybody, and so many benedictions were showered upon us, that perhaps no couple ever was so much blessed, by good wishes at least, as we were.

'My mother and her party having returned to our village, I proceeded to make the preparations for my wedding with a light heart, regardless of any event which might intervene to destroy it. When we came to discuss the money it was likely to cost, and the means of obtaining it, I was agreeably surprised to see my father walk into the room where the family was assembled, with a bag in his hand. "Here," said he, "here is money. After all, the ked khoda of Gavmishlû can provide for his son as well as the best in the country. Here, Yûsûf," said he to me, "take these ten tomauns, my son, and lay them out in the purchase of your wife's clothes."

'Upon which I knelt down, kissed his hand, and craved his blessing.

'My uncle, the priest, warmed by this generosity, said, "And here, nephew,—the church is poor indeed, and its ministers poorer,—but here —take these twenty silver abassis, and expend them in tapers for your wedding." Others of those seated in the assembly also gave me something; by which means, without being reduced to the necessity of borrowing, I found my purse sufficiently well supplied to enable me to make my purchases at once. I expressed my thanks to my benefactors; and never before having had so much money in my possession, I scarcely knew what countenance to keep. However, my impatience knew no bounds; I was anxious to be already on my road to Erivan, where the clothes were to be bought; for there was no place nearer than that city in which a bazaar was to be found. But as I was ignorant of the arts of buying, and particularly ill versed in women's dresses, it was decided that my mother should accompany me mounted on our ass, whilst I followed on foot. She had an Armenian friend at Erivan, who would take us in for a night or two; and as for sleeping on the road, we could take up our abode in the tents of the wandering tribes, whose duties bind them to hospitality towards the stranger.

'We departed, she on the ass, I with my sword by my side, and my gun on my shoulder; and followed by half the village, invoking good luck for us.

'Having reached the heights of Aberan, we discovered an immense camp of white tents; one of which, belonging to the chief, was of a magnificent size. A horseman whom we met informed us that the Serdar of Erivan was encamped there with a considerable body of cavalry; and it was supposed posted there to watch the motions of the Russians and Georgians, who, it was expected, were likely soon to move their forces forwards to the attack of Persia.

'This intelligence gave us considerable alarm. My mother was for returning home, and for putting off the wedding. Too much in love to hearken to such a proposal, I urged her to travel more expeditiously, that we might be back the sooner. We proceeded so far on the first day, that I could see the smoke of Erivan in the distance. We passed the night under a projecting rock, with the majestic mountain of Ararat in full view; and did not fail to cross ourselves when we first came in view of it, and of recommending ourselves to St. Gregorio, when we composed ourselves to sleep. The wandering tribes had gone too far out of our track for our purpose, therefore we did not think of seeking their protection; but, refreshed with our night's rest, we resumed our journey early in the morning, and reached Erivan in safety.

'My mother was received by her friend with kindness; and the day after our arrival, they went to the bazaar to make purchases of the wedding-clothes, whilst I roamed about, gaping at everything, and listening to the speeches of those who were gathered together on the market-place. Various were the rumours concerning the operations of the Serdar against the enemy. It was evident that some movement was likely soon to take place, and an attack of an extraordinary nature to be made; for the people at the arsenal, and powder works, had been more than usually employed in making ready certain instruments[1] of destruction, before unknown in Persia, and set on foot by Russian deserters themselves. I was so entirely taken up by my own affairs, and by the happiness in store for me, that this sort of intelligence passed by me totally unheeded. It just struck me, that we might endeavour to secure the protection of the Serdar, through our chief at the Three Churches, in case our village and its territory became the theatre of war; but when I reflected upon the length of time it would take to make such a deviation from our road, I abandoned the idea, and, in my impatience, trusted to my own sword and musket as sufficient protection against all invaders.

'My mother and I returned to our village by the same road we came, but not with quite so much speed; for the ass was laden with our purchases, and, in addition to my arms, I also carried a considerable share of the burden. The Serdar's camp was still in the same place, and we passed on without hindrance or any occurrence worth relating, until we reached the high ground that overlooks Gavmishlû.

'The sight of a tent first struck my mother, and she stopped.

'"What is that, Yûsûf?" she cried out to me: "see, there is a tent."

'I, who had no thoughts in my head but those that concerned my wedding, answered, "Yes, I see; perhaps they are making preparations for an entertainment for us."

'"My husband's beard with your entertainment!" exclaimed she; "what are become of your wits? Either Russians or Persians are there, as sure as I am a Christian; and in either case it is bad for us."

'We pushed on towards our dwelling with the greatest anxiety; and, as we approached it, found that my mother had judged right. The village had been just occupied by a small detachment of Russian infantry, composed of fifty men, commanded by a *penjah bashi*, or a head of fifty, who, it seems, formed the advanced posts of an army quartered at a day's distance from us. Every house in the village had been obliged to lodge a certain number of men, and ours, as the best, and belonging to the chief, was taken up by the captain.

'You may conceive our consternation on finding this state of things; and, in particular, how wretched I was from the apprehension that my

[1] It is supposed that the instruments here alluded to were hand-grenades.

wedding must be put off to an indefinite time, when perhaps ruin would have overwhelmed us, and left us naked and destitute fugitives. Oh! the idea was too overwhelming, and I hastened to give vent to my feelings to my friends at Geuklû, who perhaps might afford me some consolation. Their village being considerably out of the track of the invaders, no troops had yet made their appearance amongst them; but when they heard what was passing on our side of the country, they immediately became partakers of all our fears. I saw Mariam, dear child of nature! The customs of our country did not permit us to converse openly; but love is fertile in expedients, and we managed to pour out eternal vows of constancy, and to swear upon the holy cross of our faith, that, happen what might, we would ever be united.

'These interviews happened frequently, and I became almost mad with rage and disappointment that we could not marry. It was evident that some terrible catastrophe must take place soon—the armies might meet from day to day, and then what would become of the rejoicings of our wedding-day! To undertake the performance of a ceremony of such importance, under these circumstances, would only be mocking Providence, and preparing for ourselves a futurity of misfortune. However, I was too much in love, and too impatient, not to have married under any circumstances, therefore I only endured what I could not well resist.

'However, a fortnight had elapsed since our return, and nothing had happened. We were upon excellent terms with our guests the Russians, and as they were quiet and inoffensive, infinitely more so than Persians would have been under similar circumstances, we became very intimate. They were Christians as well as we; they made the sign of the cross; prayed at our church; ate pork and drank wine; all circumstances producing great sympathy of feeling, and strengthening the bonds of friendship between us. Their captain was a young man of great worth, and of such unpresuming manners that he gave universal satisfaction. He kept the strictest discipline among his troops, and was himself the soberest of mankind. He was anxious to gain information concerning our manners and customs, and encouraged us to converse with him upon everything that interested our family. This brought on a full exposition of our situation in regard to my wedding, to which he listened with a degree of interest so great, as to make him my friend for life.

'He said, "But why should it not take place now? There is nothing to hinder it: we are here to protect you, and whatever we can give or lend, I promise that I will procure. The Persians do not show the least sign of moving, and our army must wait for reinforcements from Teflis before it can advance farther; therefore you will have all the necessary time to perform your ceremonies in quiet and happiness, and perhaps with more splendour than if we had not been here."

'He, moreover, promised to make a present to the bride of some Georgian gold lace, and to lend me his horse, a fine Karadaghi, which I might mount on the occasion. He said so much, that he at length persuaded mine and my bride's relations not to defer the ceremony, and a day was fixed. Had any other man pressed the business so much, and appeared so personally interested in it, I should probably have been suspicious of the purity of his intentions, and certain feelings of jealousy might have arisen; but the captain was so ugly, so hideously ugly, so opposite to what passes for beauty amongst us, that I could have no fear concerning Mariam on his account; for if she could notice him, she could with the same facility become enamoured of an ape. His face was composed of a white leprous skin, with a head covered by hair, or rather quills, thrown about in a variety of stiff lines, of the colour of straw; his eyes were round holes scooped deep in their sockets, and situated behind small hillocks of cheekbones; his nose was marked by a little bit of flesh, under which were pierced two holes as if with an awl, and his chin, as lucid as glass, did not show the smallest appearance of hair. A little down grew upon his upper lip, which for length and prominence quite outdid its fellow; and this indication of a man was as carefully kept greased and blacked as a pair of immense boots in which his legs were always cased.

'"No," said I, to myself, "Mariam would sooner love her Persian giant than this creature; and when she comes to compare him to her intended (looking over myself at the same time with some complacency), I flatter myself that I may lay my jealous fears aside."

'And thus it was settled that I should wed. The evening before the wedding-day, the clothes and other articles, placed in trays borne upon men's heads, and preceded by singers and musicians (of which some are to be found in every village), were sent to my bride. My band consisted of a man who played on the *zourna*, or hautbois, a performer on the tambourine, and two who sang. As a mark of additional splendour, our Russian friends lent us a drum, the beating of which by one of our shepherd boys produced great effect all over the country. I followed my present a few hours after, for the purpose of receiving the one which my bride, according to custom, was to make me; consisting of a pair of brass mounted pistols, made in the Caucasus, which had belonged to a great uncle of hers, who had been a soldier in the troops of the *Wali* of Georgia, before the Russians had got possession of that country.

'On the following day, the day of my long-expected happiness, I and all my family arose betimes in the morning. The weather was serene but sultry; there had been a tendency to storm for several days before, and heavy clouds stood in threatening attitudes with their white heads in the horizon. But nature was beautiful, and refreshed by a shower that had fallen in the night. My friend, the captain, lent me his horse, which I caparisoned and ornamented as well as I could on the occasion. I myself put on a new suit of clothes from head to foot, and with the addition of many silver-studded belts, cartouche-boxes, daggers, and other appendages fastened about me, and which had been lent me by a Georgian in the service of the Russians, I was told, and I believe it, that I made a very handsome appearance. Accompanied by my male relations, the Russian captain, and as many of his men as could be spared in order to create a crowd, we proceeded to Geuklû, and approaching it, marshalled ourselves in procession, preceded by music, songs, and shouts. We alighted at my bride's house, where we partook of refreshments, and received the congratulations of all the village; and then, when everything was prepared for our return to Gavmishlû, where my uncle was to perform the ceremony, we mounted again. My bride, covered by a crimson veil from head to foot, which flowed over a flat platter placed on her crown, was mounted on her father's steed, led on either side by her brothers. It is the custom for the bridegroom to hold a sash or girdle by his right hand, which is held at the other end by the bride, on their way to the church, and this we did. All our friends, our relations, all the youth of the villages, some on foot, some on asses, others on horses, accompanied the procession, making shouts, and manifesting their joy by all sorts of games and jokes during the whole course of the march. When at length we had reached a small rising ground overlooking my village the procession stopped, and every one who had a part to act in the ceremony received a taper, which was forthwith lighted. The procession then moved on with slow and measured steps, headed by my uncle, who, assisted by my other uncle from the Three Churches, sang psalms as they walked forward, amidst all the noise of the surrounding lookers-on. The Russian captain had had the attention to dress his men up on the occasion, and they marched to the church with us, adding much to the dignity of the scene.

'We at length alighted at the door of the church, and, still holding each end of the girdle, my bride and I walked to the foot of the altar, which, notwithstanding our humble condition, had been ornamented with more than ordinary brilliancy by flowers, ribbons, and looking-glasses. My forehead was then placed against Mariam's in a sort of butting attitude, and the Bible opened and laid upon our heads, whilst her hand was given into mine. The priest then asked, if we agreed to take each other for husband and wife; and after we had made an inclination of our heads as marking our consent, and a suitable proportion of prayers had been read and chanted, the ceremony was at an end, and notified to all the world by the shouts of the multitude, and by the redoubled sounds of our drums, flutes, and tambours.

'Daylight by this time had entirely disappeared, and the weather, which had threatened a storm, now became very lowering. The sky was darkened, rain fell, and distant thunders were heard. This circumstance put an

end to the entertainment given by my father earlier than it otherwise
would have done; and when our guests had retired, the hour at length arrived which was to make me the happiest of men.

'Oh, shall I stop here to recollect all the horrors of that night—or shall
I pass on, and not distress you by relating them? You must conceive my
bride lovely as the morning star, innocent as an angel, and attached to me
by the purest love; and you may imagine what I felt at that moment—
I who had looked upon our union as impossible, and had thought of my
awaiting happiness as a bright spot in my existence, to which I expected
never to attain.

'But in order to give a right impression of the scene which I am about
to describe, you must know that the villages in Georgia, and in our part
of Armenia, are built partly under ground, and thus a stranger finds himself walking on the roof of a house when he thinks that he is on plain
ground, the greatest part of them being lighted by apertures at the top.
Such was the house in which my family lived, and in which my wedding
was celebrated. My nuptial chamber had one of these apertures, which had
been closed on the occasion, and was situated with its door leading at once
into the open air.

'It is the custom among the Armenians for the bridegroom to retire
first. His shoes and stockings are then taken off by his wife; and, before she
resigns her veil, has the task of extinguishing the light. The storm had
just broke—thunders were rolling over our heads—the lightning flashed
—torrents of rain were pouring down with fearful noise—there seemed
to be a general commotion of the elements, when my Mariam, unveiling
herself, extinguished the lamp. She had scarcely laid herself down, when
we heard an unusual violent noise at the aperture in the ceiling: sounds of
men's voices were mingled with the crash of the thunder; trampling of
horses was also distinctly heard; and presently we were alarmed by a heavy
noise of something having fallen in our room and near our bed, accompanied by a glare and a smell of sulphur.

'"'Tis a thunderbolt, by all that is sacred! Oh heaven protect us!"
cried I. "Fly, my soul, my wife, escape!"

'She had just time to snatch up her veil, and to get without the door,
when an explosion took place in the very room, so awful, so tremendous,
that I immediately thought myself transported to the regions of the damned.

I fell senseless, amidst the wreck of falling stones, plaster, and furniture. All I can recollect is, that an immense blaze of light was succeeded by an overpowering sulphureous smell—then a dead silence.

'I lay there for some time, unconscious of what was passing; but by degrees came to myself, and when I found that I could move my limbs, and that nothing about my person was materially hurt, I began to consider how I had got there. As for my wedding, that appeared to me a dream: all I heard about me now was the firing of muskets, loud and frequent explosions, cries and shouts of men—of men wounded and in pain—of men attacking and putting others to death—the tramplings of horses, the clashing of arms. "What, in the name of Heaven, can all this be?" said I. I still thought myself transported into another planet, when the shriek of a woman struck my ear. "It is Mariam! It is she, by all that is sacred! Where, where, shall I seek her?" I was roused: I disencumbered myself of the weight of rubbish that had fallen upon me, and, once upon my legs again, I sallied forth in search of her. The scene which presented itself was more terrible than language can express; for the first object which struck my sight was a Persian rushing by me, with a drawn sword in one hand, and a human head, dripping with blood, in another. The blackness of the night was lighted up at rapid intervals by vivid flashes of lightning, which, quick as the eye could glance, now discovered the hideous tragedy that was then acting, and now threw it again into darkness, leaving the imagination to fill up the rest. By one flash, I saw Persians with uplifted swords, attacking defenceless Russians, rushing from their beds: by another, the poor villagers were discovered flying from their smoking cottages in utter dismay. Then an immense explosion took place, which shook everything around.[1] The village cattle, loosened from their confinements, ran about in wild confusion, and mixed themselves with the horrors of the night: in short, my words fall short of any description that could be made of this awful scene of devastation; and I must bless the mercy of that Almighty hand which hath spared me in the destruction that surrounded me.

'I knew not where to turn myself to seek for my wife. I had heard her shrieks; and the shivering of despair came over me, when I thought it

---

[1] Hassan Khan Serdar, the governor of Erivan, was said to have attacked Armenian villages in the manner here described, by throwing grenades into the houses from the orifice at the top.

might have been her death groans which had struck my ears. I threw my-self into the midst of the carnage, and, armed with a firebrand, snatched from my burning nuptial chamber, I made my way through the combatants, more like a maniac at the height of his frenzy, than a bridegroom on his wedding-night. Getting into the skirts of the village again, I thought I heard the shrieks of my beloved. I ran towards the direction, and a flash of lightning, that glanced over the adjoining hill, showed me two horse-men making off with a woman, whose white veil was conspicuously seen, mounted behind one of them. Heedless of everything but my wife, I fol-lowed them with the swiftness of a mountain goat; but as the storm sub-sided, the lightning flashed no more, and I was left in utter darkness at the top of the hill, not knowing which path to take, and whether to pro-ceed or not. I was almost naked. I had been severely bruised. My feet, otherwise accustomed to the naked ground, had become quite lacerated by the pursuit I had undertaken; and altogether, I was so worn with grief, so broken-hearted, that I laid myself down on the wet earth in a state of desperation that was succeeded by a torpor of all my senses. Here I lay until the first rays of the morning glared in my eyes, and brought me gradually to a sense of my situation.

'"What has happened?" said I. "Where am I? How came I here? Either the demons and wicked angels of another world have been at work this night, or else I am most grossly abused. To see that glorious orb rising in that clear unclouded sky; to mark the soothing serenity of na-ture, the morning freshness, the song of the birds, the lowing of yon cat-tle, and the quiet and seclusion of my yonder paternal village, I ought to suppose that the images of horror, of indescribable horror, now floating in my mind, must be those of a diseased imagination. Is it possible that in this secluded spot, under this lovely sky, in the midst of these bounteous gifts of nature, I could have seen man murdering his fellow creature, the blazing cottage, the mangled corse, the bleeding head; and, O cruel, O killing thought, that I should have been bereft of my dear, my innocent wife?" and then, then only, was I restored to a full possession of every occurrence that had taken place; and tears which before had refused to flow now came to my assistance, and relieved my burning temples and my al-most suffocating bosom. I got up, and walked slowly to the village. All was hushed into quiet; a slight smoke was here and there to be seen; stray cattle were grazing on the outskirts; strangers on horseback seemed to be busily employed in preparations of some kind or other, and the wretched peasantry were seen huddled together in groups, scarcely awake from the suddenness of the destruction which had visited them, and uncertain of the fate which might still be in reserve. As for me, the loss which I had already sustained made me expect every other attendant misfortune. I had made my mind up to find my relations dead, to see the total ruin of our house, and to know that I was a solitary outcast on the face of the world, without a wife, without a home, without parents, without a friend. But no, imagination had worked up the picture too highly; for one of the first persons I met on entering our village was my poor mother, who, when she saw me, recollecting all the trouble she had been at to secure my happiness, fell on my neck, and shed a torrent of tears. When her first grief had subsided, she told me that my father had suffered much from bruises, and from a blow received on the head; but that the rest of the family were well; that our house had been considerably injured, many of our things pillaged; and that my nuptial room, in particular, had been almost totally destroyed. She informed me that the good Russian captain had been the first to fall a sacrifice to the attack of the Persians; for almost immediately after the explosion in my room, he had rushed out to see what had happened, when two Persians seized him, one of whom at once decapitated him: this was the head that I saw brandished before me, when first I sallied forth. She then took me to a place of shelter, and put on me what clothes could be found.

'The Persians, having completed their deeds of horror, had retired from the scene of action, leaving to our unfortunate villagers the melancholy task of burying the dead bodies of thirty wretched Russians, who had fallen victims to their treacherous attack, and whose heads they had carried off with them as trophies.

'After I had visited my father, and left my home in as comfortable a situation as I could, under the existing circumstances, I determined instantly to set out in pursuit of my wife. It was evident that she had been carried away by some of those who had attacked our village, and that she must have been taken to Erivan, as the nearest market for slaves, for such was no doubt the purpose for which she had been seized. My sword, pistols, and gun, which had formed part of the ornamental furniture of my bridal chamber, were found buried in its ruins, and with these for my protection, and with some pieces of silver in my purse, I bid adieu to Gavmishlû, making a vow never to return until I had found my Mariam.

'I travelled with hurried steps, taking the shortest cuts over the mountains to Erivan, and as I crossed a branch of the high road I met two horsemen, well-mounted and equipped, who stopped me, and asked whither I was going, and upon what errand.

'I did not hesitate to tell them my wretched tale, hoping they might give me some hint which might throw light upon the fate of my wife. This they did indeed, but in a manner so cruel, that their words awakened the most horrid suspicions, and almost to a certainty convinced me that my poor innocent, my hitherto unspotted, though wedded wife, had fallen into the power of a most licentious tyrant.

'"Is it possible," said I, when they had related to me the horrid expedients to which their chief, the Serdar (for it was to two of his bodyguard that I was talking), had recourse, for the accomplishment of his wickedness—"is it possible that selfishness can be carried to such an extreme, that vice can have reached to such a pitch in the heart of man? Women, by you Mussulmans, I know are treated as mere accessories to pleasure; but, after all, they are God's creatures, not made for the Serdar alone, as he seems to think, but given to us to be our help, our comfort, and our companions through life."

'My hearers only laughed at my sentiments, and tauntingly assured me, that, if I was seeking one who had got into the Serdar's harem, my labour would be in vain, and that I might just take the trouble to return whence I came.

'Little heeding what they said, I hastened my steps, without knowing why or wherefore; but impelled by a sort of feeling, that it could not be in the wisdom of the Almighty to heap such a load of misfortune upon a wretched sinner like me, without at length giving some counterbalancing reward, or some consolation which it is ever in His power to bestow.

'I was now near the camp at Aberan, where I knew the Serdar in person was settled, and, hoping to hear some favourable intelligence, I made towards it. It was greatly agitated by the arrival of the detachment of Persians who had attacked our village, and were giving proofs of the success of their enterprise, by exhibiting the Russian heads which they had brought

away, and which were laid in several heaps before the tent of the chief.
One might have supposed that a great and signal victory had been achieved,
such were the rejoicings and boastings that took place at the sight. The
horrid objects were forthwith salted, and sent off in great parade and ceremony to the Shah of Persia, who never will believe that a victory is gained
until he sees these palpable proofs of it. However, in the midst of all this
joy, a courier was seen arriving in great haste from the Russian frontier,
whose intelligence produced a change of scene. He announced that the Russian army, having heard of the late attack upon their outpost at Gavmishlû,
was now in full march against the Serdar, and coming on so rapidly, that
he must expect to be attacked even before night-close. The scene that ensued defies all description. The whole camp was ordered to be struck, and
an immediate retreat was commanded. Tents falling, mules loading, men
screaming; horses, camels, men, cannon, all were in motion at one time;
and before two hours had elapsed, the whole had disappeared, and the army
was on its march for Erivan.

'I had in the meanwhile received no account of my lost Mariam; and it
was plain that, if in the power of the Serdar, she was within the walls of
his seraglio at Erivan. Thither then I bent my steps, hoping that in this
great confusion something might turn up for my advantage.

'Upon my arrival there, I posted myself at the bridge over the Zengui,
from whence I had a full survey of that part of the Serdar's palace which
contains his women; and as the troops were crossing it at the same time in
constant succession, I was unnoticed, and passed for one of the camp followers. The building is situated upon the brink of a precipice of dark rock,
at the foot of which flows the Zengui, a clear and rapid stream, foaming
through a rocky bed, the stony projections of which form white eddies,
and increase the rush of its waters. A bridge of three arches is here thrown
over it, and forms part of the high road leading to Georgia and Turkey.
The principal saloon of the palace, in a corner of which the Serdar is usually seated, opens with a large casement on the river, and overlooks the
rugged scenery. At some distance on the same surface of building are the
windows of the women's apartments, distinguished by their lattices, and
by other contrivances of jealousy. However, I observed they were not so
well secured, but that objects passing and repassing the bridge might well
be seen from them; and I imagined that if Mariam was a prisoner there,

she might perchance make me out as I stood below. "But if she did, what then?" said I to myself in despair: "seeing me there would only add to her torture, and to my desperation." To escape from such a height appeared impossible, for a fall would be instant death; and excepting a willow tree, which grew out of the rock immediately under one of the windows, there was nothing to break the descent. However, having remained in one spot so long in meditation, I feared to be observed; and left my post for the present, determining to return to it at the close of day, and indeed at every hour when I could appear without suspicion.

'I had been watching the windows of the seraglio in this manner for more than a fortnight, and had not ceased to parade up and down the bridge at least three times every day, when one evening, as the day was about to close, I saw the lattice of the window over the willow tree open, and a female looking out of it. I watched her with breathless suspense. She appeared to recognize me. I extended my hand; she stretched forth hers. "It is she!" said I; "yes, it must be her! It is my Mariam!" Upon which, without a moment's hesitation, without thinking of the consequences, I plunged into the river, and having waded through it, stood at the foot of the precipice immediately under my beloved wife. She stretched her arms several times towards me, as if she would have thrown herself out. I almost screamed with apprehension; and yet the hope of pressing her to my heart made me half regret that she had not done so. We stood there looking wistfully at each other, fearing to speak, yet longing to do so. At length, she shut the lattice suddenly, and left me in an attitude and in all the horrors of suspense. I kept my post for some time without seeing anything more of her, when again suddenly the lattice opened, and she appeared, but with looks that spoke of intense agitation. I scarcely could tell what was about to happen, but waited in dreadful anxiety, until I saw her lean forward, retreat, lean forward again—then more and more, until, by a sudden effort, I beheld her fair form in the air, falling down the giddy height.[1] My legs refused to perform their office, my eyes were obscured by a swimming, and I should have probably sunk under the intenseness of my feelings, when I saw her half suspended, half falling, from a branch of the willow tree. I bounded up, and in an instant had mounted the tree, and had clasped her senseless in my arms. I seemed to be impelled by new

[1] This is a circumstance which is said to have really happened.

vigour and strength; to reach the ground, to recross the river, to fly with my precious burden from the inhabited outskirts into the open country, appeared but the business of a second. I was perfectly drunk with the thousand feelings which agitated me; and although I acted like one bereft of his senses, yet everything I did was precisely that which I ought to have done. Nature guided me: the animal acting only from instinct would have done like me. I had saved that which was most precious to me in this world.

'When I had worn out my first efforts of strength, and had felt that my hitherto senseless burden showed some symptoms of life, I stopped, and placed her quietly on the ground behind some broken walls. She was terribly bruised, although no bone had been broken. The branches of the tree, upon which she had alighted, had wounded her deeply in several places, and the blood had flowed very copiously. But she was alive; she breathed; she opened her eyes, and at length pronounced my name. I was almost crazy with joy, and embraced her with a fervour that amounted to madness. When she had reposed herself a little, I snatched her up again, and proceeded onwards with all the haste imaginable, in the determination to strike at once into the mountains; but recollecting that I had the river of Ashtarek to cross, and that with her in my arms it would be impossible to do so except by the bridge, I at once directed my steps thither.

'We were reposing at the foot of the bridge, when I heard the footsteps of your horses. Although nearly exhausted with my previous exertions, I still had strength enough left to clamber up the bank, and take refuge in the ruined church, where you first discovered us; and there I watched your motions with the greatest anxiety, concluding that you were a party sent in pursuit of us by the Serdar. Need I say after this, that if you will protect us, and permit us to seek our home, you will receive the overflowing gratitude of two thankful hearts, and the blessings of many now wretched people who by our return will be made supremely happy? Whoever you are, upon whatever errand you may be sent, you cannot have lost the feelings of a man. God will repay your kindness a thousand times; and although we are not of your faith and nation, still we have prayers to put up at the Throne of Grace, which must be received when they are employed in so good a cause.'

"Doctor, mashallah! you have good taste! The animal is fine!"

CHAPTER XXXVIII: SEQUEL OF THE FOREGOING HISTORY
AND OF THE RESOLUTION WHICH HAJJI BABA
TAKES IN CONSEQUENCE

THE Armenian youth here finished his narrative, and left me in astonishment and admiration at all he had related. With my permission he then quitted me to visit his wife, and promised to return immediately with the report of her present state, and how she felt after her repose. 'He surely cannot have been inventing lies to my face all this time,' said I when left to myself, 'for a bleeding woman is here in evidence to corroborate what he has advanced; but then should I permit him to proceed, and the Serdar was to hear that I had done so, what would become of me? I should certainly lose my place, and perhaps my ears. No; compassion does not suit me; for if it did, I ought not to remain a nasakchi. I will stick to what the sage Locman, I believe, once said on this occasion, which runs something to this purpose: "If you are a tiger, be one altogether; for then the other beasts will know what to trust to: but if you wear a tiger's skin, and long ears are discovered to be concealed therein, they will then treat you even worse than if you walked about in your own true character, an undisguised ass."'

I kept turning over in my mind whether I should release him or not; and was fluctuating in great perplexity between the ass and the tiger, when Yûsûf returned. He told me that his Mariam was considerably refreshed by repose; but, weak from loss of blood, and stiff by the violence of the contusions which she had received (in particular, one upon her leg, which was of consequence), it would be impossible for her to move for several days; 'except indeed we were pursued by the Serdar,' added he, 'when I believe nothing but force could hinder us from proceeding.' He said that not until now had she found strength enough to relate her own adventures from the time she had left him at Gavmishlû.

It appears that the instant she had darted from the nuptial chamber, only covered by her veil, she had been seized by a Persian, who, discovering by the glare of the lightning that she was young and handsome, ran off with her to some distance, and there detained her until, with the assistance of another, she was mounted on a horse and taken forcibly away; that these two men carried her straight to the camp at Aberan, and offered her for sale to the Serdar; who, having agreed to take her, ordered her to be conducted to his seraglio at Erivan, and there put into service; that the horrid plight in which she stood, when exhibited to the Serdar, her disfigured looks, and her weak and drooping state, made her hope that she would remain unnoticed and neglected; particularly when she heard what was his character, and to what extent he carried his cruelties on the unfortunate victims of his selfishness. Mariam, alluding to herself, then said, 'Hoping, by always talking of myself as a married woman, that I should meet with more respect in the house of a Mussulman, than if I were otherwise, I never lost an opportunity of putting my husband's name forward, and this succeeded—for little or no notice was taken of me, and I was confounded with the other slaves, and performed the different tasks of servitude which were set me. But, unfortunately, I did not long keep my own counsel; I confided my story to a Persian woman, who pretended to be my friend; hoping by that means to soften her heart so much as to induce her to help me in regaining my freedom; but she proved treacherous; she made a merit of relating it to the Serdar, who immediately forced me to confirm her words with my own lips, and then the extent of my imprudence became manifest. He announced his intention to avail himself of my situation, and ordered me to prepare for receiving him. Conceive then what were the horrors of my position. I turned over in my mind every means of escape, but all avenues to it were shut. I had never before thought of looking over the precipice upon which the windows of our prison opened; but now I seriously thought of precipitating myself, rather than submit to the tyrant. But a few hours after I had had the blessing to discover you on the bridge, I had been ordered to hold myself in readiness to receive him; and it was then that I had positively determined in my own mind to throw myself headlong out, either once more to be joined to you, or to die in the attempt. When I shut the lattices in haste, several women had just come into the room to conduct me to the hot bath previously to being dressed; and when I had made some excuse for delaying it, and had sent them out of the room, it was then that I opened the lattice a second time, and put my resolution into practice.'

Yûsûf having finished the recital of his and his wife's adventures, was very anxious to know what part I would take, and earnestly entreated me to befriend him by my advice and assistance.

The morning was far spent. My men were already mounted, and ready to proceed on our reconnoitring expedition, and my horse was waiting for me, when a thought struck me, which would settle every difficulty with regard to the young Armenian and his wife.

I called him to me, and said, 'After what you have related, it will be impossible to leave you at liberty. You have, by your own account, run off with a woman from the Serdar's seraglio, a crime which you perhaps do not know, in a Mussulman country, is punished with death, so sacred is the harem held in our estimation. If I were to act right, I ought not to lose a moment in sending you both back to Erivan; but that I will not do, provided you agree to join us in our present expedition, and to serve us as guide in those parts of the country with which you are best acquainted.' I then explained to him the nature of my office, and what was the object of the expedition.

'If you are zealous in our cause,' said I, 'you will then have performed a service which will entitle you to reward, and thus enable me to speak in your favour to the Serdar and to my chief, and, *Inshallah!* please God, to procure your release. In the meanwhile, your wife may remain here, in all safety, in the hands of the good folks of this village; and by the time we return, she will, I hope, have been restored to health.'

The youth, upon hearing this language, took my hand and kissed it, agreed to everything I had said, and having girt on his arms, he was ready to attend us. I permitted him to go to his wife, to give her an account of this arrangement, and to console her, with proper assurances, that they would soon be restored to each other. He again thanked me; and, with the agility of an antelope, had already gained the summit of the first hill before we had even begun to ascend it.

CHAPTER XXXIX: THE ARMENIAN YUSUF PROVES HIMSELF WORTHY OF HAJJI BABA'S CONFIDENCE

WE proceeded towards the Georgian frontier, shaping our track over unfrequented parts of the mountains, in which we were very materially assisted by Yûsûf, who appeared to be acquainted with every landmark, and who knew the directions of places with a precision that quite surprised us. He did not seem anxious to visit his own village; and, in fact, he assured me, that had he even permission so to do, he could not, because he felt himself bound by the oath which he had taken upon last quitting it, not to return, except accompanied by his wife.

The intelligence which had been brought to the Serdar of the advance of the Moscovites proved false, for we found them posted on the banks of the Pembaki river, occupying the village of Hamamlû, and fortifying themselves in Kara Klisseh. We were not far from the former place; and as we approached it, I became anxious to acquire some precise intelligence concerning the numbers and the dispositions of the enemy. A thought struck me, as I pondered over the fate of my Armenian protégé—'I will either save this youth or lose him,' thought I, 'and never was there a better opportunity than the present. He shall go to Hamamlû: if he brings me the intelligence we want, nothing can prevent me from procuring both his pardon and his wife for him—if he proves a traitor, I get rid of him, and demand a reward from the Serdar, for restoring his fugitive slave.'

I called him to me, and proposed the undertaking. Quicker than thought, he seized all the different bearings of the question, and without hesitation accepted of my proposal. He girt himself afresh, he tucked the skirts of his coats into his girdle, putting his cap on one side, and slinging his long gun at his back, he darted down the mountain's side, and we very soon lost him amid the sloping woods.

'*Ruft ke ruft*. He is gone and doubly gone,' said the young delikhan; 'we shall never see him again.'

'And why should he not return?' said I. 'Have we not got a hostage? Armenian though he is, he will not leave his wife.'

'Yes,' said the youth, 'he is an Armenian; but he is also an Isauvi (a Christian). The Russians too are Isauvis; and we all know, that when these infidels get together, they will rather die than return to the sons of Islam. No; were he the chaste Joseph himself, and his wife Zuleikha in person, I will bet this horse,' pointing to the beast under him, 'that we see him no more.'

'Do not coin false words, my little gentleman!' said a sturdy old cavalier, whose sunburnt face was harrowed by a thousand wrinkles, and shaded by a shaggy beard, mustachios, and eyebrows,—'why, without any use, do you eat dirt? The horse is the Shah's, not yours: and do you pretend to make the *bahs* (bets) upon it?'

'The Shah's property is mine, and mine is my own,' retorted the youth.

I and my party kept up this sort of desultory talk for a little while before we thought of settling ourselves, when, seeing a spot where there was much grass, we made for it, and dismounted from our horses. We dispersed ourselves here and there, each making a temporary establishment of horse-cloths and cloaks spread upon the ground, whilst our steeds, picketed among the grass, fed at pleasure. I announced my intention of passing the night here in case Yûsûf did not appear before its close; and preparatory to this, two of our best marauders set off in quest of a sheep, fowls, or anything they could get for our evening's meal. After an hour's absence, they returned with a sheep which they had seized from a flock

grazing in the neighbourhood of the river. It was soon killed, and preparations were made for roasting it. Two stakes with hooks at the top were
cut from the forest and stuck into the ground; then a long stick was passed
through the animal in lieu of a spit, and placed on the hooks. A fire having
been lighted, one of our men was stationed near it to turn the animal at
intervals; and it was not long before it was ready for eating. By way of
variety, some of the prime bits, with the fat of the tail, were cut off, spitted
upon a ramrod, and thus roasted. The sheep was served up on its stake,
and our party fell upon it with an intense appetite, whilst, by way of distinction, the ramrod was handed over to me for my share.

By this time the day had entirely closed in, and Yûsûf had not appeared. We then composed ourselves to sleep, leaving one or two to keep
watch and to attend upon the horses. About an hour after midnight, when
the moon was about going down, a distant shout was heard—presently a
second, more distinctly and nearer to us. We were immediately upon the
alert, and the shouts being repeated, we could no longer doubt but that
the Armenian was at hand. We then shouted in return, and not very long
after we saw him appear. He was almost exhausted with fatigue, but
still strong enough to be able to relate his adventures since he had
left us.

He informed me that having reached Hamamlû, he was recognized by
some of the Russian soldiers who had escaped the attack of the Persians
upon his village, and who immediately introduced him into the fort, and
treated him very kindly. He was taken before the commanding officer,
who questioned him narrowly upon the object of his visit; but the ready
pretext which he advanced, of seeking his wife, answered every difficulty;
besides which, the ruin of his village, the destruction of his family property, and the acquaintances which he had on the spot, furnished him with
so much matter of conversation, that no suspicion of his designs could be
entertained. He was then permitted to walk about the fort, and by asking
his questions with prudence, and making his own observations, was enabled to furnish me with the information I required on the strength and
position of the enemy, with some very good conjectures on the nature and
probability of their future operations. He then managed to slip away unperceived before the gates of the place were closed, and regained the mountains without the smallest impediment.

Having permitted Yûsûf to refresh himself with food and rest, and being now perfectly satisfied that his story was true, and that all confidence might be placed in his integrity, I ordered my party to hold themselves in readiness to return to Erivan. He was permitted to ride behind either of the horsemen when tired with walking, and in this manner, taking the shortest cuts over the mountains, we regained the village of Ashtarek. Whilst we stopped here to refresh ourselves and horses, and to gain intelligence of the movements of the Serdar and the chief executioner, I permitted the youth to visit his wife. He returned beaming with joy, for he had found her almost cured of her bruises, and full of thanks for the kindness and hospitality with which she had been treated.

The Serdar and the chief executioner had moved from Erivan, and were now encamped close to the residence of the Armenian patriarch; and thither we bent our steps, accompanied by Yûsûf.

CHAPTER XL: HAJJI BABA GIVES AN ACCOUNT OF
HIS PROCEEDINGS TO HIS SUPERIORS AND SHOWS HIMSELF
A FRIEND TO THE DISTRESSED

THE monastery of Etchmiazin, so called in the Armenian tongue, or Utch Klisseh, or the Three Churches, by the Turks and Persians, is situated in a large and well-cultivated plain, watered by the Araxes, and several smaller streams. It stands at the foot of the high mountain of Agri Dagh[1], which the Christians, and in particular the Armenians, hold in great veneration, because (so Yûsûf informed me) upon its conspicuous snow-capt summit the ark of Noah rested. The monastery and church, celebrated throughout Asia for the riches which they contain, are enclosed within high walls, and secured by strong and massive gates. It is here that the head of the Armenian church constantly resides, together with a large retinue of bishops, priests, and deacons, who form the stock which provides clergy for most of the Armenian churches in Asia. The title by which he is known in Persia is *khalifeh* or caliph, a designation which, comprising the head of the civil as well as the religious government, the Mussulmans used formerly to bestow on the sovereigns who held their sway at Bagdad and elsewhere. By the Christians he is generally known by the name of patri-

[1] Ararat.

arch, and his church is an object of pilgrimage for the Armenians, who flock there at particular seasons in great numbers from different parts of the world.

Hither we bent our steps. We discovered the united camps of the Serdar and the chief executioner, spreading their white tents in an irregular figure all round the monastery; and before we had reached its walls, we heard that the two chiefs had taken up their abode within it, and were the guests of the caliph.

'We'll burn the fathers of these *giaours* (infidels),' said the young delikhan, as he rode up to me in great joy at this intelligence; 'and will make up for the fatigues we have undergone, by drinking abundantly of their wine.'

'Are you a Mussulman,' said I, 'and talk of drinking wine? You yourself will become a giaour.'

'Oh, as for that,' answered he, 'the Serdar drinks wine like any Christian, and I do not see why I should not.'

As we approached the monastery, I called Yûsûf to me, and told him to be in readiness whenever he should be called for, and be prepared to confirm any oath that I might think it necessary to take for his interests. He was particularly enjoined, when he came to talk of the services he had rendered, to deviate from the truth as much as he chose, to set forth every sort of danger he had or had not incurred, and in particular to score up an account of sums expended, all for the use and advantage of the Serdar and of the Shah's government. 'I hope at that rate,' said I to him, 'your accounts may be balanced by having your wife restored to you; for which, after considerable difficulty, you may agree to give a receipt in full of all demands.'

Thus agreed, we passed through the heavy archway which leads into the first court of the monastery. This we found encumbered by the equipages and servants of the Serdar and the chief executioner. Here and there were strings of horses picketed by ropes and pegs, with their grooms established in different corners among their saddles and horse furniture; and a corner was taken up by a set of mules, distinguished by the eternal jingle of their bells, and the no less eternal wranglings of their drivers.

In the second yard were the horses of the chief servants, who themselves inhabited small rooms that surrounded two sides of the court.

We alighted at the first court, and I immediately inquired for the quarters of my master, the chief executioner. It was noon, and I was informed he was then with the Serdar, before whom, in all the boots, dust, and dirt of my travelling dress, I was immediately conducted.

They seemed to have entirely taken possession of the Armenian sanctuary, and to have dispossessed the Caliph of his place and authority; for they had taken up their abode in his very rooms, whilst the poor priests were skulking about with humble and downcast looks, as if fearful and ashamed of being the lawful inhabitants of their own possessions. The favourite horses of both the Persian chiefs were picketed close to the very walls of the church, more care being taken of their comforts than of the convenience of the Armenians.

My reader is already acquainted with the person and character of the chief executioner; and, before I proceed further, I must also make him acquainted with the Serdar. A man of a more sinister aspect was never seen. His eyes, which, in the common expression of his countenance, were like opaque bits of glass, glared terribly whenever he became animated, and almost started out of their old shrivelled sockets; and when this happened, it was always remarked that a corresponding smile broke out upon his mouth, which made the Shah's poet say, that Hassan Khan's face was like *Agri dagh*, the mountain near which he lived. When clouded at the top, and the sun shone in the plain, a storm was sure to ensue. Time had worn two deep wrinkles down his cheeks, which were not hid by a scanty beard, notwithstanding all the pains he took to make it thick; and the same enemy having despoiled him of all his teeth save one, which projected from his mouth, had produced deep cavities, that made the shaggy hairs, thinly spread over them, look like burnt stubble on the slopes of a valley. Altogether, it was difficult to say whether the goat or the tiger was most predominant; but this is most certain, that never was the human form so nearly allied to that of the brute as in this instance. His character corresponded to his looks; for no law, human or divine, ever stood in the way of his sensuality; and when his passions were roused, he put no bounds to his violence and cruelty. But with all this, he had several qualities, which attached his followers to him. He was liberal and enterprising. He had much quickness and penetration, and acted so politically towards the Shah and his government, that he was always treated with the greatest confidence and consideration. He lived in princely magnificence; was remarkable for his hospitality, and making no mystery of his irregularity as a Mussulman, was frank and open in his demeanour, affable to his inferiors, and the very best companion to those who shared in his debaucheries. No bolder drinker of wine existed in Persia, except perhaps his present companion, the executioner, who, as long as he could indulge without incurring the Shah's displeasure, had ratified an eternal treaty of alliance between his mouth and every skin of wine that came within his reach.

It was before these two worshipful personages that I was introduced, followed by two or three of my principal attendants. I stood at the end of the compartment until I was spoken to.

'You are welcome,' said the chief executioner. 'Hajjî, by my soul, tell me, how many Russians have you killed? have you brought a head— let me see?'

Here the Serdar took him up, and said, 'What have you done? What Russians are on the frontier? and when shall we get at them?'

To all of which I answered, after making the usual prefatory speech, 'Yes, Agas, I have done all that was in my power to do. It was a lucky hour when we set off, for everything that you wish to know I can explain! and it is evident that the destinies of the Serdar and of my master are much on the rise, since so insignificant a slave as I can be of use to them.'

'Good luck is no bad thing, that's true,' said the Serdar, 'but we trust a great deal to our swords, too,'—rolling his eyes about at the same time, and smiling in the face of the chief executioner.

'Yes, yes,' said his companion, 'swords and gunpowder, spears and pistols,—those are our astrologers. It will always be a fortunate hour that will bring me within slice of an infidel's neck. As for me, I am a *kizzel bash* (a red head), and pretend to nothing else. A good horse, a sharp sword, a spear in my hand, and a large maidan (an open space) before me, with plenty of Muscovites in it—that is all I want.'

'And what do you say to good wine too?' said the Serdar. 'I think that is as good a thing as any you have mentioned. We'll have the Caliph in, and make him give Hajjî a cup of his best. But tell us first,' addressing himself to me, 'what have you seen and done?—where are the Russians posted?—how many of them are there—have they any guns?—who commands them?—where are their Cossacks?—have you heard anything of the Georgians?—where is the Russian commander-in-chief?—what are the Lesgî about?—where is the renegade Ismael Khan?—Come, tell us all: and you, Mirza,' addressing himself to his scribe, 'write down all he says.'

Upon this I drew myself up, and, putting on a face of wisdom, I made the following speech:

'By the soul of the Serdar! by the salt of the chief executioner! the Muscovites are nothing. In comparison to the Persians, they are mere dogs. I, who have seen with my own eyes, can tell you, that one Persian, with a spear in his hand, would kill ten of those miserable, beardless creatures.'

'Ah, you male lion!' exclaimed my master, apparently delighted with what I said, 'I always knew that you would be something. Leave an Ispahani alone: he will always show his good sense.'

'They are but few Muscovites on the frontier. Five, six, seven, or eight hundred,—perhaps a thousand or two thousand—but certainly not more than three. They have some ten, twenty, or thirty guns; and as for the Cossacks, *pûtch and*, they are nothing. It is very inconvenient that they are to be found everywhere when least wanted, with those thick spears of theirs, which look more like the goad of an ox than a warlike weapon, and they kill, 'tis true; but then, they are mounted upon *yabous* (jades), which can never come up to our horses, worth thirty, forty, fifty tomauns each, and which are out of sight before they can even get theirs into a gallop.'

'Why do you waste your breath upon the Cossacks and their horses?' said the chief executioner; 'you might as well talk of monkeys mounted upon bears. Who commands the infidels?'

'They call him the *deli mayor*, or the mad major; and the reason why he is called so, is because he never will run away. Stories without number are related of him. Among others, that he has got the pocket Koran of his excellency the Serdar in his possession, which he shows to every one as a great trophy.'

'Aye, that's true,' exclaimed the Serdar. 'These bankrupt dogs surprised me last year, when encamped not five parasangs hence, and I had only time to save myself, in my shirt and trousers, on the back of an unsaddled horse. Of course, they pillaged my tent, and among other things stole my Koran. But I'll be even with them. I have shown them what I can do at Gavmishlû, and we still have much more to perform upon their fathers' graves. How many guns, did you say, they had?'

'Four or five, or six,' said I.

'I wrote down twenty or thirty just now,' remarked the Mirza, who was writing at the edge of the carpet,—'which of the two is right?'

'Why do you tell us lies?' exclaimed the Serdar, his eyes becoming more animated as he spoke. 'If we find that any part of what you say be false, by the head of Ali! you will soon discover that our beards are not to be laughed at with impunity.'

'In truth, then,' said I, 'this intelligence is not of my own acquiring. The greatness of the Serdar's, and my Aga's good fortune, consists in my having fallen upon a means of getting the most perfect information through a young Armenian, who risked his life for us, upon my making him a promise of recompense in the name of the Serdar.'

'A recompense in my name!' exclaimed the Serdar: 'who is this Armenian?—and what Armenian was ever worthy of a recompense?'

Upon this I related the whole of Yûsûf's history, from the beginning to the end. In pleading his cause in this public manner, I hoped that the Serdar would feel it impossible to resist the justice of the demand which I made upon him, and that my young protégé would at once be released from his fears and apprehensions of the chief's resentment, and restored to the undisputed possession of his wife.

When I had done speaking, nothing was said, but here and there *Allah! Allah! il Allah!* (there is but one God!) in suppressed exclamations from the lips of the Mohammedans present; whilst the Serdar, having rolled his eyes about, and twitched his mouth into various odd shapes, at length mumbled out, 'the Armenian has performed wonders'; and then called aloud to his servants to bring his *kaliân* or pipe.

Having smoked two or three long whiffs, he said, 'Where is this Armenian? Order the Caliph also to come before us.'

Upon which Yûsûf was ushered in, with the shoves and thrusts by which a poor man of his nation is generally introduced before a Persian grandee; and he stood in face of the assembly as fine a specimen of manly beauty as was ever seen, evidently creating much sensation upon all present by the intrepidity of his appearance. The Serdar, in particular, fixed his eyes upon him with looks of approbation; and turning round to the executioner in chief, made signs, well known among Persians, of his great admiration.

The Caliph, a heavy, coarse man, of a rosy and jovial appearance, dressed in the black hood peculiar to the Armenian clergy, appeared soon after, followed by two or three of his priests. Having stood for a short time before the Serdar and his companion, he was invited to sit, which he did, going through all the ceremonial of complimentary phrases, and covering the feet and hands in a manner usual on such occasions.

The Serdar then, addressing himself to the Caliph, said, 'It is plain that we Mussulmans are become less than dogs in the land of Irân. The Armenians now break into our harems, steal our wives and slaves from before our faces, and invite men to defile our fathers' graves. What news is this, O Caliph? Is this Allah's work or yours?'

The Caliph, attacked in this unexpected manner, looked very much alarmed, and the dew broke out upon his ample and porous forehead. Experience had taught him that these sorts of attacks were generally the forerunners of some heavy fine, and he already put himself in a posture of defence to resist it.

'What language is this?' said he in answer. 'We, whose dogs are we, who should dare even to think upon the evil of which your highness speaks? We are the Shah's subjects—You are our protector, and the Armenians sit in peace under your shade. What manner of man is this who has brought these ashes upon our heads?'

'That is he,' answered the Serdar, pointing to Yûsûf. 'Say, fellow, have you stolen my slave or not?'

'If I am guilty,' said the youth, 'of having taken aught from any man, save my own, here am I, ready to answer for myself with my life. She who threw herself out of your windows into my arms was my wife before she was your slave. We are both the Shah's *rayats*, and it is best known to yourself if you can enslave them or no. We are Armenians, 'tis true, but we have the feelings of men. It is well known to all Persia, that our illustrious Shah has never forced the harem of even the meanest of his subjects; and, secure in that feeling, how could I ever suppose, most noble Serdar, that we should not receive the same protection under your government? You were certainly deceived when told that she was a Georgian prisoner; and had you known that she was the wife of your peasantry, you never would have made her your property.'

The Caliph, frightened at the language of the youth, stopped him, by loud and angry exclamations; but the Serdar, apparently struck by language so unusual to his ears, instead of appearing angry, on the contrary, looked delighted (if the looks of such a countenance could ever express delight); and, staring with astonished eyes upon the youth, seemed to forget even the reason of his having been brought before him. Of a sudden, as if dispelling his former indignation, he stopped all further discussion by saying to him, 'Enough, enough; go, take your wife, and say no more; and, since you have rendered us a service at Hamamlû, you shall remain my servant, and wait upon my person. Go, my head valet will instruct you in your duties; and when attired in clothes suited to your situation, you will return again to our presence. Go, and recollect that my condescension towards you depends upon your future conduct.' Upon this Yûsûf, in the fullness of his heart, ran up to him with great apparent gratitude, fell upon his knees, and kissed the hem of his garment, not knowing what to say, or what countenance to keep upon such unlooked-for good fortune.

Every one present seemed astonished: the chief executioner gave a shrug, and indulged in a deep yawn; the Caliph, as if he had been disencumbered of a heavy weight, stretched his limbs, and the huge drops that were before glittering on his brow now disappeared, and his face again expanded into good humour. All congratulated the Serdar upon his humanity and benevolence, and compared him to the celebrated Noushirwan. *Barikallah* and *Mashallah* was repeated and echoed from mouth to mouth, and the story of his magnanimity was spread abroad, and formed the talk of the whole camp. I will not pretend to explain what were the Serdar's real sentiments; but those who well knew the man were agreed that he could be actuated by no generous motive.

CHAPTER XLI: HE DESCRIBES AN EXPEDITION AGAINST THE RUSSIANS, AND DOES AMPLE JUSTICE TO THE COWARDICE OF HIS CHIEF

MY chief and the Serdar having acquired all the information which Yûsûf and I could give them upon the force and position of the Muscovites, it was determined that an attack should immediately be made, and the army was ordered to march upon Hamamlû.

Everything was soon in motion; the artillery began its tedious and difficult march through the mountains; the infantry made their way in the best manner they could, and the cavalry were seen in unconnected groups all over the plain. I must not omit to say, that before the march began I received a visit from the Armenian. He was no longer, in appearance, the rude mountaineer with his rough sheepskin cap, his short Georgian tunic, his sandalled feet, his long knife hung over his knee, and his gun slung obliquely across his body; but he was now attired in a long vest of crimson velvet, trimmed with gold lace and gold buttons; a beautiful Cashmerian shawl was tied gracefully round his waist; his small cap, of Bokhara lamb-skin, was duly indented at the top, and the two long curls behind his ears were combed out with all proper care. He had now more

the appearance of a woman than a man, so much were his fine limbs hid
by his robes; and as he approached me, he could not help blushing and
looking awkward at the metamorphosis. He thanked me with expressions
that indicated much gratitude, and assured me, that so far from having expected this result to his interview with the Serdar, he had, in fact, made up
his mind to the loss of both his wife and life, and therefore had spoken
with the boldness of one determined to die. 'But,' said he, 'notwithstanding this great change in my fortunes, this new existence of mine will never
do. I cannot endure the degradation of being a mere idle appendage to the
state of the Serdar; and be not angry if, ere long, I decline the honour of
his service. I will submit to everything as long as my wife is not in a place
of safety; but when once I have secured that, then adieu. Better live a
swineherd in the Georgian mountains, naked and houseless, than in all
these silks and velvets, a despised hanger on, be it even in the most lux-
urious court of Persia.'

I could not help applauding such sentiments, although I should have
been happy had he made any one else his confidant, conscious that if he
did run away I should in some measure be made answerable for him.

In the meanwhile the army proceeded on its march. As we passed
Ashtarek, Yûsûf got permission to take possession of Mariam, who, now
transformed into the wife of one who had the reputation of being in the
good graces of the Serdar, travelled with great respectability and consideration on horseback, and formed one among the numerous camp-follow-
ers that are always attached to a Persian army. The camp was pitched between Gavmishlû and Aberan, where all that was not necessary for the
expedition was ordered to remain until its return. It was settled that the
Serdar and the chief executioner, each accompanied by their own men,
with two pieces of artillery, should form the expedition, and towards the
close of the evening it set off.

As we approached the scene of action, the Serdar became impatient of
delay, and, like every Persian who despises the utility of infantry, expressed
his wish to push on with the cavalry. I will not say as much for the impatience of my chief. He continued his boastings to the last, 'tis true, and
endeavoured to make every one believe that he had only to appear, and
the enemy would instantly be seized with a panic; but at length he ceded
to the Serdar's wishes of bringing on the rear-guard, whilst the latter

pushed on to Hamamlû with the main body of the cavalry. I, of course, remained behind, to act under the orders of my chief. The Serdar intended to reach Hamamlû before break of day in order to surprise the gates, and deviated from the road to ford the Pembaki river. We continued our march straight for that place, and were to appear as the day dawned, to give a retreat to the Serdar, in case he should be beaten back.

The morning had just broke when we reached the banks of the river. The chief executioner was surrounded by a body of about five hundred cavalry, and the infantry was coming up as well as it could. We were about fording the river, when of a sudden we were accosted by a voice on the other side, which shouting out two or three strange words in a language unknown to us, explained their meaning by a musket shot. This stopped our career, and called the attention of our chief, who came up, looking paler than death.

'What's the news?' exclaimed he, in a voice far below its usual pitch— 'what are we doing?—where are we going?—Hajjî Baba,' accosting me, 'was it you that fired?'

'No,' said I, catching rather more of his apprehension than was convenient; 'no, I did not fire. Perhaps there are *ghôls* here among the Muscovites, as well as at Ashtarek among the Armenians.'

In another minute more barbarous cries were heard, and another shot was fired, and by this time day had sufficiently advanced to show two men, on the other bank, whom we discovered to be Russian soldiers. As soon as our chief saw the extent of the danger, and the foe opposed to us, his countenance cleared up, and he instantly put on the face of the greatest resolution and vigour. 'Go, seize, strike, kill!' he exclaimed, almost in one breath, to those around him—'Go, bring me the heads of yonder two fellows.'

Immediately several men dashed into the river, with drawn swords, whilst the two soldiers withdrew to a small rising ground, and, placing themselves in a convenient position, began a regular, though alternate, discharge of their muskets upon their assailants, with a steadiness that surprised us. They killed two men, which caused the remainder to retreat back to our commander, and no one else seemed at all anxious to follow their example. In vain he swore, entreated, pushed, and offered money for their heads: not one of his men would advance. At length, he said, with a most magnanimous shout, 'I myself will go; here, make way! will nobody follow me?' Then, stopping, and addressing himself to me, he said, 'Hajji! my soul, my friend, won't you go and cut those men's heads off? I'll give you everything you can ask.' Then, putting his hand round my neck, he said, 'Go, go; I am sure you can cut their heads off.'

We were parleying in this manner, when a shot from one of the Russians hit the chief executioner's stirrup, which awoke his fears to such a degree, that he immediately fell to uttering the most violent oaths. Calling away his troops, and retreating himself at a quick pace, he exclaimed, 'Curses be on their beards! Curse their fathers, mothers, their ancestry, and posterity! Whoever fought after this fashion? Killing, killing, as if we were so many hogs. See, see, what animals they are! They will not run away, do all you can to them. They are worse than brutes;—brutes have feeling,—they have none. O Allah, Allah, if there was no dying in the case, how the Persians would fight!'

By this time we had proceeded some distance, and then halted. Our chief, expecting to find the Russians back to back under every bush, did not know what course to pursue, when the decision was soon made for us by the appearance of the Serdar, who, followed by his cavalry, was seen retreating in all haste from before the enemy. It was evident that his enterprise had entirely failed, and nothing was left for the whole army but to return whence it came.

I will not attempt to draw a picture of the miserable aspect of the Serdar's troops; they all looked harassed and worn down by fatigue, and seemed so little disposed to rally, that one and all, as if by tacit consent, proceeded straight on their course homewards without once looking back. But as much as they were depressed in spirits, in the same degree were raised those of our commander. He so talked of his prowess, of the wound he had received, and of his intended feats, that at length, seizing a spear, he put his horse at the full gallop, and overtaking his own cook, who was making the best of his way to his pots and pans, darted it at him, in the exuberance of his valour, and actually pierced him in the back through his shawl girdle.

Thus ended an expedition which the Serdar expected would have given him a great harvest of glory and of Muscovites' heads; and which, the chief executioner flattered himself, would afford him exultation and boasting for the remainder of his life. But, notwithstanding its total failure, still he had ingenuity enough to discover matter for self-congratulation.

Surrounded by a circle of his adherents, amongst whom I was one, he was in the midst of a peal of boasting, when a message came from the Serdar, requesting that Hajjî Baba might be sent to him. I returned with the messenger, and the first words which the Serdar said, upon my appearing before him, were, 'Where is Yûsûf? Where is his wife?'

It immediately occurred to me that they had escaped; and putting on one of my most innocent looks, I denied having the least knowledge of their movements.

The Serdar then began to roll his eyeballs about, and to twist up his mouth into various shapes. Passion burst from him in the grossest and most violent expressions; he vowed vengeance upon him, his race, his village, and upon everything and everybody in the least connected with him; and whilst he expressed a total disbelief of all my protestations of ignorance, he gave me to understand, that if I was found to have been in the smallest degree an accessory to his escape, he would use all his influence to sweep my vile person from the face of the earth.

I afterwards heard that he had sent a party of men to Gavmishlû, to seize and bring before him Yûsûf's parents and kindred, with everything that belonged to them; to take possession of their property, and to burn and destroy whatever they could not bring away: but the sagacious and active youth had foreseen this, and had taken his measures with such prudence and promptitude, that he had completely baffled the tyrant. He, his wife, his wife's relations, his own parents and family, with all their effects (leaving only their tilled ground behind them), had concerted one common plan of migration into the Russian territory. It had fully succeeded, as I afterwards heard, for they were received with great kindness, both by the government and by their own sect; lands were allotted, and every help afforded them for the re-establishment of their losses.

CHAPTER XLII: HE PROCEEDS TO THE KING'S CAMP, AND GIVES A SPECIMEN OF LYING ON A GRAND SCALE

I RETURNED to my chief full of apprehension at the threat which I had received; and knowing how very tenacious all our great men are of power over their own servants, I did not fail immediately to inform him of the language which the Serdar had entertained me with. He became furious, and I had only to fan the flame which I had raised in order to create a quarrel between them; but, having more fears about the Serdar's power of hurting me than I had confidence in the ability of the chief executioner to protect me, I thought it best for all parties that I should retire from the scene, and craved my master's permission to return to Tehran. Pleased with an opportunity of showing the Serdar that nobody but himself could control his servants, he at once assented to my proposal; and forthwith began to give me instructions concerning what I should say to the grand vizier touching the late expedition, and particularly in what light I was to place his own individual prowess.

'You yourself were there, Hajjî,' said he to me, 'and therefore can describe the whole action as well as I could.—We cannot precisely say that we gained a victory, because, alas! we have no heads to show; but we also were not defeated. The Serdar, ass that he is, instead of waiting for the artillery, and availing himself of the infantry, attacks a walled town with his cavalry only, and is very much surprised that the garrison shut their gates, and fire at him from the ramparts: of course he can achieve nothing, and retires in disgrace. Had I been your leader, things would have gone otherwise; and as it was, I was the only man who came hand to hand with the enemy. I was wounded in a desperate manner; and had it not been for the river between us, not a man of them would have been left to tell the tale. You will say all this, and as much more as you please'; then, giving me a packet of letters to the grand vizier, and to the different men in office, and an *arizeh* (a memorial) to the Shah, he ordered me to depart.

I found the Shah still encamped at Sultanieh, although the autumn was now far advanced, and the season for returning to Tehran near at hand. I presented myself at the grand vizier's levée, with several other couriers, from different parts of the empire, and delivered my dispatches. When he had inspected mine, he called me to him, and said aloud, 'You are welcome! You also were at Hamamlû? The infidels did not dare to face the *Kizzil bashes*, eh? The Persian horseman, and the Persian sword, after all, nobody can face. Your khan, I see, has been wounded; he is indeed one of the Shah's best servants. Well it was no worse. You must have had hot work on each bank of the river.'

To all of this, and much more, I said 'Yes, yes,' and 'no, no,' as fast as the necessity of the remark required; and I enjoyed the satisfaction of being looked upon as a man just come out of a battle. The vizier then called to one of his mirzas or secretaries, 'Here,' said he, 'you must make out a *fatteh nameh* (a proclamation of victory), which must immediately be sent into the different provinces, particularly to Khorassan, in order to overawe the rebel khans there; and let the account be suited to the dignity and character of our victorious monarch. We are in want of a victory just at present; but, recollect, a good, substantial, and bloody victory.'

'How many strong were the enemy?' inquired the mirza, looking towards me. '*Bisyar, bisyar*, many, many,' answered I, hesitating and embarrassed how many it would be agreeable that I should say—'Put down fifty thousand,' said the vizier coolly. 'How many killed?' said the mirza, looking first at the vizier, then at me. 'Write ten to fifteen thousand killed,' answered the minister: 'remember these letters have to travel a great distance. It is beneath the dignity of the Shah to kill less than his thousands and tens of thousands. Would you have him less than *Rustam*, and weaker than *Afrasiab?*[1] No, our kings must be drinkers of blood, and slayers of men, to be held in estimation by their subjects, and surrounding nations. Well, have you written?' said the grand vizier.

'Yes, at your highness's service,' answered the mirza; 'I have written' (reading from his paper) 'that the infidel dogs of Moscovites (whom may Allah in his mercy impale on stakes of living fires!) dared to appear in

[1] An invading Tartar prince who was repulsed by Rustam, in command of the Persians.

arms to the number of fifty thousand, flanked and supported by a hundred mouths spouting fire and brimstone; but that as soon as the all-victorious armies of the Shah appeared, ten to fifteen thousand of them gave up their souls; whilst prisoners poured in in such vast numbers, that the prices of slaves have diminished 100 per cent. in all the slave-markets of Asia.'

'Barikallah! Well done,' said the grand vizier. 'You have written well. If the thing be not exactly so, yet, by the good luck of the Shah, it will, and therefore it amounts to the same thing. Truth is an excellent thing when it suits one's purpose, but very inconvenient when otherwise.'

'Yes,' said the mirza, as he looked up from his knee, upon which he rested his hand to write his letter, and quoting a well-known passage in Saadi, 'Falsehood mixed with good intentions, is preferable to truth tending to excite strife.'

The vizier then called for his shoes, rose from his seat, mounted the horse that was waiting for him at the door of his tent, and proceeded to the audience of the Shah, to give an account of the different dispatches that he had just received. I followed him, and mixed in with his large retinue of servants, until he turned round to me, and said, 'You are dismissed; go, and take your rest.'

CHAPTER XLIII: HE RELATES A HORRID TALE,
THE CONSEQUENCES PLUNGE HIM IN THE GREATEST MISERY

IN a few days after the camp was struck, and the Shah returned to his winter quarters at Tehran, in the same pomp and parade with which he had left it. I had resumed my post as sub-lieutenant to the chief executioner, and was busily engaged in disposing of the men under my command, that the best order might be preserved during the march, when I was commanded to send off a messenger to Tehran, with orders that the *bazigers*, the dancers and singers, should be in readiness to receive the Shah on his arrival at Sulimanieh. This place, as I have said before, is a palace situated on the banks of the Caraj, about nine parasangs from the capital.

On receiving this order, my long-forgotten Zeenab came again to my recollection, and all my tender feelings which, owing to my active life, had hitherto lain dormant, were now revived. Seven months were elapsed since we had first become acquainted; and although during that time I had lived with men of a nature sufficiently barbarous to destroy every good feeling, yet there was something so terrible in what I imagined must now be her situation, and I felt myself so much the cause of it, that my heart smote me every time that the subject came across my mind. 'We shall soon see,' thought I, 'if my fears be well founded. In a few days more we reach Sulimanieh, and then her fate will be decided.'

On the day of our arrival I headed the procession, to see that every proper arrangement had been made within the palace; and as I approached the walls of the harem, within which the bazigers had already taken their station, I heard the sounds of their voices and of their musical instruments. What would I not have given to have spoken to Zeenab, or even to have observed her at a distance! But I knew that it would not be prudent to ask many questions concerning her, as suspicions, dangerous both to her and me, might arise, and probably involve us in immediate ruin. Indeed, had I been inclined to give myself much stir on the subject, it would have been to no purpose; for very shortly after I heard the salute fired from the *Zamburek* camels,[1] which indicated that the Shah had alighted from his horse.

After he had smoked one pipe in his hall of state, and had dismissed the courtiers who attended him, he retired to the harem.

Upon his entrance there, I heard the songs of the women, accompanied by tambourines, guitars, and little drums, rending the air as they walked in procession before him. Well did I listen with all my ears to discover Zeenab's voice; but every endeavour was baffled, and I remained in a disagreeable state of vibration betwixt hope and fear, until a hasty order was issued for my old master, Mirza Ahmak, the king's physician, to appear immediately before the Shah. Combinations of the mind in all matters of deep interest are formed as quick as thought, and act like the foretellings of prophecy. When I heard that the hakîm was sent for, a cold thrill ran through my veins, and I said to myself, 'Zeenab is lost for ever!'

He came, was soon dismissed, and seeing me at the door of the harem, took me on one side, and said, 'Hajjî, the Shah is much enraged. You remember the Cûrdish slave, which I presented to him at the festival of the No Rûz. She has not appeared among the dancing-women, and pretends to be ill. He loves her, and had set his heart upon seeing her. He has called

[1] Artillery: camels carrying swivel guns.

me to account for her conduct, as if I could control the caprice of this daughter of the devil; and says, that if he does not find her in full health and beauty when he reaches the *ark* (the palace), which will be on the next best fortunate hour, he will pluck my beard out by the roots. Curse the unlucky moment which made her my slave; and still more the hour when I first invited the Shah into my house.'

Upon this he left me, to set off immediately for Tehran, whilst I retired to my tent, to ruminate over the horrid fate that awaited this unfortunate girl. I endeavoured to rally my spirits by the hope that perhaps she was actually ill, and that it had been impossible for her to appear before the king; and then I consoled myself with the idea, that if my fears were well founded, the doctor's heart might be softened, and he might screen her from the Shah's observation, by giving some evasive reason for her non-appearance. Then, after all, as if braving my feelings, I repeated to myself the lines of one of our poets, who, like me, had lost his mistress.

'Is there but one pair of stag eyes, or one cypress waist, or one full-moon face in the world, that I should so mourn the loss of my cruel one?

'Why should I burn, why should I cut myself, and sigh out my griefs under the windows of the deaf-eared charmer?

'No, let me love where love is cheap; for I am a miser of my feelings.'

Thus I endeavoured to make light of the subject, and to show myself a true Mussulman by my contempt for womankind. But still, turn where I would, go where I would, the image of Zeenab, a torn and mangled corpse, was ever before my eyes, and haunted my imagination at all seasons and at all hours.

At length the fortunate hour for the Shah's entry was announced, and he entered Tehran amidst the whole of its population, who had been turned out to greet his arrival. My most pressing want was to see the hakîm, as if by chance, in order that no suspicion might fall upon me, in case poor Zeenab was found guilty. On the very evening of our arrival, my wishes (alas! how fatally!) were accomplished. As I was taken up in giving some orders to a nasakchi, I saw him come out of the Shah's private apartment, looking full of care, with one hand stuck in his girdle, the other in his side, his back more bent than usual, and with his eyes fixed on the ground. I placed myself in his way, and gave him the salutation of peace, which caused him to look up. When he had recognized me, he stopped, saying, 'You are the very man I was seeking. Come hither;' and he took me on one side. 'Here is a strange story afloat,' said he; 'this Cûrd has brought all sorts of ashes on my head. *Wallah!* by Heaven, the Shah has run clean mad. He talks of making a general massacre of all that is male, within and without his harem, beginning with his viziers, and finishing by the eunuchs. He swears by his own head, that he will make me the first example if I do not find out the culprit.'

'What culprit? who? what?' said I, 'what has happened?'

'Why, Zeenab,' answered he, 'Zeenab.'

'Oh! I understand,' said I; 'Aye! she you used to love so much.'

'I?' answered the Hakîm, as if afraid of being himself suspected, 'I? *Astaferallah!* Heaven forbid! Do not say so for pity's sake, Hajjî, for if such a suspicion were once hinted, the Shah would put his threat into immediate execution. Where did you ever hear that I loved Zeenab?'

'Many things were reported concerning you at that time,' said I, 'and all were astonished that a man of your wisdom, the Locman of his time, the Galenûs of Persia, should have embarked in so frail and dangerous a commodity as a Cûrdish maid, one of the undoubted progeny of the devil himself, whose footsteps could not be otherwise than notoriously unfortunate; who, of herself, was enough to bring ill luck to a whole empire, much more to a single family like yours.'

'You say true, Hajjî,' said Mirza Ahmak, as he shook his head from side to side, and struck his left hand on the pit of his stomach. 'Ah! marvellous fool was I ever to have been caught by her black eyes! in fact, they were not eyes, they were spells,—the devil himself looked out of them, not she, and if he is not in her now, may I be called *Gorumsak* all the rest of my days. But, after all, what shall I do?'

'What can I say?' answered I. 'What will the Shah do with her?'

'Let her go to Jehanum,' answered the doctor; 'let her go to her father's mansion, and a good journey to her. I am only thinking of my own skin.'

Upon this, looking up tenderly at me, he said, 'Ah, Hajjî! you know how much I have always loved you: I took you into my house when you were houseless—I placed you in a good situation, and you have risen in your profession all through me—allow that there is, or that there ought

to be such a thing in the world as gratitude——you have now an opportunity of exercising it:' then pausing for a while, and playing with the tip
of my beard, he said, 'Have you guessed what I wished to say?'

'No,' said I, 'it has not yet reached my understanding.'

'Well, then,' said he, 'in two words, own that you are the culprit. A
great loss of consideration would accrue to me, but none to you; you are
young, and can bear such a story to be told of you.'

'Loss of consideration, indeed!' exclaimed I, 'what is that when the
loss of life will ensue? Are you mad, oh Hakîm, or do you think me so?
Why should I die? why do you wish to have my blood upon your head?
All I can say, if I am questioned on the subject, is, that I do not think you
guilty, because you were ever too much in fear of the khanum, your wife;
but I will never say that I am guilty.'

Whilst in the middle of our conversation, one of the Shah's eunuchs
came up to me, and said that his chief had been ordered to see that the
sub-lieutenant to the chief executioner, with five men, were in waiting at
the foot of the high tower at the entrance of the harem, at the hour of midnight; and that they were to bring a *taboot*, or hand-bier, with them, to
bear away a corpse for interment.

All I could say in answer was '*be cheshm* (by my eyes)'; and lucky was it
for me that he quitted me immediately, that Mirza Ahmak had also left
me, and that it was dusk, or else the fear and anguish which overwhelmed
me upon hearing this message must have betrayed me. A cold sweat broke
out all over my body, my eyes swam, my knees knocked under me, and I
should perhaps have fallen into a swoon, if the counter fear of being seen
in such a state, in the very centre of the palace, had not roused me.

'What,' said I to myself, 'is it not enough that I have been the cause of
her death, must I be her executioner too? must I be the grave-digger to
my own child? must I be the ill-fated he who is to stretch her cold limbs in
the grave, and send my own life's blood back again to its mother earth?
Why am I called upon to do this, oh cruel, most cruel destiny? Cannot I
fly from the horrid scene? Cannot I rather run a dagger into my heart?
But no, 'tis plain my fate is ordained, sealed, fixed! and in vain I struggle,
——I must fulfil the task appointed for me! Oh world, world! what art thou,
and how much more wouldst thou be known, if each man was to lift up
the veil that hideth his own actions, and show himself as he really is!'

With these feelings, oppressed as if the mountain of Demawend and all its sulphurs were on my heart, I went about my work doggedly, collecting the several men who were to be my colleagues in this bloody tragedy; who, heedless and unconcerned at an event of no unfrequent occurrence, were indifferent whether they were to be the bearers of a murdered corpse, or themselves the instruments of murder.

The night was dark and lowering, and well suited to the horrid scene about to be acted. The sun, unusual in these climates, had set, surrounded by clouds of the colour of blood; and, as the night advanced, they rolled on in unceasing thunders over the summits of the adjacent range of Albors. At sudden intervals the moon was seen through the dense vapour, which covered her again as suddenly, and restored the night to its darkness and solemnity. I was seated lonely in the guard-room of the palace, when I heard the cries of the sentinels on the watch-towers, announcing midnight, and the voices of the muezzins from the mosques, the wild notes of whose chant floating on the wind ran through my veins with the chilling creep of death, and announced to me that the hour of murder was at hand! They were the harbingers of death to the helpless woman. I started up,—I could not bear to hear them more,—I rushed on in desperate haste, and as I came to the appointed spot, I found my five companions already arrived, sitting unconcerned on and about the coffin that was to carry my Zeenab to her eternal mansion. The only word which I had power to say to them was, 'Shoud? Is it done?' to which they answered, 'Ne shoud, It is not done.' To which ensued an awful silence. I had hoped that all was over, and that I should have been spared every other horror, excepting that of conducting the melancholy procession to the place of burial; but no, the deed was still to be done, and I could not retreat.

On the confines of the apartments allotted to the women in the Shah's palace stands a high octagonal tower, some thirty gez in height, seen conspicuous from all parts of the city, at the summit of which is a chamber, in which he frequently reposes and takes the air. It is surrounded by unappropriated ground, and the principal gate of the harem is close to its base. On the top of all is a terrace (a spot, ah! never by me to be forgotten!) and it was to this that our whole attention was now riveted. I had scarcely arrived, when, looking up, we saw three figures, two men and a female, whose forms were lighted up by an occasional gleam of moonshine, that shone in a wild and uncertain manner upon them. They seemed to drag their victim between them with much violence, whilst she was seen in attitudes of supplication, on her knees, with her hands extended, and in all the agony of the deepest desperation. When they were at the brink of the tower her shrieks were audible, but so wild, so varied by the blasts of wind that blew round the building, that they appeared to me like the sounds of laughing madness.

We all kept a dead and breathless silence: even my five ruffians seemed moved—I was transfixed like a lump of lifeless clay, and if I am asked what my sensations were at the time, I should be at a loss to describe them,—I was totally inanimate, and still I knew what was going on. At length, one loud, shrill, and searching scream of the bitterest woe was heard, which was suddenly lost in an interval of the most frightful silence. A heavy fall, which immediately succeeded, told us that all was over. I was then roused, and with my head confused, half crazed and half conscious, I immediately rushed to the spot, where my Zeenab and her burden lay struggling, a mangled and mutilated corpse. She still breathed, but the convulsions of death were upon her, and her lips moved as if she would speak, although the blood was fast flowing from her mouth. I could not catch a word, although she uttered sounds that seemed like words. I thought she said, 'My child! my child!' but perhaps it was an illusion of my brain. I hung over her in the deepest despair, and having lost all sense of prudence and of self-preservation, I acted so much up to my own feelings, that if the men around me had had the smallest suspicion of my real situation, nothing could have saved me from destruction. I even carried my frenzy so far as to steep my handkerchief in her blood, saying to myself, 'This, at least, shall never part from me!' I came to myself, however, upon hearing the shrill and demon-like voice of one of her murderers from the tower's height, crying out—'Is she dead?' 'Aye, as a stone,' answered one of my ruffians. 'Carry her away, then,' said the voice. 'To hell yourself,' in a suppressed tone, said another ruffian; upon which my men lifted the dead body into the taboot, placed it upon their shoulders, and walked off with it to the burial-ground without the city, where they found a grave ready dug to receive it. I walked mechanically after them, absorbed in most melancholy thoughts, and when we had arrived at the burial-place, I sat myself down on a grave-stone, scarcely conscious of what was going on. I watched the operations of the nasakchies with a sort of unmeaning stare; saw them place the dead body in the earth; then shovel the mould over it; then place two stones, one at the feet and the other at the head. When they had finished, they came up to me and said 'that all was done': to which I answered, 'Go home; I will follow.' They left me seated on the grave, and returned to the town.

The night continued dark, and distant thunders still echoed through the mountains. No other sound was heard, save now and then the infant-like cries of the jackal, that now in packs, and then by two or three at the time, kept prowling round the mansions of the dead.

The longer I remained near the grave, the less I felt inclined to return to my home, and to my horrid employment of executioner. I loathed my existence, and longed to be so secluded from the world, and from all dealings with those of high authority in it, that the only scheme which I could relish was that of becoming a real dervish, and passing the rest of my days in penitence and privations. Besides, the fear of having disclosed, both by my words and actions, how much I was involved in the fate of the deceased, came across my mind, and added to my repugnance of returning.

Day by this time began to dawn, and impelled, both by a sense of my danger and by my desire to quit a place which had become odious to me, I determined to proceed on foot to Kinaragird, the first stage to Ispahan, and then take advantage of the first caravan that should be going to that city.

'I will go and seek consolation in retirement, and in the bosom of my family,' said I to myself; 'I will see what is become of my parents—perhaps I may reach the paternal roof in time to receive my father's dying blessing, and by my presence give him in his old age the happiness of seeing his long-lost son restored to him—How shall I be able to go through my duties, with this misfortune about my neck?—I have lived long enough in vice, and it is time that I should make the *tobeh*, or renounce my wicked ways.'

In short, this horrid event produced such an effect upon my mind, that had I continued in the sentiments it inspired me with through life, I might well have aspired to be placed at the head of our most holy dervishes.

CHAPTER XLIV: HAJJI BABA MEETS WITH AN OLD FRIEND WHO CHEERS HIM UP, GIVES HIM GOOD ADVICE, AND SECURES HIM FROM DANGER

PULLING out the handkerchief from my breast, still wet with the blood of the unfortunate Zeenab, I contemplated it with feelings of the most bitter anguish; then spreading it before me on her grave, I went through a ceremony to which I had long been unaccustomed,—I said my prayers. Refreshed by this act, and strengthened in my resolutions of leaving Tehran, I tore myself away, and stept valiantly onwards towards Ispahan.

Having reached Kinaragird, without seeing the trace of a caravan, and feeling myself sufficiently strong to proceed on my journey, I pushed on for the caravanserai of the Sultan's Reservoir, where I intended to halt for the night.

As I came in sight of the building, at some distance in the desert, I saw a man putting himself into strange attitudes, playing antics by himself, and apparently addressing himself to something on the ground. I approached him, and found that he was talking with great animation to his cap, which was thrown some yards before him. Going still nearer to him, I discovered a face that was familiar to me.

'Who can it be?' said I to myself: 'it must be one of my old friends, the dervishes of Meshed.'

In fact, it proved to be the *Kessehgou*, the story-teller, who was practising a new story by himself, making his cap act audience. As soon as he saw, he recognized me, and came up to embrace me with seeming rapture.

'Ahi, Hajjî,' said he, 'peace be with you! Where have you been these many years? Your place has long been empty. My eyes are refreshed by the sight of you.' Then he repeated himself in the same strain several times over, until we at length got upon more rational subjects.

He related his adventures since we had last met; which consisted in the detail of long and painful journeys, and of the various methods which his ingenuity had suggested to him of gaining his bread. He was now on his return from Constantinople, from whence he had walked, and had it in contemplation to make his way in the same manner to Delhi, after having passed a summer at Ispahan, whither he was now proceeding.

Although little inclined to talk, in the melancholy mood in which my mind had been plunged, still I could not refrain in some measure from catching the exuberance of spirits with which my companion seemed to overflow, and I also gave him an account of myself since the day I left Meshed with Dervish Sefer, when I had just recovered from the bastinado on the soles of my feet.

As I proceeded in my narrative, showing him how, step by step, I had advanced in station and dignity, it was amusing to see with what increased reverence he treated me. At length, when I came to my promotion to the rank of sub-lieutenant to the chief executioner, I verily believe that he would have prostrated himself before me, with such extreme respect had experience taught him to treat gentlemen of that profession. But when he heard the sequel of my story; how for a woman I had abandoned my high situation and all the prospects of advancement which it held out to me; I perceived the low estimation to which I fell in his opinion. He exclaimed that I was not worthy of the *kalaât* (the dress of distinction), which fortune had cut out, fashioned, and invested me with. 'So, because the Shah thinks it fitting to destroy a faithless slave,' said he, 'in whose guilt you have at most only half the share, you think it necessary to abandon the excellent station in life to which you had reached, and to begin again the drudgery of an existence lower and more uncertain than even the one which I enjoy. Well' (making a pause), 'there is no accounting for the different roads which men take in their search after happiness: some keep the high road; some take short cuts; others strike out new paths for themselves; and others again permit themselves to be led on without asking the road: but I never yet heard of one, but yourself, who, having every road and every path thrown open to him, preferred losing his way, with the risk of never

again finding it.' And then he finished by quoting a reflection of the poet
Ferdûsi, applicable to the uncertainty of a soldier's life, by way of consoling me for the vicissitudes of mine, saying, '*Gahi pûsht ber zeen, gahi zeen
ber pûsht* (sometimes a saddle bears the weight of his back, and sometimes
his back the weight of a saddle).'

Whilst we were conversing, a caravan appeared on the road from Ispahan, and making straight for the caravanserai, took up its abode there for
the night.

'Come,' said the dervish, who was a merry sociable fellow, 'come, forget your sorrows for the present; we will pass an agreeable evening, notwithstanding we are in the midst of this dreary and thirsty desert. Let us
get together the travellers, the merchants, and the mule-drivers who compose the caravan, and after we have well supped and smoked I will relate
to you a story that has recently happened at Stamboul, and which I am
sure cannot yet have been imported into Persia.'

Most willingly did I accede to his proposal; for I was happy to drive
melancholy from my thoughts at any rate, and we strolled into the building together. Here we found men from different parts of Persia, unloading
their beasts and putting their effects in order, settling themselves in the
different open rooms which look upon the square of the caravanserai. A
dervish, and a story-teller too, was a great acquisition, after the fatigue
and dullness of a journey across the Salt Desert; and when we had made a
hearty meal he collected them on the square platform in the middle of the
court, making them sit round, whilst he took his station in the midst. He
then related his promised story.

I endeavoured to pay every attention to it; but I found that my mind
so constantly strayed from the narrative to the scenes I had lately witnessed, that it became impossible for me to retain what he said. I remarked,
however, that he interested his audience in the highest degree; for when
plunged in one of my deepest reveries I was frequently roused by the
laughter and applause which the dervish excited. I promised myself on
some future occasion to make him relate it over again, and in the meanwhile continued to give myself up wholly to my feelings. Much did I envy
the apparent light-heartedness that pervaded my companions and which at
intervals made the vaulted rooms of the building resound with shouts of
merriment. I longed for the time when I should again be like them, and

Being a nasakchi gave me consequence in the bazaar

enjoy the blessings of existence without care; but grief, like every other passion, must have its course, and, as the spring which gushes with violence from the rock, by degrees dwindles into a rivulet; so it must be let to pass off gradually until it becomes a moderate feeling, and at length is lost in the vortex of the world.

Day had closed by the time that the dervish had finished his story. The blue vault of heaven was completely furnished with bright twinkling stars, which seemed to have acquired a fresh brilliancy after the storms of the preceding night; and the moon was preparing to add her soft lustre to the scene, when a horseman, fully equipped, entered the porch that leads into the caravanserai.

The principal persons of the caravan had still kept their stations on the platform, quietly smoking their pipes and discussing the merits of the tale they had just heard; the servants had dispersed to spread their masters' beds; and the muleteers had retired for the night to nestle in among their mules and their baggage: I, destitute of everything, had made up my mind to pass my night on the bare ground with a stone for my pillow; but when I looked at the horseman, as he emerged from the darkness of the porch into the light, my ideas took another turn.

I recognized in him one of the nasakchies, who under my orders had witnessed the death of the wretched Zeenab; and I very soon guessed what the object of his journey might be, when I heard him ask if the caravan was coming from or going to Tehran; and whether they had seen a person whom, by the description he gave, I instantly recognized to be myself.

My friend the dervish immediately divined how the matter stood; and deeply versed in every stratagem of deceit, without hesitation took upon himself to answer for the whole company.

He said that all were going to the capital, with the exception of himself and his friend, who, both dervishes, were just arrived from Constantinople; but that he had met one answering to the person he had described, one who seemed oppressed with care and worn with grief, wandering about in a sort of chance manner through the wilds of the desert. He added many more particulars which corresponded so entirely to my appearance and history that the horseman could not doubt for a moment but that this was the person he was in search of, and rode off in great haste according to the directions of the dervish, who, as may be imagined, purposely led him wrong.

When he had been gone some time the dervish took me on one side, and said, 'If you want to secure yourself from this man, you must instantly depart; for when he finds his search fruitless, and is tired of wandering about the desert, he will certainly return here, and then what can hinder your being discovered?'

'I will do anything rather than be discovered by him,' said I: 'he is evidently sent to seize me. I can expect no mercy from such a ruffian, particularly as I have not enough money to offer him, for I know his price. Where can I go?'

The dervish reflected a while, and said, 'You must go to Kom: you will reach it before morning, and as soon as you arrive there, lose not a moment in getting within the precincts of the sanctuary of the tomb of Fatimeh. You will then, and not till then, be safe, even from the Shah's power. Should you be caught without its walls, there is no hope for you. You will be seized; and then may Allah take you into his holy keeping!'

'But when I am there,' said I, 'what shall I do? how shall I live?'

'Leave that to me,' said the dervish; 'I shall soon overtake you, and as I know the place and many of the people in it, *inshallah*, please God, you will not fare so ill as you may imagine. I myself was once obliged to do the same thing, for having been the means of procuring poison for one of the Shah's women, who used it to destroy a rival. Orders were sent to seize me, and I managed to reach the *bust* (the refuge seat) at Shahabdul Azîm just five minutes before the executioner who was to have apprehended me. I never fared better in my life: for I did nothing; I was supported by the charity of those who came to say their prayers at the shrine of the saint: and the women, who constantly travelled thus far to pray and take their pleasure, always contrived to comfort me in my confinement. The only evil you have to fear is an order from the Shah, that no one on pain of death shall give you food: if so, you will be starved into a surrender, and then the Prophet be your protector! But your case is not one of sufficient consequence to make you fear this. The Shah cannot care so much for one slave, when he has a hundred others to fill her place. After all, men do not die so easily as we Persians imagine. Recollect what the Sheikh says, "Clouds and wind, the moon, the sun, the firmament (and he might have added dervishes), all are busied, that thou, O man, mayest obtain thy bread: only eat it not in neglect."'

'I am not the man,' said I, 'who will forget your kindness. Perhaps my fortune may again be on the rise, and then I will put my beard into your hand. You know Hajjî Baba of old, and that he is not one of those who "exposes his virtues on the palm of his hand, and hides his vices under his armpit." What I was at Meshed, the same I am now: the seller of adulterated smoke and the deputy lieutenant to the chief executioner, are one and the same.'

'Well, then, go,' said the dervish, as he embraced me, 'and God be with you! Take care of the *ghôls* and *gins* as you cross the Salt Desert; and again, I repeat, may Allah, peace, and safety attend you!'

As the day broke I could distinguish the gilt cupola of the tomb at a considerable distance before me; and this beacon of my security inspired me with fresh vigour in my solitary march over the dreary waste. I had scarcely reached the outskirts of the town of Kom before I perceived the horseman at some distance behind, making the best of his way in search of me; and therefore I looked neither right nor left until the massive chain that hangs across the principal gateway of the sanctuary was placed between myself and my pursuer. I then exclaimed, '*Ilhamd'illah!* Praises to Allah! O Mahomed! O Ali!' and kissing the threshold of the tomb I said my prayers with all the fervency of one who having escaped a tempest has got safe into port.

I had scarcely time to look about me before I perceived the nasakchi coming towards me. He accosted me with a cold salutation of peace, and then said, 'that he had a royal order to conduct me into the Shah's presence wherever I might be found.'

I told him that, with all reverence for his firman, it was my intention to avail myself of the acknowledged privilege of every true believer, to seek refuge at the shrine of the saint, and that, of course, he could not violate it by dragging me from it. 'Besides, this is the favourite saint of the King of Kings,' said I, 'and he respects this shrine more than any other.'

'What shall I do then, Hajjî?' said he. 'You know this is not written in the order. If I go back without you, perhaps the Shah may cut off my ears instead of yours.'

'*Inshallah!* please God,' said I.

'Please God, do you say?' said he in a fury: 'am I come all this way that men should call me ass? I am not a man if I do not make you return with me.' And forthwith we began to wrangle to such a degree that several of the priests, attached to the endowment, came from their rooms to inquire into the cause of the disturbance.

'Here is one,' exclaimed I, 'who presumes to violate the sanctuary. I have taken refuge in it, and he talks of forcing me away! You, that are men of God,' addressing myself to the mollahs, 'speak, and say whether you will allow this?'

They all took my part. 'This is unheard of,' said they, 'in Persia. If you dare to take one from the *bust*, you will not only have the vengeance of the saint on your head, but the whole corps of the Ullemah will be upon you; and be you protected by the King of Kings, or the king of demons, nothing can screen you from their fury.'

The nasakchi remained quite uncertain what to do, and at length, softening his tone, he endeavoured to make a virtue of necessity, and began to negotiate with me upon what he might get if he went away without further molesting me. I did not deny the right he had of being paid for his trouble, for it is precisely what I should have expected myself had I been in his place; but I made him recollect how little I was able to requite him; for he knew as well as I all the circumstances of my flight, and that I had brought nothing away with me from Tehran.

He suggested that I might give him what effects I had left behind me; to which I did not in the least agree, but recommended him to go whence he came, and to leave the afflicted to their miseries.

The fact is, as I afterwards found out, the rogue had already taken possession of my property, which consisted of clothes, trunks, bedding, horse-furniture, pipes, &c., having himself been the cause of denouncing me to the Shah. He had watched the effect which the murderous death of the unhappy Cûrd had produced upon me, and immediately had laid his plan for my destruction, and for stepping into my situation.

Finding that he could not exert the power which had been vested in him, and that his firman was so much waste paper, as long as I continued to hold fast to my refuge-place, he thought it best to return to Tehran; but in so doing he delivered his powers into the hands of the governor of the town, with strict injunctions to keep watch over my actions, and in case I stirred from the sanctuary, to seize and send me a prisoner to the seat of government.

CHAPTER XLV: HE TAKES REFUGE
IN A SANCTUARY WHERE HIS MELANCHOLY THOUGHTS
ARE DIVERTED BY A CURIOUS STORY

 HAD scarcely got rid of the nasakchi, when I heard the voice of my friend the dervish, who was announcing his arrival in the holy city, by all the different invocations of the Almighty and his attributes, which are frequently made by true believers.

Very soon after, I was delighted to see him coming towards me, and to hear him express his satisfaction that I had reached my resting-place before my pursuer had had time to come up with me.

He proposed to keep me company for a short time, and we took possession of one of the cells situated in the square court forming part of the buildings in the centre of which the tomb is placed. I had by good luck brought away my ready money, consisting of twenty tomauns in gold, besides some silver; and we expended some of this in articles of the first necessity, such as a mat to cover the bare floor of our room, and an earthen jug for our water.

But before we had got any further in our domestic arrangements, the dervish accosted me in the following manner: 'I must be informed of one thing before we proceed. Do you ever say your prayers? do you keep your fasts? do you make your ablutions regularly? or do you continue to live in that fit state for eternal perdition which we were wont to do at Meshed?'

'Why do you speak thus to me?' said I. 'What can it be to you whether I pray or not?'

'It is not much to me,' answered the dervish, 'but it is a great deal to yourself. This Kom is a place that, excepting on the subject of religion, and settling who are worthy of salvation and who to be damned, no one opens his lips. Every man you meet is either a descendant of the Prophet or a man of the law. All wear long and mortified faces, and seem to look upon that man as an appointed subject for the eternal fires, who happens to have a rosy cheek and a laughing eye. Therefore, as soon as I approach the place, I always change the atmosphere of my countenance from fair to haze, and from haze to downright clouds and darkness, according as circumstances may require. My knees, which scarcely ever touch the praying carpet, now perform their functions five good times per day; and I, who in any other place never consult any *kebleh*[1] but that of my own pleasure and inclinations, now know the direction of the true one, as well as I know the way to my mouth.'

'All this is very well,' said I; 'but what may be the use of it? I am a Mussulman, 'tis true, but to such a pitch as this—no never.'

'The use?' answered the dervish. 'The use is this; that it will save you from being starved or stoned to death. These priests will hearken to no medium—either you are a true believer or you are not. If they were to have the least suspicion that you doubted any of the articles of the faith— that you did not look upon the Koran as a living miracle, and did not read it with becoming reverence, whether you understand or not—they would soon show you what power they possess. And if they were to suppose you to be a *sûfi* (a free thinker), by the death of your father and mother, they would tear you into little pieces, and then feel contented that they had got on another post on the high road to paradise. Perhaps, friend Hajjî, you do not know that this is the residence of the celebrated Mirza Abdul Cossim, the first *mushtehed* (divine) of Persia; a man who, if he were to give himself sufficient stir, would make the people believe any doctrine that he

[1] i. e. Mecca, to which all Mohamedans turn in their prayers.

might choose to promulgate. Such is his influence, that many believe he could even subvert the authority of the Shah himself, and make his subjects look upon his firmans as worthless, as so much waste paper. But the truth is, he is a good man; and, except stoning his *sûfi*, and holding us wandering dervishes as the dirt under his feet, I know of no fault in him.'

Having heard him out, I agreed that, however I might deplore the want of habit in my religious duties, yet, situated as I was, it was necessary that I should acquire them, in order to be held in proper estimation by the great authorities, under whose eye I was immediately placed; and forthwith I set about saying my prayers and making my ablutions, as if my very existence depended upon my regularity. Indeed, what I had formerly looked upon as irksome ceremony, now became an agreeable pastime, and helped greatly to soften the tedium of my melancholy life. I never omitted to rise at the first call; to make my ablutions at the cistern—using all the forms of the strictest shiah—and then to pray in the most conspicuous spot I could find. The intonations of my *Allah ho akbar* were to be heard in each corner of the tomb, and I hoped they came to the ear of every inhabitant of it. No face wore a more mortified appearance than mine: even the dervish, who was the best mimic possible, could not beat me in the downcast eye, the hypocritical ejaculation, the affected taciturnity of the sour, proud, and bigoted man of the law.

It became known that I was a refugee at the sanctuary; and I very soon discovered the advantages which the dervish had promised me, from taking upon me the airs of the place, and assuming the character of a rigid Mussulman. He spread abroad the history of my misfortune—of course much to my advantage, giving me out for one who was suffering for the sins of another, and asserting that the doctor ought, in fact, to have been the sufferer.

I became acquainted with the principal personages of the town, who were agreed that they had never known a better model of a true believer than I; and had I not been confined to the walls of the sanctuary, it was in contemplation to have made me a *peish namaz* (a leader of the prayers) at their religious meetings in the mosque. I found that the profound taciturnity which I had adopted was the best help towards the establishment of a high reputation for wisdom; and that, by the help of my beads—which I kept constantly counting—a mumble of my lips, and occasional groans and pious exclamations, the road to the highest consideration was open to me.

My dervish and I lived almost free of expense, so plentifully were we supplied with food. The women, in particular, did not lose an opportunity of bringing me presents of fruit, honey, bread, and other necessaries, for which I repaid them with kind thanks, and now and then with a talisman, written with my own hand.

But although our life was one of ease, yet it was so dull, and so void of incident, that even the spirits of my companion began to sink under it. In order to fill up some of the long hours of listlessness which oppressed us, I encouraged him to recite all his stories, one by one, not forgetting the one which he had related with so much effect in the caravanserai of the Sultan's Reservoir, and we found this a very agreeable mode of closing the day.

> *I feel, O reader, that you also may partake*
> *of that same dullness which oppressed me; and*
> *I think it but fair that I should endeavour to*
> *dissipate it, in the same manner as mine was by*
> *the dervish — therefore I will repeat the story*
> *which he related to me; and, whether it amuses*
> *you or not, yet perhaps you will be glad to know*
> *how the mind of a poor prisoner, in the sanctu-*
> *ary at Kom, was diverted from its miseries.*

Told by the Dervish

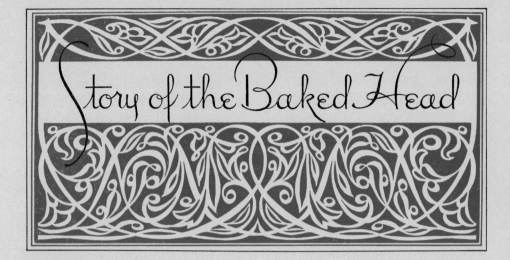

Story of the Baked Head

THE present Khon-khor[1] of Roum is a staunch Mussulman and a rigid upholder of the true faith. Upon his coming to the throne, he announced his intention of doing away with many customs common to the infidels, which had crept into the administration of the state during the reign of his predecessor; and he thought it his duty to endeavour to restore things to their primitive simplicity and to adopt a mode of government purely Turkish. Accordingly he resumed a custom which had almost got into disuse—that of going about the city in *tebdil*, or disguise; and he was so careful about the disguises which he adopted, and the people whom he admitted into his secrets on these occasions, that he took all sorts of precautions, and invented all sorts of schemes of secrecy, in whatever related to his dresses, and the characters in which he chose to appear.

It is not long ago that considerable discontent prevailed throughout Turkey, and rebellion threatened to break out in Constantinople itself. He was then very anxious to ascertain the temper of the public

mind; and, in his usual wary manner, determined to get a suit made that would make him undiscoverable by even his own immediate attendants.

He usually sent for different tailors at different times, and in different places. On this occasion he ordered his favourite slave, the white eunuch Mansouri, to bring him one of no repute, with all the requisite secrecy, at midnight, in order that he might receive instructions about a dress.

The slave in great humility made his *bash ustun* (on my head be it), and went his way to execute the command.

Close to the gate of the *Bezesten,* or cloth-market, he saw an old man in a stall, so narrow that he could scarce turn himself about in it, who was taken up in patching an old cloak. He was almost bent double with constant labour at his shopboard; and his eyes seemed not to have benefited by his application, for a pair of glasses were mounted on his nose. "This is precisely the man I want," said the slave to himself: "I am sure he can be of no repute." So intent was he upon his work, that he did not heed the salutation of "Peace be with you, friend!" with which Mansouri accosted him; and when he did look

[1] *Khon-khor*—literally 'Blood drinker'; so the Sultan of *Roum* or Turkey is styled in Persia.

I

up, and saw the well-dressed personage whom he thought had spoken, he continued his work, without making the usual reply; for he could not suppose that the salutation was meant for such a poor devil as he.

However, finding that he was the object of the eunuch's attention, he doffed the spectacles, threw away his work, and was about getting on his legs, when he was stopped, and requested not to disturb himself.

"What is your name?" said Mansouri.

"Abdallah," said the tailor, "at your service; but I am generally called Babadul by my friends and the world at large."

"You are a tailor, are you not?" continued the slave.

"Yes," said the other, "I am a tailor as well as the muezzin at the little mosque in the fish-market. What more can I do?"

"Well, Babadul," said Mansouri, "have you a mind for a job—a good job?"

"Am I a fool," answered the old man, "that I should dislike it? Say what it is."

"Softly, my friend," remarked the eunuch; "we must go on slow and sure. Will you suffer yourself to be led blindfolded at midnight wherever I choose to take you, for a job?"

"That's another question," said Babadul; "times are critical, heads fly in abundance, and a poor tailor's may go as well as a vizier's or a capitan pacha's. But pay me well, and I believe I would make a suit of clothes for Eblis, the foul fiend, himself."

"Well, then, you agree to my proposal?" said the eunuch, who at the same time put two pieces of gold in his hand.

"Yes, most surely," said Babadul, "I agree. Tell me what I am to do, and you may depend upon me."

Accordingly they settled between them that the eunuch was to come to the stall at midnight, and lead him away blindfolded.

Babadul, being left alone, continued his work, wondering what could be the job upon which he was to be so mysteriously employed; and, anxious to make his wife

a partaker of the news of his good luck, he shut up his stall earlier than usual, and went to his house, that was situated not far from the little mosque in the fish-market, of which he was the muezzin.

Old Dilferîb, his wife, was almost as much bent double as her husband; and in consequence of the two gold pieces, and in contemplation of more which they expected to receive, they treated themselves to a dish of smoking kabobs, a salad, dried grapes, and sweetmeats, after which they consoled themselves with some of the hottest and most bitter coffee which the old woman could make.

True to his appointment, Babadul was at his stall at midnight, where he was as punctually met by Mansouri. Without any words, the former permitted himself to be blindfolded, whilst the latter led him away by the hand, making many and devious turns, until they reached the imperial seraglio; there, stopping only to open the private iron gate, Mansouri introduced the tailor into the very heart of the Sultan's private apartments. The bandage over his eyes was taken off in a dark chamber, lighted up only by a small lamp, which stood on the shelf surrounding the top of the room, but which was splendidly furnished by sofas of the richest brocade, and by carpets of the most costly manufacture. Here Babadul was commanded to sit, until Mansouri returned with a bundle, wrapped in a large shawl handkerchief: this being opened, a sort of dervish's dress was displayed to the tailor, and he was requested to look at it, to consider how long he would be making such a one, and then to return it again, duly folded up, to its shawl covering. In the meanwhile, Mansouri told him to stay there until he should return to take him away again, and then left him.

Babadul, having turned the dress over and over again, calculated each stitch, and, come to his proper conclusions, packed it

2

up in the handkerchief, as he had been commanded; but no sooner had he done this than a man of lofty demeanour and appearance, whose look made the poor tailor shrink within himself, came into the room, took up the bundle, and walked away with it, without uttering a single word.

A few minutes after, as Babadul was pondering over the strangeness of his situation, and just recovering from the effects of this apparition, a door opened in another part of the apartment, and a mysterious figure, richly dressed, came in, bearing a bundle, equally covered with a shawl, about the size of that which had just been taken away; and making the lowest prostrations before the tailor, in great apparent trepidation, approached him, placed it at his feet, kissed the ground, and retreated without saying a word, or even looking up.

"Well," said Babadul to himself, "this may be something very fine, and I may be some very great personage, for aught I know; but this is very certain, that I had rather be patching my old cloak in the stall than doing this job, however grand and lucrative it may be. Who knows what I may have been brought here for? These comings in and goings out of strange-looking people, apparently without tongues in their heads, do not argue well. I wish they would give me fewer bows and a greater supply of words, from which I might learn what I am to get by all this. I have heard of poor women having been sewn up in sacks and thrown into the sea. Who knows? perhaps I am destined to be the tailor on such an occasion."

E HAD scarcely got thus far in his soliloquy when the slave Mansouri re-entered the room and told him, without more words, to take up the bundle; which having done, his eyes were again blindfolded, and he was led to the spot from whence he came. Babadul, true to his agreement, asked no questions, but agreed with the slave that in three days the dress should be ready for delivery at his stall for which he was to receive ten more pieces of gold.

Having got rid of his companion, he proceeded with all haste to his house, where he knew his wife would be impatiently waiting his return; and as he walked onwards he congratulated himself that at length he had succeeded in getting indeed a job worth the having, and that his fate had finally turned up something good for his old age. It was about two o'clock in the morning when he reached the door of his house. He was received by his wife with expressions of great impatience at his long absence; but when he held up the bundle to her face, as she held up the lamp to his, and when he said, "Mujdeh, give me a reward for good news: see, I have got my work, and a handsome reward we shall get when it is finished," she was all smiles and good humour.

"Leave it there till we get up, and let us go to bed now," said the tailor.

"No, no," said the wife, "I must look at what you have got before I retire, or I shall not be able to sleep": upon which, whilst he held up the lamp she opened the bundle. Guess, guess at the astonishment of the tailor and his wife, when, instead of seeing a suit of clothes, they discovered, wrapped in a napkin, in its most horrid and ghastly state, a human head!

It fell from the old woman's hands and rolled away some paces, whilst the horror-struck couple first hid their faces with their hands, and then looked at each other with countenances which nothing can describe.

"Work!" cried the wife, "work, indeed! pretty work you have made of it! Was it necessary to go so far, and to take such precautions, to bring this misfortune on our heads? Did you bring home this dead man's head to make a suit of clothes of?"

3

"*Anna senna! Baba senna! Curses be on his mother! Perdition seize his father!*" exclaimed the poor tailor, "*for bringing me into this dilemma. My heart misgave me as that dog of a eunuch talked of blindfolding and silence to me: I thought, as true as I am a Turk, that the job could not consist only in making a suit of clothes; and sure enough this dog's son has tacked a head to it. Allah! Allah! what am I to do now? I know not the way to his home, or else I would take it back to him immediately, and throw it in his face. We shall have the Bostangi Bashi and a hundred other Bashis here in a minute, and we shall be made to pay the price of blood; or, who knows, be hanged, or drowned, or impaled! What shall we do, eh, Dilferîb, my soul, say?*"

"*Do?*" said his wife; "*get rid of the head, to be sure: we have no more right to have it palmed upon us than anybody else.*"

"*But the day will soon dawn,*" said the tailor, "*and then it will be too late. Let us be doing something at once.*"

"*A thought has struck me,*" said the old woman. "*Our neighbour, the baker, Hassan, heats his oven at this hour, and begins soon after to bake his bread for his morning's customers. He frequently has different sorts of things to bake from the neighbouring houses, which are placed near the oven's mouth overnight: suppose I put this head into one of our earthen pots and send it to be baked; nobody will find it out until it is done, and then we need not send for it, so it will remain on the baker's hands.*"

BABADUL admired his wife's sagacity, and forthwith she put her plan into execution. When the head had been placed in a baking-pan, she watched a moment when nobody was at hand, and set it on the ground, in the same row with the other articles that were to be inserted in Hassan's oven. The old couple then double-barred the door of their house,

and retired to rest, comforting themselves with the acquisition of the fine shawl and napkin in which the head had been wrapped.

The baker Hassan and his son Mahmûd were heating their oven, inserting therein thorns, chips, and old rubbish at a great rate, when their attention was arrested by the extraordinary whinings and barking of a dog, that was a constant customer at the oven for stray bits of bread, and much befriended by Hassan and his son, who were noted for being conscientious Mussulmans.

"*Look, Mahmûd,*" said the father to the son, "*see what is the matter with the dog: something extraordinary is in the wind.*"

The son did what his father bade him, and seeing no reason for the dog's noises, said, "*Bir chey yok, there is nothing,*" and drove him away.

But the howlings not ceasing, Hassan went himself, and found the dog most extremely intent upon smelling and pointing at the tailor's pipkin. He jumped upon Hassan, then at the pot, then upon Hassan again, until the baker no longer doubted that the beast took great interest in its contents. He therefore gently drew off the lid, when need I mention his horror and surprise at seeing a human head staring him in the face?

"*Allah! Allah!*" cried the baker; but being a man of strong nerves, instead of letting it fall, as most people would have done, he quietly put on the lid again, and called his son to him.

"*Mahmûd,*" said he, "*this is a bad world, and there are bad men in it. Some wicked infidel has sent a man's head to bake; but thanks to our good fortune, and to the dog, our oven has been saved from pollution, and we can go on making our bread with clean hands and clear consciences. But since the devil is at work, let others have a visit from him as well as ourselves. If it be known that we have had a dead man's head to bake, who will ever employ us again? we must starve, we must* shut up our oven; we shall get the reputation of mixing up our dough with human grease, and if perchance a hair is found, it will immediately be said that it came from the dead man's beard."

Mahmûd, a youth of about twenty, who partook of his father's insensibility and coolness, and who, moreover, had a great deal of dry humour and ready wit, looked upon the incident in the light of a good joke, and broke out into a hearty laugh when he saw the ugly picture which the grinning head made, set in its earthen frame.

"*Let us pop it into the shop of Kior Ali, the barber, opposite,*" said the youth; "*he is just beginning to open it, and as he has but one eye, we shall be better able to do so without being seen. Do, father,*" said Mahmûd, "*let me; nobody shall discover me; and let it be done before there is more daylight.*"

The father consented, and Mahmûd catching the moment when the barber had walked to the corner of the street to perform certain ablutions, stepped into his shop, and placed the head on a sort of *takcheh*, or bracket on the wall, arranged some shaving towels about it, as if it had been a customer ready seated to be shaved, and, with a boy's mischief in his heart, stepped back to his oven again, to watch the effects which this new sort of customer would have upon the blind barber.

IOR ALI hobbled into his shop, which was but ill lighted by a glimmering of daylight that hardly pierced through the oil-papered windows, and looking about him, saw this figure, as he supposed, seated against the wall ready to be operated upon.

"*Ha! peace be unto you!*" said he to it: "*you are rather early this morning; I did not see you at first. My water is not yet hot. Oh, I see you want your head shaved! but why do you take off your fese (skull-cap) so soon? you will catch cold.*" Then he paused. "*No answer,*" said the barber to himself. "*I suppose he is dumb, and deaf too perhaps. Well, I am half blind: so we are nearly upon equal terms: however, if I were even to lose my other eye,*" addressing himself to the head, "*I dare say, my old uncle, I could shave you for all that; for my razor would glide as naturally over your head, as a draught of good wine does over my throat.*"

He went methodically about his preparations; he took down his tin basin from a peg, prepared his soap, then stropped his razor on the long bit of leather that was fastened to his girdle. Having made his lather, he walked up to the supposed customer, holding the basin in his left hand, whilst his right was extended to sprinkle the first preparation of water on the sconce. No sooner had he placed his hand on the cold head, than he withdrew it, as if he had been burnt. "*Eh! why, what's the matter with you, friend?*" said the barber: "*you are as cold as a piece of ice.*" But when he attempted a second time to lather it, down it came with a terrible bounce from the shelf to the floor, and made the poor shaver jump quite across his shop with the fright.

"*Aman! aman! O mercy, mercy!*" cried Kior Ali, as he thrust himself into the furthermost corner without daring to move: "*take my shop, my razors, my towels,—take all I have; but don't touch my life! If you are the Shaitan, speak; but excuse my shaving you!*"

But when he found that all was hushed after the catastrophe, and that nothing was to be feared, he approached the head, and taking it up by the lock of hair at the top, he looked at it in amazement. "*A head, by all the Imams!*" said he, accosting it: "*and how did you get here? Do you want to disgrace me, you filthy piece of flesh? but you shall not! Although Kior Ali has lost one* eye, yet his other is a sharp one, and knows what it is about. I would give you to the baker Hassan there, if his rogue of a son, who is now looking this way, was not even sharper than this self-same eye; but now I think of it, I will take you where you can do no harm. The Giaour Yanaki, the Greek Kabobchi[1] (roast meat man), shall have you, and shall cut you up into mincemeat for his infidel customers." Upon this Kior Ali, drawing in one hand, in which he carried the head, through the slit on the sides of his *beniche*, or cloak, and taking up his pipe in the other, he walked down two streets to the shop of the aforesaid Greek.

He frequented it in preference to that of a Mussulman, because he could here drink wine with impunity. From long practice he knew precisely where the provision of fresh meat was kept, and as he entered the shop, casting his eye furtively round, he threw the head in a dark corner, behind one of the large sides of a sheep that was to be used for the kabobs of the day. No one saw him perform this feat; for the morning was still sufficiently obscure to screen him. He lighted his pipe at Yanaki's charcoal fire, and as a pretext for his visit, ordered a dish of meat to be sent to him for breakfast; a treat to which he thought himself fully entitled after his morning's adventure.

Y ANAKI, meanwhile, having cleaned his platters, put his skewers in order, lit his fires, made his sherbets, and swept out his shop, went to the larder for some meat for the shaver's breakfast. Yanaki was a true Greek: cunning, cautious, deceitful; cringing to his superiors,

[1] The *kabob* shops at Constantinople are eating-houses where, at a moment's notice, a dish of roast meat, and small bits of meat done on skewers, are served up to whoever asks for them.

6

tyrannical towards his inferiors; detesting with a mortal hatred his proud masters, the Osmanlies, yet fawning, flattering, and abject whenever any of them, however low in life, deigned to take notice of him. Turning over his stock, he looked about for some old bits that might serve the present purpose, muttering to himself that any carrion was good enough for a Turk's stomach. He surveyed his half sheep from top to bottom; felt it, and said, "*No, this will keep*"; but as he turned up its fat tail, the eye of the dead man's head caught his eye, and made him start, and step back some paces. "*As ye love your eyes,*" exclaimed he, "*who is there?*" Receiving no answer, he looked again, and again; then nearer,—then, thrusting his hand among sheep's heads and trotters, old remnants of meat, and the like, he pulled out the head—the horrid head—which he held extended at arm's length, as if he were afraid it would do him mischief. "*Anathemas attend your beard!*" exclaimed Yanaki, as soon as he discovered, by the tuft of hair on the top, that it had belonged to a Mussulman, "*Och! if I had but every one of your heads in this manner, ye cursed race of Omar! I would make kabobs of them, and every cur in Constantinople should get fat for nothing. May ye all come to this end! May the vultures feed on your carcasses! and may every Greek have the good fortune which has befallen me this day, of having one of your worthless skulls for his football!*" Upon which, in his rage, he threw it down and kicked it from him; but recollecting himself, he said, "*But, after all, what shall I do with it? If it is seen here, I am lost for ever: nobody will believe but what I have killed a Turk.*"

All of a sudden he cried out, in a sort of malicious ecstasy, "*'Tis well I remembered,—the Jew! the Jew!—a properer place for such a head was never thought or heard of; and there you shall go, thou vile remnant of a Mohamedan!*"

Upon which he seized it, and hiding it under his coat, ran with it down the street to where the dead body of a Jew lay extended, with its head placed immediately between its legs.

In Turkey, you must know, when a Mohamedan is beheaded, his head is placed under his arm, by way of an honourable distinction from the Christian or Jew, who, when a similar misfortune befalls them, have theirs inserted between their legs, as close to the seat of dishonour as possible.

IT WAS in that situation then that Yanaki placed the Turk's head, putting it as near, cheek by jowl, with the Jew's, as the hurry of the case would allow. He had been able to effect this without being seen, because the day was still but little advanced, and no one stirring; and he returned to his shop, full of exultation at having been able to discharge his feelings of hatred against his oppressors, by placing one of their heads on the spot in nature, which, according to his estimation, was the most teeming with opprobrium.

The unfortunate sufferer on this occasion had been accused of stealing and putting to death a Mohamedan child (a ceremony in their religion, which they have been known to practice both in Turkey and Persia), and which created such an extraordinary tumult among the mob of Constantinople, that, in order to appease it, he had been decapitated. His execution had taken place purposely before the door of a wealthy Greek, and the body was ordered to remain there three days before it was permitted to be carried away for interment. The expectation that the Greek would be induced to pay down a handsome sum, in order that this nuisance might be removed from his door, and save him from the ill luck which such an object is generally supposed to bring, made the officer entrusted with the execution prefer this spot to every other.

But, careless of the consequences, the Greek shut up the windows of his house, determined to deprive his oppressors of their expected perquisite; and so the dead Jew remained exposed his full time. Few excepting those of the true faith ventured to approach the spot, fearful that the Mohamedan authorities would, in their wanton propensities to heap insults upon the Giaours, oblige some one of them to carry the carcass to the place of burial; and thus the horrid and disgusting object was left abandoned to itself, and this had given an opportunity to the kabobchi, Yanaki, to dispose of the head in the manner above related, unseen and unmolested. But when, as the day advanced, and as the stir of the streets became more active, this additional head was discovered, the crowd, which gathered about it, became immense. It was immediately rumoured that a miracle had been performed; for a dead Jew was to be seen with two heads. The extraordinary intelligence flew from mouth to mouth, until the whole city was in an uproar, and all were running to see the miracle. The Sanhedrim immediately pronounced that something extraordinary was about to happen to their persecuted race. Rabbis were to be seen running to and fro, and their whole community was now poured around the dead body, in expectation that he would perhaps arise, put on his heads, and deliver them from the grip of their oppressors.

But as ill luck would have it for them, a Janissary, who had mixed in the crowd, and had taken a close survey of the supernumerary head, exclaimed in a mixture of doubt and amazement, *"Allah, Allah, il Allah! these are no infidel's heads. One is the head of our lord and master, the Aga of the Janissaries."* Upon which, seeing more of his companions, he called them to him, and making known his discovery, they became violent with rage, and set off to communicate the intelligence to their Orta.

7

The news spread like wildfire throughout the whole of the corps of the Janissaries, and a most alarming tumult was immediately excited: for it seems that it was unknown in the capital that their chief, to whom they were devotedly attached, and one of their own selection, had been put to death.

"What!" said they, "is it not enough to deal thus treacherously with us, and deprive us of a chief to whom we are attached; but we must be treated with the greatest contempt that it is possible for men to receive? What! the head of our most noble Aga of the Janissaries to be placed upon the most ignoble part of a Jew! what are we come to? We alone are not insulted; the whole of Islam is insulted, degraded, debased! No: this is unheard-of insolence, a stain never to be wiped off, without the extermination of the whole race! And what dog has done this deed? How did the head get there? Is it that dog of a Vizier's work, or has the Reis Effendi and those traitors of Frank ambassadors been at work? Wallah, Billah, Tallah! by the holy Caaba, by the beard of Osman, and by the sword of Omar, we will be revenged!"

WE MUST leave the tumult to rage for a short time; we must request the reader to imagine a scene, in which the Jews are flying in all directions, hiding themselves with great precaution against enraged Turks, who with expressions like those just mentioned in their mouths, are to be seen walking about in groups, armed to their teeth with pistols and scimitars, and vowing vengeance upon everything

which came in their way. He must imagine a city of narrow streets and low houses, thronged with a numerous population, in dresses the most various in shape and the most lively in colours, all anxious, all talking, all agog as if something extraordinary was to happen; in the midst of whom I will leave him, to take a look into the interior of the Sultan's seraglio, and to inquire in what his eminency himself had been engaged since we last noticed him.

On the very same night of the tailor's attendance, the Sultan had given a secret order for taking off the head of the Aga of the Janissaries (the fomenter of all the disturbances which had lately taken place among his corps, and consequently their idol); and so anxious was he about its execution, that he had ordered it to be brought to him the moment it was off. The man entrusted with the execution, upon entering the room where he had been directed to bring the head, seeing some one seated, naturally took him for the Sultan, and, without daring to look up, immediately placed the burden at his feet, with the prostrations which we have already described as having been performed before the tailor. The Sultan, who not a minute before had taken away the bundle containing the Dervish's dress, had done so in the intention of deceiving his slave Mansouri himself; so anxious was he of being unknown in his new disguise even to him; and intended to have substituted another in its stead; but not calculating either upon the reception of the head, or upon Mansouri's immediate return to the tailor, he was himself completely puzzled how to act when he found the tailor was gone, led off by his slave. To have sent after them would have disconcerted his schemes, and therefore he felt himself obliged to wait Mansouri's return, before he could get an explanation of what had happened; for he knew that they would not have gone away without the dress, and that dress he had then in his possession. In the meanwhile, anxious and impatient to know what had become of the expected head, he sent for the officer who was entrusted with the execution; and the astonishment of both may be imagined when an explanation took place.

"*By my beard!*" *exclaimed the Sultan, having thought awhile within himself; "by my beard, the tailor must have got the head!*"

His impatience for Mansouri's return then became extreme. In vain he fretted, fumed, and cried "*Allah! Allah!*" It did not make the slave return a minute the sooner, who, good man, would have gone quietly to rest had he not been called upon to appear before the Sultan.

As soon as he was within hearing, he called out, "*Ahi! Mansouri, run immediately to the tailor—he has got the head of the Aga of the Janissaries instead of the Dervish's dress—run, fetch it without loss of time, or something unfortunate will happen!*" He then explained how this untoward event had occurred. Mansouri now, in his turn, felt himself greatly embarrassed; for he only knew the road to the tailor's stall, but was totally unacquainted with his dwelling-house. However, rather than excite his master's anxiety in a higher degree, he set off in quest of the tailor, and went straight to his stall, in the hopes of hearing from the neighbours where his house was. It was too early in the day for the opening of the Bezesten, and except a coffee-house that had just prepared for the reception of customers, where he applied and could gain no intelligence, he found himself completely at a standstill. By the greatest good luck, he recollected Babadul had told him that he was the muezzin to the little mosque in the fish-market, and thither he immediately bent his steps. The azan, or morning invitation to prayers, was now chanting forth from all the minarets, and he expected that he might catch the purloiner of his head in the very act of inviting the faithful to prayers.

AS HE approached the spot, he heard an old broken and tremulous voice, which he imagined might be Babadul's, breaking the stillness of the morning by all the energy of its lungs; and he was not mistaken, for as he stood under the minaret, he perceived the old man walking round the gallery which encircles it, with his hand applied to the back of his ear, and with his mouth wide open, pouring out his whole throat in the execution of his office. As soon as the tailor saw Mansouri making signs to him, the profession of faith stuck in his throat; and between the fright of being brought to account for the head, and the words which he had to pronounce, it is said that he made so strange a jumble, that some of the stricter Mussulmans, his neighbours, who were paying attention to the call, professed themselves quite scandalized at his performance. He descended with all haste, and locking the door after him which leads up the winding staircase, he met Mansouri in the street. He did not wait to be questioned respecting the fate of the horrid object, but at once attacked the slave concerning the trick, as he called it, which had been put upon him.

"*Are you a man,*" *said he, "to treat a poor Emir like me in the manner you have done, as if my house was a charnel-house? I suppose you will ask me the price of blood next!*"

"*Friend,*" *said Mansouri, "what are you talking about? do not you see that it has been a mistake?*"

"*A mistake, indeed!*" *cried the tailor, "a mistake done on purpose to bring a poor man into trouble. One man laughs at my stupid beard, and makes me believe that I am to make a suit of clothes for him—another takes away the pattern—and a third substitutes a dead man's head for it. Allah! Allah! I have got into the hands of a pretty nest of rogues, a set of ill-begotten knaves!*"

Upon which Mansouri placed his hand upon the tailor's mouth, and said, "*Say no*

more, say no more; you are getting deeper into the dirt. Do you know whom you are abusing?"

"I know not, nor care not," answered Babadul; "all I know is, that whoever gives me a dead man's head for a suit of clothes can only be an infidel dog."

"Do you call God's viceregent upon earth, you old demi-stitching, demi-praying fool, an infidel dog?" exclaimed Mansouri in a rage, which entirely made him forget the precaution he had hitherto maintained concerning his employer. "Are your vile lips to defile the name of him who is the Alem penah, the refuge of the world? What dirt are you eating, what ashes are you heaping on your head? Come, no more words; tell me where the dead man's head is, or I will take yours off in his stead."

Upon hearing this, the tailor stood with his mouth wide open, as if the doors of his understanding had just been unlocked.

"Aman, aman, Mercy, mercy, O Aga!" cried Babadul to Mansouri, "I was ignorant of what I was saying. Who would have thought it? Ass, fool, dolt, that I am, not to have known better. Bismillah! in the name of the Prophet, pray come to my house; your steps will be fortunate, and your slave's head will touch the stars."

"I am in a hurry, a great hurry," said Mansouri. "Where is the head, the head of the Aga of the Janissaries?"

When the tailor heard whose head it had been, and recollected what he and his wife had done with it, his knees knocked under him with fear, and he began to exude from every pore.

"Where is it, indeed?" said he. "Oh! what has come upon us! Oh! what cursed kismet (fate) is this?"

"Where is it?" exclaimed the slave, again and again, "where is it? speak quick!"

The poor tailor was completely puzzled what to say, and kept floundering from one answer to another until he was quite entangled as in a net.

"Have you burnt it?"

"No."

"Have you thrown it away?"

"No."

"Then in the name of the Prophet what have you done with it? Have you ate it?"

"No."

"Is it lying in your house?"

"No."

"Is it hiding at any other person's house?"

"No."

Then at last quite out of patience, the slave Mansouri took Babadul by his beard, and shaking his head for him, exclaimed with a roar, "Then tell me, you old dotard! what is it doing?"

"It is baking," answered the tailor, half choked: "I have said it."

"Baking! did you say?" exclaimed the slave, in the greatest amazement; "what did you bake it for? Are you going to eat it?"

"True, I said: what would you have more?" answered Babadul, "it is now baking." And then he gave a full account of what he and his wife had done in the sad dilemma in which they had been placed.

"Show me the way to the baker's," said Mansouri; "at least, we will get it in its singed state, if we can get it in no other. Who ever thought of baking the head of the Aga of the Janissaries? Allah il allah!"

They then proceeded to the baker Hassan's, who was now about taking his bread from his oven. As soon as he became acquainted with their errand, he did not hesitate in telling all the circumstances attending the transmission of the head from the pipkin to the barber's bracket; happy to have had an opportunity of exculpating himself of what might possibly have been brought up against him as a crime.

The three (Mansouri, the tailor, and the baker) then proceeded to the barber's, and inquired from him what he had done with the head of his earliest customer.

Kior Ali, after some hesitation, made great assurances that he looked upon this horrid object as a donation from Eblis himself, and consequently that he had thought himself justified in transferring it over to the Giaour Yanaki, who, he made no doubt, had already made his brother-infidels partake of it in the shape of ka-bobs. Full of wonder and amazement, invoking the Prophet at each step, and uncertain as to the result of such un-heard-of adventures, they then added the barber to their party, and proceeded to Yanaki's cook-shop.

The Greek, confounded at seeing so many of the true believers enter his house, had a sort of feeling that their business was not of roast meat, but that they were in search of meat of a less savoury nature. As soon as the question had been put to him concerning the head, he stoutly denied having seen it, or knowing anything at all concerning it.

The barber showed the spot where he had placed it, and swore it upon the Koran.

Mansouri had undertaken the investigation of the point in question, when they discovered symptoms of the extraordinary agitation that prevailed in the city in consequence of the discovery which had been made of the double-headed Jew, and of the subsequent discovery that had produced such great sensation among the whole corps of Janissaries.

Mansouri, followed by the tailor, the baker, and the barber, then proceeded to the spot where the dead Israelite was prostrate; and there, to their astonishment, they each recognized their morning visitor—the head so long sought after.

Yanaki, the Greek, in the meanwhile, conscious of what was likely to befall him, without loss of time gathered what money he had ready at hand, and fled the city.

"Where is the Greek?" said Mansouri, turning round to look for him in the supposition that he had joined his party; "we must all go before the Sultan."

"I dare say he is run off," said the barber. "I am not so blind but I can see that he it is who gifted the Jew with his additional head."

Mansouri now would have carried off the head; but surrounded as it was by a band of enraged and armed soldiers, who vowed vengeance upon him who had deprived them of their chief, he thought it most prudent to withdraw. Leading with him his three witnesses, he at once proceeded to the presence of his master.

WHEN Mansouri had informed the Sultan of all that had happened, where he had found the head of the Aga of the Janissaries, how it had got there, and of the tumult it had raised, the reader may better imagine than I can describe the state of the monarch's mind. To tell the story with all its particulars he felt would be derogatory to his dignity, for it was sure to cover him with ridicule; but at the same time to let the matter rest as it now stood was impossible, because the tumult would increase until there would be no means of quelling it, and the affair might terminate by depriving him of his crown together with his life.

He remained in a state of indecision for some time, twisting up the ends of his mustachios, and muttering Allah! Allah! in low ejaculations, until at length he ordered the Prime Vizier and the Mûfti to his presence.

Alarmed by the abruptness of the summons, these two great dignitaries arrived at the imperial gate in no enviable state of mind; but when the Sultan had informed them of the tumult then raging in the capital, they resumed their usual tranquillity.

After some deliberation it was resolved, that the tailor, the baker, the barber, and the kabobchi should appear before the tribunal of the Mûfti, accused of having entered into a conspiracy against the Aga of the Janissaries, and stealing his head, for the purposes of baking, shaving, and roasting it, and that they should be condemned to pay the price of his blood; but as the kabobchi had been the immediate cause of the tumult by treating the head with such gross and unheard-of insult, and as he was a Greek and an infidel, it was further resolved that the Mûfti should issue a *fetwah*, authorizing his head to be cut off, and placed on the same odious spot where he had exposed that of the Aga of the Janissaries.

It was then agreed between the Sultan and his grand vizier, that in order to appease the Janissaries a new Aga should be appointed who was agreeable to them, and that the deceased should be buried with becoming distinction. All this (except killing the Greek, who had fled) was done, and tranquillity again restored to the city. But it must further be added to the honour of the Sultan, that he not only paid every expense which the tailor, the baker, and the barber were condemned to incur, but also gave them each a handsome reward for the difficulties into which they had so unfortunately been thrown.

the Baked Head

I have much curtailed the story, particularly where Mansouri proceeds to relate to the Sultan the fate of the head, because, had I given it with all the details the dervish did, it would have been over long. Indeed I have confined myself as much as possible to the outline; for to have swelled the narrative with the innumerable digressions of my companion a whole volume would not have contained it. The art of a story-teller (and it is that which marks a man of genius) is to make his tale interminable, and still to interest his audience. So the dervish assured me; and added, that with the materials of the one which I have attempted to repeat, he would bind himself to keep talking for a whole moon, and still have something to say.

CHAPTER XLVI: HE BECOMES A SAINT AND ASSOCIATES
WITH THE MOST CELEBRATED DIVINE IN PERSIA

T length Mirza Abdul Cossim himself, having heard much of my sanctity, took an opportunity, when visiting the shrine of the saint, to send for me. This was an event which I contemplated with apprehension; for how could I possibly conceal my ignorance from one who would certainly put my pretensions of knowledge to the test?—an ignorance so profound, that I could scarcely give an account of what were the first principles of the Mohamedan faith.

I, therefore, began to take myself to task upon what I did know. 'Let me see,' said I, 'I know, 1st, That all those who do not believe in Mohamed, and in Ali his lieutenant, are infidels and heretics, and are worthy of death. 2nd, I also know that all men will go to *Jehanum* (hell), excepting the true believers; and I further believe that it is right to curse Omar. —I am certain that all the Turks will go to Jehanum, that all Christians and Jews are *nejis* (unclean), and will go to Jehanum—that it is not lawful to drink wine or eat pork, that it is necessary to say prayers five times a day, and to make the ablution before each prayer, causing the water to run from the elbow to the fingers, not contrariwise, like the heretical Turks.'

I was proceeding to sum up the stock of my religious knowledge, when the dervish came into the room; and I made no scruple of relating to him my distress and its cause.

'Have you lived so long in the world,' said he, 'and not yet discovered that nothing is to be accomplished without impudence? The stories which Dervish Sefer, his companion, and I related to you at Meshed, have they made so little impression upon you?'

'The effect of those stories upon my mind,' said I, 'produced such a bastinado upon the soles of my feet, by way of a moral, that I request you to be well assured I shall neither forget you nor them as long as I live: the *felek* is a great help to the memory. And now, according to your own account, instead of the bastinado, I am likely to get stoned, should I be found wanting; a ceremony which, if it be the same to you, I had rather dispense with. Say then, O dervish, what shall I do?'

'You are not that Hajjî Baba which I always took you to be,' said the dervish, 'if you have not the ingenuity to deceive the mûshtehed. Keep to your silence, and your sighs, and your shrugs, and your downcast looks, and who is there that will discover you to be an ass? No, even I could not.'

'Well,' said I, 'be it so: *Allah kerim!* God is great!—but it is being in very ill luck to be invited to an entertainment to eat one's own filth.'

Upon which I set forward with my most mortified and downcast looks to visit the mûshtehed, and, thanks to my misfortunes, I truly believe that no man in the whole city could boast of so doleful a cast of countenance as I could. However, as I slowly paced the ground, I recollected one of the tales recited by our great moralist Saadi, in his chapter upon the Morals of Dervishes, which applied so perfectly to my own case, that I own it cheered me greatly, and gave me a degree of courage to encounter the scrutiny of the mûshtehed which otherwise I never could have acquired. It is as follows:

'A devout personage was once asked, what he thought of the character of a certain holy man, of whom others had spoken with slight and disrespect? He answered, "In his exterior I can perceive no fault, and of what is concealed within him I am ignorant. He who weareth an exterior of religion, doubt not his goodness and piety, if you are ignorant of the recesses of his heart. What hath the *mohtesib* to do with the inside of the house?"'

I then recollected some sentences from the same chapter, which would apply admirably in case I were called upon to show my learning and humility at the same time; for I promised to say to the holy man, should he offer me an opportunity, 'Do unto me that which is worthy of thee, treat me not according to my desert. Whether you slay or whether you pardon, my head and face are on thy threshold. It is not for a servant to direct; whatsoever thou commandest I shall perform.'

The mûshtehed had just finished his midday prayer, and was completing the last act of it by turning his head first over the right shoulder then over the left, when I entered the open apartment where he was seated. It was lined with his disciples, on each side and at the top, all of whom looked upon him with the reverence and respect due to a master. Here he held his lectures. A mollah, with whom I was acquainted, mentioned who I was, and forthwith I was invited to take my place on the carpet, which I did, after having with great humility kissed the hem of the holy man's cloak. 'You are welcome,' said he; 'we have heard a great deal concerning you, Hajjî, and *inshallah*, your steps will be fortunate. Sit up higher!'

I made all sorts of remonstrances against sitting higher up in the room (for I had taken the lowest place); and when I had crept up to the spot to which he had pointed with his finger, I carefully nestled my feet closely under me, covering both them and my hands with my coat.

'We have heard,' said he, 'that you are a chosen slave of the Most High; one whose words and whose acts are the same; not wearing a beard of two colours, like those who are Mussulmans in outward appearance, but who are Kafirs in their hearts.'

'May your propitious condescension never be less!' said I: 'your servant is the most abject of the least of those who rub their forehead on the threshold of the gate of Almighty splendour.'

Here ensued a pause and dead silence, when we each appeared absorbed in deep meditation. The mûshtehed then breaking the silence, said to me:

'Is it true, O Hajjî! that your *talleh*, your destiny, has turned its face upon you, and that you have come hither to seek refuge? We and the world have long bid adieu to each other; so my questions are not to satisfy curiosity, but to inform me whether I can be of use to you. Our holy Prophet (upon whom be blessings and peace!) sayeth, "Let our faithful followers help each other: those who see, let them lead the blind; those who prosper, let them help those who are in adversity."'

Upon this I took courage, spoke my sentences from Saadi, as already recited, and told my tale in such a modified manner, that my auditors, I verily believe, began to look upon me as very little short of a martyr.

'If it is so,' said the mûshtehed, 'perhaps the day is not far off, when I may be the instrument, in the hands of God, to see justice done you. The Shah is to visit the tomb before this month is expired, and as he looks upon me with the eyes of approbation, be assured that I will not be deficient in endeavouring to procure your release.'

'What can such a sinner as I say to one of your high sanctity? I will pray for you; the dust of your path shall be collyrium for my eyes. Whatever you will do for me will be the effect of your goodness.'

'It is plain that you are one of us,' said the mûshtehed, apparently well satisfied at the almost divine honours which I paid him. 'True Mussulmans always recognize each other in the same manner, as I have heard to be the case among a sect of the Franks, called *Faramooshi*,[1] who by a word, a look, or a touch, will discover one another even among thousands.'

'*Allah ho akbar!* God is great'; and '*La Allah il Allah!* there is but one God!' was echoed by the company, in admiration of the mûshtehed's knowledge; and then he continued to address me thus:

'There is an ajem with you, who calls himself a dervish. Is he an acquaintance of yours? He says that he and you are *hem dum*, of one breath. Is it so?'

'*Che arz bekunum?* what supplication can I make?' said I, not knowing precisely whether to acknowledge my friend or not.

'Yes, he is a *fakîr*, a poor man, to whom I have given a path near me. He has done me some little service, and I am mindful of him.'

'You must be mindful of yourself,' said an old mollah, who sat next to me. 'Whatever is thief, whatever is knave, you will be sure to find it among these ajems.'

'Yes,' said the mûshtehed, as he rested both his hands upon his girdle, whilst his disciples (who knew this to be his favourite attitude when about to make a speech) settled their faces into looks of attention—'yes, these, and all who call themselves dervishes, be they the followers of *Nûr Ali Shahi*, be they *Zahabîes*, be they *Nakshbendies*, or be they of that accursed race of *Uweisîes*; all are kafirs or heretics—all are worthy of death. The

[1] So the Persians call Freemasons, about whom they are very inquisitive.

one promulgate, that the fastings of the Ramazan, our ablutions, the forms
and number of our daily prayers, are all unnecessary to salvation; and that
the heart is the test of piety, and not the ceremonies of the body. The
other acknowledge the Koran, 'tis true; but they reject everything else:
the sayings of the Prophet, opinions of saints, &c. are odious to them; and
they show their religious zeal by shouting out the blessed name of Allah,
until they foam at the mouth, like so many roaring lions; and this they
are pleased to call religion. Another set pretend to superior piety, by dis-
figuring the outward man, making vows, and performing acts of penance,
that partake more of the tricks of mountebanks than of the servants of the
Almighty. The fourth, the most heretical of all, would make us believe
that they live in eternal communion with supernatural powers; and whilst
they put on a patched and threadbare garment, affect to despise the goods
of this world, and keep themselves warm by metaphysical meditations,
which neither they nor any one else understand. No distinction of clean or
unclean (may they enjoy the eternal grills!) stands in their way; lawful
and unlawful is all one to them; they eat and drink whatever they choose,
and even the Giaours, the infidels, are undefiled in their sight. And these
call themselves Sûfies; these are your wise men; these are your lights of
the world! Curses on their beard!' To which all the company answered
'*ameen*,' or amen. 'Curses on their fathers and mothers! Curses on their

children! Curses on their relations! Curses on Sheikh Attar![1] Curses on
Jelâledîn Rûmi!' After each curse the whole assembly echoed 'Ameen!'

When he had concluded, all the company, whilst they expressed their
admiration at his doctrine, looked at me to see if I was not struck with
amazement. I was not backward in making the necessary exclamations,
and acted my part so true to the life, that the impression in my favour
was universal.

The mûshtehed, warmed by his own words, continued to harangue
against the Sûfies with such vehemence, that I believe had there been one
at hand, they would have risen in a body and put him to death. I hugged
myself in the success which had accompanied my attempt to appear a good
Mussulman, and now began to think that I was one in right earnest.

'If what I do,' said I, 'constitutes a religious man, and is to acquire me
the world's consideration, nothing is more easy. Why then should I toil
through life, a slave to some tyrant, exposed to every vicissitude, uncertain of my existence beyond the present moment, and a prey to a thousand
and one evils?'

I left the mûshtehed, and returned to my cell, determined to persevere
in my pious dispositions. When I met my companion again, I told him all
that had happened, and everything that had been said about him and dervishes in general; and advised him, considering the temper in which I had
left the assembly, to make the best of his way out of a place in which every
man's mind and hand were turned against him. 'If they catch you, they
stone you, friend!' said I; 'upon that make your mind easy.'

'May the stones alight on their own heads!' exclaimed the dervish: 'a
set of blood-thirsty heathens! What sort of religion can theirs be which
makes them seek the life of an inoffensive man? I come here, having no one
thing to do with either Sûni or Shiah, Sûfi or Mohamedan: on the contrary, out of compliment to them, I go through all the mummery of five
washings and five prayings per day, and still that will not satisfy them;
however, I will be even with them. I will go; I will leave their vile hypocritical town; and neither will I wash nor pray until necessity obliges me
to pass through it again.'

I must own that I was not sorry when I heard the dervish make this
resolution. I saw him with pleasure gird on his broad leathern belt, from

[1]*Sheikh Attar* and *Jelâledîn Rûmi* are the two great doctors of the Sûfies.

which was suspended great bunches of beads, and stick his long spoon in it. I helped to fasten his deer-skin to his back; and when he had taken up the iron weapon, which he carried on his shoulder, in one hand, whilst his other bore his calabash suspended with three chains, we bade each other adieu with great apparent cordiality.

Leaving me to the full possession of my cell, he sallied forth with all the lightness and gaiety of heart of one who had the world at his command, instead of the world before him, with nothing but his two feet and his ingenuity to carry him through it.

'May the mercy of Allah be poured over you,' said I, as I saw the last of him, 'you merry rogue! and mayest thou never want a pair of shoes to your feet, nor a pleasant story to your tongue, with both of which thou mayest go through life with more pleasure both to thyself and others than the rich man, who is the slave of a thousand wants, a dependant upon his dependants for the commonest necessaries of his existence.'

CHAPTER XLVII: HAJJI BABA IS ROBBED
BY HIS FRIEND AND LEFT UTTERLY DESTITUTE
BUT IS RELEASED FROM HIS CONFINEMENT.

MY mind now dwelt upon the promise which the mûshtehed had made of procuring my pardon and release from the Shah, when he came to visit the sanctuary at Kom; and it occurred to me, that to secure the favour of so powerful an advocate, I ought to make him a present, without which nothing is ever accomplished in Persia. But of what it was to be composed was the next consideration. The money left in my purse was all that I had to subsist upon until I should acquire a new livelihood; and, little as it was, I had kept it safely buried in an unfrequented corner near my cell.

I fixed upon a praying-carpet, as the best present for one who is always upon his knees, and had laid my plan for getting some brought to me from the bazaar to look at.

'Every time the good man prays,' said I, 'he will think of me; and as one is apt to make good resolutions in such moments, perhaps he will be put in mind of his promises to endeavour to release me.'

I forthwith resorted to my secret corner for my purse, in the determination of sacrificing one of my remaining tomauns to this purpose. But here let me stop, and let me request the reader to recollect himself, and reflect upon his feelings after the most severe disappointment which it may have been his lot to sustain, and let me tell him, that it was nothing to my grief, to my rage, to my exasperation, when I found my purse was gone.

My soul came into my mouth; and without a moment's hesitation I exclaimed, 'O thou bankrupt dog! thou unsainted dervish! You have brought me safe into harbour, 'tis true; but you have left me without an anchor. May your life be a bitter one, and may your daily bread be the bread of grief! And so, after all, Hajjî Baba has become a beggar!'

I then took to making the most sorrowful moanings and lamentations; for the fear of starvation now stared me in the face notwithstanding the charity of the people of Kom; and as despair is a malady which increases the more the mind dwells upon its misfortune, I seemed to take delight in reverting to all the horrors which I had lately witnessed in the death of Zeenab; then I dwelt upon my confinement, then upon my loss, and at length wound myself up to look upon my situation as so desperate, that if I had had poison by me, I should certainly have swallowed it.

At this moment passed by my cell the old mollah, who, during my visit to the mûshtehed, had warned me against putting too much confidence in the dervish. I told him of my misfortune, and raised such doleful wailings, that his heart was touched.

'You spoke but too well, O mollah!' said I, 'when you warned me against the dervish. My money is gone, and I am left behind. I am a stranger; and he who called himself my friend has proved my bitterest enemy! Curses on such a friend! Oh! whither shall I turn for assistance?'

'Do not grieve, my son,' said the mollah; 'we know that there is a God, and if it be his will to try you with misfortune, why do you repine? Your money is gone,—gone it is, and gone let it be; but your skin is left, —and what do you want more? A skin is no bad thing, after all!'

'What words are these?' said I: 'I know that a skin is no bad thing; but will it get back my money from the dervish?'

I then requested the old man to state my misfortune to the mûshtehed, and, moreover, my impossibility of showing him that respect by a present, which was due to him, and which it had been my intention to make.

He left me with promises of setting my case in its proper light before

the holy man; and, to my great joy, on the very same day the news of the
approaching arrival of the Shah was brought to Kom by the chief of the
tent-pitchers, who came to make the necessary preparations for his accommodation.

The large open saloon in the sanctuary in which the king prays was
spread with fine carpets, the court was swept and watered, the fountain in
the centre of the reservoir was made to play, and the avenues to the tomb
were put into order. A deputation, consisting of all the priests, was collected, to go before him, and meet him on his entry; and nothing of ceremony was omitted which was due to the honour and dignity of the Shadow
of the Almighty upon earth.

I now became exceedingly anxious about my future fate; for it was
long since I had heard from Tehran, and I was ignorant of the measure of
the Shah's resentment against me. Looking upon the dark side of things,
my imagination led me to think that nothing short of my head would satisfy him; but then, cheering myself with a more pleasing prospect, I endeavoured to believe that I was too insignificant a personage that my
death should be of any consequence, and built all my hopes upon the intercession of the mûshtehed.

The chief tent-pitcher had formerly been my friend, and among his as-
sistants I recognized many of my acquaintance. I soon made myself known
to them; and they did not, for a wonder, draw back from recognizing me,
although one of our greatest sages hath said, 'that a man in adversity is
shunned like a piece of base money, which nobody will take; and which, if
perchance it has been received, is passed off to another as soon as possible.'

The newcomers gave me all the intelligence of what had happened at
court since I had left it; and although I professed to have renounced the
world, and to have become a recluse, a sitter in a corner, as it is called,
yet still I found that I had an ear for what was passing in it. They informed me that the chief executioner had returned from his campaign
against the Russians, and had brought the Shah a present of two Georgian
slaves, a male and a female, besides other rarities, in order the better to
persuade him of his great feats and generalship. The present had been accepted, and his face was to be whitened by a dress of honour, provided he
made the *tobeh*, oath of penance, restraining himself from the use of wine
for the future. I also learnt, notwithstanding it was known how deeply I

was implicated in Zeenab's guilt, that my former master, the hakîm, had still been obliged to make a large present to the Shah, besides having had half his beard pulled out by the roots, for the loss which his majesty had incurred by her death, and for his disappointment at not finding her ready to dance and sing before him on his return from Sultanieh. The king's wrath for the loss of the Cûrdish slave had in great measure subsided, owing to the chief executioner's gift of the Georgian one, who was described as being the finest person of the sort who had been exhibited at the slave-market since the days of the celebrated *Taous*, or Peacock; and was, in short, the pearl of the shell of beauty, the marrow of the spine of perfection. She had a face like the full moon, eyes of the circumference of the chief tent-pitcher's forefinger and thumb, a waist that he could span, and a form tall and majestic as the full-grown cypress. And they moreover assured me, that the Shah's anger against me would very easily cede to a present of a few tomauns.

Here again my anathemas against the dervish broke forth; 'and but for him,' said I, 'I might have appeared not empty-handed.' However, I was delighted to hear that my case was not so desperate as I had imagined; and, seated on the carpet of hope, smoking the pipe of expectation, I determined to await my fate with that comfortable feeling of predestination which has been so wisely dispensed by the holy Prophet for the peace and quiet of all true believers.

The King of Kings arrived the next day, and alighted at his tents, which were pitched without the town. I will not waste the reader's time in describing all the ceremonies of his reception, which, by his desire, were curtailed as much as possible, inasmuch as his object in visiting the tomb of Fatimeh was not to reap worldly distinctions, but to humble himself before God and men, in the hope of obtaining better and higher reward.

His policy has always been to keep in good odour with the priesthood of his country; for he knew that their influence, which is considerable over the minds of the people, was the only bar between him and unlimited power. He therefore courted Mirza Abdul Cossim, the mûshtehed of Kom, by paying him a visit on foot, and by permitting him to be seated before him, an honour seldom conferred on one of the laity. He also went about the town on foot, during the whole time of his stay there, giving largely to the poor, and particularly consecrating rich and valuable gifts at the shrine of the saint. The king himself, and all those who composed his train, thought it proper to suit their looks to the fashion of the place; and I was delighted to find that I was not singular in my woe-smitten face and my mortified gait. I recollected to have heard, when I was about the court, that the Shah, in point of fact, was a Sûfi at heart, although very rigid in the outward practices of religion; and it was refreshing to me to perceive, among the great officers in his train, one of the secretaries of state, a notorious sinner of that persuasion, who was now obliged to fold up his principles in the napkin of oblivion, and clothe himself in the garments of the true faith.

On the morning of the Shah's visit to the tomb for the purpose of saying his prayers, I was on the alert, in the hopes of being remarked by the mûshtehed, who would thus be reminded of his promises to me.

About an hour before the prayer of midday, the Shah, on foot, escorted by an immense concourse of attendants, priests, and of the people, entered the precincts of the sanctuary. He was dressed in a dark suit, the sombre colours of which were adapted to the solemn looks of his face, and he held in his hand a long enamelled stick, curiously inlaid at the pommel. He had put by all ornament, wearing none of his customary jewellery, not even his dagger, which on other occasions he is never without. The only article of great value was his rosary, composed of large pearls (the produce of his fishery at Bahrein), of the most beautiful water and symmetry, and this he kept constantly in his hand.

The mûshtehed walked two or three steps behind him on the left hand, respectfully answered the interrogatories which the king was pleased to make, and lent a profound attention to all his observations.

When the procession came near me (for it passed close to my cell), I seized an opportunity, when no officer was at hand, to run forward, throw myself on my knees, make the prostration with my face to the ground, and exclaim, 'Refuge in the King of Kings, the asylum of the world! In the name of the blessed Fatimeh, mercy!'

'Who is this?' exclaimed the king to the mûshtehed, 'Is he one of yours?'

'He has taken the *bust* (the sanctuary),' answered the mirza, 'and he claims the accustomed pardon of the Shadow of the Almighty to all unfortunate refugees whenever he visits the tomb. He and we all are your sacrifice; and whatever the Shah ordains, so let it be.'

'But who and what are you?' said the Shah to me; 'why have you taken refuge here?'

'May I be our sacrifice!' said I. 'Your slave was the sub-deputy executioner to the Centre of the Universe, Hajjî Baba by name; and my enemies have made me appear criminal in the eyes of the Shah, whilst I am innocent.'

'*Yaftéh îm*, we have understood,' rejoined the king, after a minute's pause. 'So you are that Hajjî Baba? *Mûbarek*, much good may it do you. Whether it was one dog or another that did the deed, whether the hakîm or the sub-deputy, it comes to the same thing,—the end of it has been that the king's goods have burnt. That is plain enough, is it not, Mirza Abdul Cossim?' said he, addressing himself to the mûshtehed.

'Yes, by the sacred head of the king,' answered the holy man; 'generally in all such cases between man and woman, they, and they alone, can speak to the truth.'

'But what does our holy religion say in such cases?' observed the king: 'the Shah has lost a slave—there is a price of blood for the meanest of human beings—even a Frank or a Muscovite have their price, and why should we expend our goods gratis, for the amusement of either our chief physician or our sub-deputy executioner?'

'There is a price upon each of God's creatures, and blood must not be spilt without its fine; but there is also an injunction of forgiveness and lenity towards one's fellow creatures,' said the mûshtehed, 'which our holy Prophet (upon whom be eternal blessings!) has more particularly addressed to those invested with authority, and which, O king, cannot be better applied than in this instance. Let the Shah forgive this unfortunate sinner, and he will reap greater reward in Heaven than if he had killed twenty Muscovites, or impaled the father of all Europeans, or even if he had stoned a Sûfi.'

'Be it so,' said the Shah; and turning to me, he said with a loud voice, '*Murakhas*, you are dismissed; and recollect it is owing to the intercession of this man of God,' putting his hand at the same time upon the shoulder of the mûshtehed, 'that you are free, and that you are permitted to enjoy the light of the sun. *Bero!* Go! open your eyes, and never again stand before our presence.'

CHAPTER XLVIII: HAJJI BABA REACHES ISPAHAN AND HIS PATERNAL ROOF JUST TIME ENOUGH TO CLOSE THE EYES OF HIS DYING FATHER.

I DID not require to be twice ordered to depart; and, without once looking behind me, I left Kom and its priests, and bent my steps towards Ispahan and my family. I had a few *reals* in my pocket, with which I could buy food on the road; and, as for resting-places, the country was well supplied with caravanserais, in which I could always find a corner to lay my head. Young as I was, I began to be disgusted with the world; and perhaps had I remained long enough at Kom, and in the mood in which I had reached it, I might have devoted the rest of my life to following the lectures of Mirza Abdul Cossim, and acquired worldly consideration by my taciturnity, by my austerity, and strict adherence to Mahomedan discipline. But fate had woven another destiny for me. The *maidan* (the racecourse) of life was still open to me, and the courser of my existence had not yet exhausted half of the bounds and curvets with which he was wont to keep me in constant exercise. I felt that I deserved the misfortunes with which I had been afflicted, owing to my total neglect of my parents.

'I have been a wicked son,' said I. 'When I was a man in authority, and was puffed up with pride at my own importance, I then forgot the poor barber at Ispahan; and it is only now, when adversity spreads my path, that I recollect the authors of my being.' A saying of my schoolmaster, which he frequently quoted with great emphasis in Arabic, came to my mind. 'An old friend,' used he to say, 'is not to be bought, even if you had the treasures of Hatem to offer for one. Remember then, O youth, that thy first, and therefore thy oldest friends are thy father and thy mother.'

'They shall still find that they have a son,' said I, feeling a great rush of tenderness flow into my heart, as I repeated the words; 'and, please God, if I reach my home, they shall no longer have to reproach me with want of proper respect.' A still soft voice, however, whispered to me that I should be too late; and I remembered the prognostics of my mind, when, filled with grief for the loss of Zeenab, I left Tehran full of virtuous intentions and resolutions.

When I could first distinguish the peak in the mountain of the *Colah Cazi*, which marks the situation of Ispahan, my heart bounded within me; and at every step I anxiously considered in what state I should find my family. Would my old schoolmaster be alive? Should I find our neighbour the *Baqal* (or chandler), at whose shop I used to spend in sweetmeats all the copper money that I could purloin from my father, when I shaved for him, would he be still in existence? And my old friend the *Capiji*, the door-keeper of the caravanserai, he whom I frightened so much at the attack of the Turcomans, is the door of his life still open, or has it been closed upon him for ever?

In this manner did I muse by the wayside, until the tops of the minarets of Ispahan actually came in view; when, enraptured with the sight, and full of gratitude for having been preserved thus far in my pilgrimage, I stopped and said my prayers; and then taking up one stone, which I placed upon another as a memorial, I made the following vow: 'O Ali, if thou wilt grant to thy humblest and most abject of slaves the pleasure of reaching my home in safety, I will, on arrival, kill a sheep, and make a pilau for my friends and family.'

Traversing the outskirts of the city with a beating heart, every spot was restored to my memory, and I threaded my way through the long vaulted bazaars and intricate streets without missing a single turn, until I found myself standing opposite both my father's shop and the well-known gate of the caravanserai.

The door of the former was closed, and nothing was stirring around it that indicated business. I paused a long time before I ventured to proceed, for I looked upon this first aspect of things as portentous of evil; but, recollecting myself, I remembered that it was the *Sheb-i-Jumah*, the Friday eve, and that probably my father, in his old age, had grown to be too scrupulous a Mussulman to work during those hours which true believers ought to keep holy.

However, the caravanserai was open, and presented the same scene to my eyes which it had done ever since I had known it. Bales of goods heaped up in lots, intermixed with mules, camels, and their drivers. Groups of men in various costumes, some seated, some in close conversation, others gazing carelessly about, and others again coming and going in haste, with faces full of care and calculation. I looked about for the friend of my boyhood the capiji, and almost began to fear that he too had closed his door, when I perceived his well-known figure crawling quietly along with his earthen water-pipe, seeking his bit of charcoal wherewith to light it.

His head had sunk considerably between his shoulders, and reclined more upon his breast since last I had seen him; and the additional bend in his knees showed that the passing years had kept a steady reckoning with him. 'It is old Ali Mohamed,' said I, as I stepped up towards him. 'I should know that crooked nose of his from a thousand, so often have I clipped the whisker that grows under it.'

When I accosted him with the usual salutation of peace, he kept on trimming his pipe, without even looking up, so much accustomed was he to be spoken to by strangers; but when I said, 'Do not you recognize me, Ali Mohamed?' he turned up his old bloodshot eye at me, and pronounced 'Friend! a caravanserai is a picture of the world; men come in and go out of it, and no account is taken of them. How am I then to know you? Ali Mohamed is grown old, and his memory is gone by.'

'But you will surely recollect Hajjî Baba—little Hajjî, who used to shave your head, and trim your beard and mustachios!'

'There is but one God!' exclaimed the door-keeper in great amazement. 'Are you indeed Hajjî? Ah! my son, your place has long been empty

—are you come at last? Well, then, praise be to Ali, that old Kerbelai Hassan will have his eyes closed by his only child, ere he dies.'

'How!' said I, 'tell me where is my father? Why is the shop shut? What do you say about death?'

'Yes, Hajjî, the old barber has shaved his last. Lose not a moment in going to his house, and you may stand a chance to be in time to receive his blessing ere he leaves this world. Please God, I shall soon follow him, for all is vanity. I have opened and shut the gates of this caravanserai for fifty years, and find that all pleasure is departed from me. My keys retain their polish, whilst I wear out with rust.'

I did not stop to hear the end of the old man's speech, but immediately made all speed to my father's house.

As I approached the well-remembered spot, I saw two mollahs loitering near the low and narrow entrance.

'Ha!' thought I, 'ye are birds of ill-omen; wherever the work of death is going on, there ye are sure to be.'

Entering, without accosting them, I walked at once into the principal room, which I found completely filled with people, surrounding an old man, who was stretched out upon a bed spread upon the floor, and whom I recognized to be my father.

No one knew me, and, as it is a common custom for strangers who have nothing to do with the dying to walk in unasked, I was not noticed. On one side sat the doctor, and on the other an old man, who was kneeling near the bed-head, and in him I recognized my former schoolmaster. He was administering comfort to his dying friend, and his words were something to this purpose: 'Do not be downcast: please God you still have many days to spend on earth. You may still live to see your son; Hajjî Baba may yet be near at hand. But yet it is a proper and a fortunate act to make your will, and to appoint your heir. If such be your wish, appoint any one here present your heir.'

'Ah,' sighed out my father, 'Hajjî has abandoned us—I shall never see him more—He has become too much of a personage to think of his poor parents—He is not worthy that I should make him my heir.' These words produced an immediate effect; I could no longer restrain my desire to make myself known, and I exclaimed, 'Hajjî is here!—Hajjî is come to receive your blessing—I am your son—do not reject him!' Upon which I knelt down by the bedside, and taking up the dying man's hand, I kissed it, and added loud sobs and lamentations, to demonstrate my filial affection.

The sensation which I produced upon all present was very great. I saw looks of disappointment in some, of incredulity in others, and of astonishment in all.

My father's eyes, that were almost closed, brightened up for one short interval as he endeavoured to make out my features, and clasping his trembling hands together, exclaimed, '*Il hem dillah!* Praise be to God, I have seen my son, I have got an heir!' Then addressing me, he said, 'Have you done well, O my son, to leave me for so many years? Why did you not come before?' He would have gone on, but the exertion and the agitation produced by such an event were too much for his strength, and he sunk down inanimate on his pillow.

'Stop,' said my old schoolmaster, who had at once recognized me— 'stop, Hajjî; say no more: let him recover himself; he has still his will to make.'

'Yes,' said a youngish man, who had eyed me with looks of great hostility—'yes, we have also still to see whether this is Hajji Baba, or not.' I afterwards found he was son to a brother of my father's first wife, and had expected to inherit the greatest part of the property; and when I inquired who were the other members of the assembly, I found that they were all relations of that stamp, who had flocked together in the hope of getting a share of the spoil, of which I had now deprived them.

They all seemed to doubt whether I was myself, and perhaps would have unanimously set me down for an impostor, if the schoolmaster had not been present: and from his testimony there was no appeal.

However, all doubts as to my identity were immediately hushed when my mother appeared, who, having heard of my arrival, could no longer keep to the limits of her anderûn, but rushed into the assembly with extended arms and a flowing veil, exclaiming, 'Where, where is he? where is my son? Hajjî, my soul, where art thou?'

As soon as I had made myself known, she threw herself upon my neck, weeping aloud, making use of every expression of tenderness which her imagination could devise, and looking at me from head to foot with an eagerness of stare, and an impetuosity of expression, that none but a mother can command.

In order to rouse my father from the lethargy into which he had apparently fallen, the doctor proposed administering a cordial, which, having prepared, he endeavoured to pour down his throat; during the exertion of raising the body, the dying man sneezed once, which every one present knew was an omen so bad, that no man in his senses would dare venture to give the medicine until two full hours had expired: therefore, it remained in the cup.

After having waited the expiration of the two hours, the medicine was again attempted to be administered, when, to the horror of all present, and to the disappointment of those who expected that he should make his will, he was found to be stone dead.

'In the name of Allah, arise,' said the old mollah to him; 'we are now writing your will.' He endeavoured to raise my father's head, but to no purpose; life had entirely fled.

Water steeped in cotton was then squeezed into his mouth, his feet were carefully placed towards the Kebleh, and as soon as it was ascertained that no further hope was left, the priest at his bed-head began to read the Koran in a loud and sing-song emphasis. A handkerchief was then placed under his chin, fastened over his head, and his two great toes were also tied together. All the company then pronounced the *Kelemeh Shehâdet* (the profession of faith), a ceremony which was supposed to send him out of this world a pure and well-authenticated Mussulman; and during this interval a cup of water was placed upon his head.

All these preliminaries having been duly performed, the whole company, composed of what were supposed to be his friends and relations, gathered close round the corpse, and uttered loud and doleful cries. This was a signal to the two mollahs (whom I before mentioned), who had mounted on the house-top, and they then began to chant out in a sonorous cadence portions of the Koran, or verses used on such occasions, and which are intended as a public notification of the death of a true believer.

The noise of wailing and lamentation now became general, for it soon was communicated to the women, who, collected in a separate apartment, gave vent to their grief after the most approved forms. My father, from his gentleness and obliging disposition, had been a great favourite with all ranks of people, and my mother, who herself was a professional mourner, and a principal performer at burials, being well acquainted with others of her trade, had managed to collect such a band around her on this occasion, that no Khan, it was said, ever had so much mourning performed for him on his death-day as my father.

As for me, whose feelings had previously been set to the pitch-pipe of misfortune, I became a real and genuine mourner; and the recollection of all the actions of my life, in which my total neglect of my parents made so conspicuous a figure, caused me to look upon myself in no enviable light.

I was seated quietly in a corner, adding my sincere sobs to the artificial ones of the rest of the whole company, when a priest came up to me, and said, that of course it was necessary for me to tear my clothes, as I could not prove myself to be a good son without so doing, and that if I permitted him, he would perform that operation for me without spoiling my coat. I let him do what he required, and he accordingly ripped open the seam of the breast flap, which then hung down some three or four inches. He also told me that it was the custom to keep the head uncovered, and the feet naked, at least until all the ceremonies of burial had been performed.

To this I freely consented, and had the satisfaction afterwards to learn, that I was held up as the pattern of a good mourner.

My mother's grief was outrageous: her hair was concealed, and she enveloped her head in a black shawl, making exclamations expressive of her anguish, calling upon the name of her husband.

By this time the neighbours, the passers-by, the known or unknown to the family, flocked round the house for the purpose of either reading the Koran or hearing it read, which is also esteemed a meritorious act on that occasion. Among these, many came in the character of comforters, who, by their knowledge in the forms of speech best adapted to give consolation, are looked upon as great acquisitions in the event of a mourning.

My old schoolmaster, an eminent comforter, took me in hand, and seating himself by my side, addressed me in the following words:

'Yes, at length your father is dead. So be it. What harm is done? Is not death the end of all things? He was born, he got a son, he ran his course, and died. Who can do more? You now take his place in the world; you are the rising blade, that with millions of others promise a good harvest, whilst he is the full ripened ear of corn, that has been cut down and gathered into the granary. Ought you to repine at what is a subject for joy? Instead of shaving men's heads, he is now seated between two houris, drinking milk and eating honey. Ought you to weep at that? No; rather weep that you are not there also. But why weep at all? Consider the many motives for which, on the contrary, you have to rejoice. He might have been an unbeliever—but he was a true Mussulman. He might have been a Turk—but he was a Persian. He might have been a Sûni—but he was a Shiah. He might have been an unclean Christian—he was a lawful son of Islam. He might have died accursed like a Jew—he has resigned his breath with the profession of the true faith in his mouth. All these are subjects of joy!'

After this manner did he go on; and, having expended all he had to say, left me, to join his voice to the general wailing.

Those unclean men, the *mûrdeshûr*, or washers of the dead, were then called in, who brought with them the bier, in which the corpse was to be carried to the grave. I was consulted, whether they should make an *imareh* of it, which is a sort of canopy, adorned with black flags, shawls, and other stuffs—a ceremony practised only in the burials of great personages; but I referred the decision to my friend the schoolmaster, who immediately said, that considering my worthy father to have been a sort of public character, he should certainly be for giving him such a distinction. This was accordingly done; and the corpse having been brought out by the distant relations, and laid therein, it was carried to the place of ablution, where it was delivered over to the washers, who immediately went to work. The body was first washed with clear cold water, then rubbed over with lime, salt, and camphor, placed in the winding-sheet, again consigned to the bier, and at length conveyed to the place of burial.

The many who offered themselves to carry the body was a proof how much my father must have been beloved. Even strangers feeling that it was a praiseworthy action to carry a good Mussulman to the grave, pressed forward to lend their shoulder to the burden, and by the time it had reached its last resting-place, the crowd was considerable.

I had followed at a small distance, escorted by those who called themselves friends and relations; and after a mollah had said a prayer, accompanied by the voices of all present, I was invited, as the nearest relative,, to place the body in the earth, which having done, the ligatures of the winding-sheet were untied, and another prayer, called the *talkhi*, was pronounced. The twelve Imâms, in rotation, were then invoked; and the *talkhi* being again read, the grave was covered in. After this, the *Fatheh* (the first chapter of the Koran) was repeated by all present, and the grave having been sprinkled over with water, the whole assembly dispersed, to meet again at the house of the deceased. A priest remained at the head of the grave, praying.

I was now called upon to act a part. I had become the principal personage in the tragedy, and an involuntary thought stole into my mind.

'Ah,' said I, 'the vow which I made upon first seeing the city must now be performed, whether I will or no. I must spend boldly, or I shall be esteemed an unnatural son'; therefore, when I returned to the house, I blindly ordered every thing to be done in a handsome manner.

Two rooms were prepared, one for the men, the other for the women. According to the received custom, I, as chief mourner, gave an entertainment to all those who had attended the funeral; and here my sheep and my pilau were not forgotten. I also hired three mollahs, two of whom were appointed to read the Koran in the men's apartment, and the other remained near the tomb, for the same purpose, inhabiting a small tent, which was pitched for its use. The length of the mourning, which lasts, according to the means of the family, three, five, seven days, or even a month, I fixed at five days, during which each of the relations gave an entertainment. At the end of that period, some of the elders, both men and women, went round to the mourners, and sewed up their rent garments, and on that day I was again invited to give an entertainment, when separate sheets of the Koran were distributed throughout the whole assembly, and read by each individual, until the whole of the sacred volume had been completely gone through.

After this my mother, with several of her relations and female friends, proceeded in a body to my father's tomb, taking with them sweetmeats and baked bread for the purpose, which they distributed to the poor, having partaken thereof themselves. They then returned, weeping and bewailing.

Two or three days having elapsed, my mother's friends led her to the bath, where they took off her mourning, put her on a clean dress, and dyed her feet and hands with the *khena*.

This completed the whole of the ceremonies: and, much to my delight, I was now left to myself, to regulate my father's affairs, and to settle plans for my own future conduct.

CHAPTER XLIX: HE BECOMES HEIR TO PROPERTY WHICH IS NOT TO BE FOUND AND HIS SUSPICIONS THEREON

MY father having died without a will, I was, of course, proclaimed his sole heir without any opposition, and consequently, all those who had aspired to be sharers of his property, balked by my unexpected appearance, immediately withdrew to vent their disappointment in abusing me. They represented me as a wretch, devoid of all respect for my parents, as one without religion, an adventurer in the world, and the companion of *Lûties* and wandering dervishes.

As I had no intention of remaining at Ispahan, I treated their endeavours to hurt me with contempt; and consoled myself by giving them a full return of all their scurrility, by expressions which neither they nor their fathers had ever heard; expressions I had picked up from amongst the illustrious characters with whom I had passed the first years of my youth.

When we were left to ourselves, my mother and I, after having bewailed in sufficiently pathetic language, she the death of a husband, I the loss of a father, the following conversation took place: 'Now tell me, O my mother—for there can be no secrets between us—tell me the state of Kerbelai Hassan's concerns. He loved you, and confided in you, and you must therefore be better acquainted with them than any one else.'

'What do I know of them, my son?' said she, in great haste, and seeming confusion.

I stopped her, to continue my speech. 'You know that according to the law, his heir is bound to pay his debts: they must be ascertained. Then, the expenses of the funeral are to be defrayed; they will be considerable; and at present I am as destitute of means as on the day you gave me birth. To meet all this, money is necessary; or else both mine and my father's name will be disgraced among men, and my enemies will not fail to overcome me. He must have been reputed wealthy, or else his death-bed would never have been surrounded by that host of blood-suckers and time-servers which have been driven away by my presence. You, my mother, must tell me where he was accustomed to deposit his ready cash; who were, or who are, likely to be his debtors; and what might be his possessions, besides those which are apparent.'

'Oh, Allah!' exclaimed she, 'what words are these? Your father was a poor, good man, who had neither money nor possessions. Money, indeed! We had dry bread to eat, and that was all! Now and then, after the arrival of a great caravan, when heads to be shaved were plentiful, and his business brisk, we indulged in our dish of rice, and our skewer of *kabob*, but otherwise we lived like beggars. A bit of bread, a morsel of cheese, an onion, a basin of sour curds—that was our daily fare; and, under these circumstances, can you ask me for money, ready money too? There is this house, which you see and know; then his shop, with its furniture; and when I have said that, I have nearly said all. You are just arrived in time, my son, to step into your father's shoes, and take up his business; and *Inshallah*, please God, may your hand be fortunate! may it never cease wagging, from one year's end to the other!'

'This is very strange!' exclaimed I, in my turn. 'Fifty years, and more, hard and unceasing toil! and nothing to show for it! This is incredible! We must call in the diviners.'

'The diviners?' said my mother, in some agitation; 'of what use can they be? They are only called in when a thief is to be discovered. You will not proclaim your mother a thief, Hajjî, will you? Go, make inquiries of your friend, and your father's friend, the *âkhon*.[1] He is acquainted with the whole of the concerns, and I am sure he will repeat what I have said.'

'You do not speak amiss, mother,' said I. 'The âkhon probably does know what were my father's last wishes, for he appeared to be the principal director in his dying moments; and he may tell me, if money there was left, where it is to be found.'

Accordingly I went straightway to seek the old man, whom I found seated precisely in the very same corner of the little parish mosque, surrounded by his scholars, in which some twenty years before I myself had received his instructions. As soon as he saw me he dismissed his scholars, saying, my footsteps were fortunate, and that others, as well as himself, should partake of the pleasure I was sure to dispense wherever I went.

'Ahi, âkhon,' said I, 'do not laugh at my beard. My good fortune has entirely forsaken me; and even now, when I had hoped that my destiny, in depriving me of my father, had made up the loss by giving me wealth, I am likely to be disappointed, and to turn out a greater beggar than ever.'

'*Allah kerim*, God is merciful,' said the schoolmaster; and, lifting up his eyes to heaven, whilst he placed his hands on his knees, with their palms uppermost, he exclaimed, 'O Allah, whatever is, thou art it.' Then addressing himself to me, he said, 'Yes, my son, such is the world, and such will it ever be, as long as man shuts not up his heart from all human desires. Want nothing, seek nothing, and nothing will seek you.'

'How long have you been a *Sûfi*,' said I, 'that you talk after this manner? I can speak on that subject also, since my evil star led me to Kom, but now I am engrossed with other matters.' I then informed him of the object of my visit, and requested him to tell me what he knew of my father's concerns. Upon this question he coughed, and, making up a face of great wisdom, went through a long string of oaths and professions, and finished by repeating what I had heard from my mother; namely, that he believed my father to have died possessed of no *nagd*, ready cash (for that, after all, was the immediate object of my search); and what his other property was, he reminded me that I knew as well as himself.

I remained mute for some time with disappointment, and then ex-

[1] A mollah who is a schoolmaster is also styled *âkhon*.

pressed my surprise in strong terms. My father, I was aware, was too good a Mussulman to have lent out his money upon interest, for I recollected a circumstance, when I was quite a youth, which proved it. Osman Aga, my first master, wanting to borrow a sum from him, for which he offered an enormous interest, my father put his conscience into the hands of a rigid mollah, who told him that the precepts of the Koran entirely forbade it. Whether since that time he had relaxed his principles, I could not say; but I was assured that he always set his face against the unlawful practice of taking interest, and that he died, as he had lived, a perfect model of a true believer.

I left the mosque in no very agreeable mood, and took my way to the spot where I had made my first appearance in life, namely, my father's shop, turning over in my mind as I went what steps I should take to secure a future livelihood. To remain at Ispahan was out of the question—the place and the inhabitants were odious to me; therefore, it was only left me to dispose of everything that was now my own, and to return to the capital, which, after all, I knew to be the best market for an adventurer like myself. However, I could not relinquish the thought that my father had died possessed of some ready money, and suspicions would haunt my mind, in spite of me, that foul play was going on somewhere or other. I was at a loss to whom to address myself, unknown as I was in the city, and I was thinking of making my case known to the Cadi, when, approaching the gate of the caravanserai, I was accosted by the old capiji. 'Peace be unto you, Aga!' said he; 'may you live many years, and may your abundance increase! My eyes are enlightened by seeing you.'

'Are your spirits so well wound up, Ali Mohamed,' said I in return, 'that you choose to treat me thus? As for the abundance you talk of, 'tis abundance of grief, for I have none other that I know of. Och!' said I, sighing, 'my liver has become water, and my soul has withered up.'

'What news is this?' said the old man. 'Your father (peace be unto him!) is just dead—you are his heir—you are young, and, *Mashallah!* you are handsome—your wit is not deficient—what do you want more?'

'I am his heir, 'tis true; but what of that? what advantage can accrue to me, when I only get an old mud-built house, with some worn-out carpets, some pots and pans and decayed furniture, and yonder shop with a brass basin and a dozen of razors? Let me spit upon such an inheritance.'

'But where is your money, your ready cash, Hajjî? Your father (God be with him!) had the reputation of being as great a niggard of his money as he was liberal of his soap. Everybody knows that he amassed much, and never passed a day without adding to his store.'

'That may be true,' said I; 'but what advantage will that be to me, since I cannot find where it was deposited? My mother says that he had none—the âkhon repeats the same—I am no conjuror to discover the truth. I had it in my mind to go to the Cadi.'

'To the Cadi?' said Ali Mohamed. 'Heaven forbid! Go not to him—you might as well knock at the gate of this caravanserai, when I am absent, as try to get justice from him, without a heavy fee. No, he sells it by the miscal, at a heavy price, and very light weight does he give after all.—He does not turn over one leaf of the Koran, until his fingers have been well plated with gold, and if those who have appropriated your father's sacks are to be your opponents, do not you think that they will drain them into the Cadi's lap, rather than he should pronounce in your favour?'

'What, then, is to be done?' said I. 'Perhaps the diviners might give me some help.'

'There will be no harm in that,' answered the doorkeeper. 'I have known them make great discoveries during my service in this caravan-serai. Merchants have frequently lost their money, and found it again through their means.—It was only in the attack of the Turcomans, when much property was stolen, that they were completely at their wits' end. Ah! that was a strange event. It brought much misery on my head; for some were wicked enough to say that I was their accomplice, and, what is more extraordinary, that you were amongst them, Hajjî!—for it was on account of your name, which the dog's son made use of to induce me to open the gate, that the whole mischief was produced.'

Lucky was it for me, that old Ali Mohamed was very dull of sight, or else he would have remarked strange alterations in my features when he made these observations. However, our conference ended by his promising to send me the most expert diviner of Ispahan; 'a man,' said he, 'who would entice a piece of gold out of the earth, if buried twenty *gez* deep, or even if it was hid in the celebrated well[1] of Kashan.'

---

[1] It is a popular belief, that near the city of Kashan there exists a well, of fabulous depth, at the bottom of which are found enchanted groves and gardens.

CHAPTER L: SHOWING THE STEPS
HE TAKES TO DISCOVER HIS PROPERTY, AND THE
IDENTITY OF THE DIVINER, TEEZ NEGAH

THE next morning, soon after the first prayers, a little man came into my room, whom I soon discovered to be the diviner. He was a humpback, with an immense head, with eyes so wonderfully brilliant, and a countenance so intelligent, that I felt he could look through and through me at one glance. He wore a dervish's cap, from under which flowed a profusion of jet black hair, which, added to a thick bush of a beard, gave an imposing expression to his features. His eyes, which by a quick action of his eyelid (whether real or affected, I know not) twinkled like stars, made the monster, who was not taller than a good bludgeon, look like a little demon.

He began by questioning me very narrowly; made me relate every circumstance of my life—particularly since my return to Ispahan—inquired who were my father's greatest apparent friends and associates, and what my own suspicions led me to conclude. In short, he searched into every particular, with the same scrutiny that a doctor would in tracing and unravelling an intricate disorder.

When he had well pondered over every thing that I had unfolded, he then required to be shown the premises, which my father principally inhabited. My mother having gone that morning to the bath, I was enabled, unknown to her, to take him into her apartments, where he requested me to leave him to himself, in order that he might obtain a knowledge of the localities necessary to the discoveries which he hoped to make. He remained there a full quarter of an hour, and when he came out requested me to collect those who were in my father's intimacy, and in the habit of much frequenting the house, and that he would return, they being assembled, and begin his operations.

Without saying a word to my mother about the diviner, I requested her to invite her most intimate friends for the following morning, it being my intention to give them a breakfast; and I myself begged the attendance of the âkhon, the capiji, my father's nephew by his first wife, and a brother of my mother, with others who had free entrance into the house.

They came punctually; and when they had partaken of such fare as I could place before them, they were informed of the predicament in which I stood, and that I had requested their attendance to be witnesses to the endeavours of the diviner to discover where my father was wont to keep his money, of the existence of which, somewhere or other, nobody who knew him could doubt. I looked into each man's face as I made this speech, hoping to remark some expression which might throw a light upon my suspicions, but everybody seemed ready to help my investigation, and maintained the most unequivocal innocence of countenance.

At length the dervish, Teez Negah (for that was the name of the conjuror), was introduced, accompanied by an attendant who carried something wrapped up in a handkerchief. Having ordered the women in the anderûn to keep themselves veiled, because they would probably soon be visited by men, I requested the dervish to begin his operations.

He first looked at every one present with great earnestness, but more particularly fixed his basilisk eyes upon the âkhon, who evidently could not stand the scrutiny, but exclaimed '*Allah il Allah!*—there is but one God'—stroked down his face and beard, and blew first over one shoulder and then over the other, by way of keeping off the evil spirit. Some merriment was raised at his expense; but he did not appear to be in a humour to meet any one's jokes.

After this, the dervish called to his attendant, who from the handker-chief drew forth a brass cup, of a plain surface, but written all over with quotations from the Koran, having reference to the crime of stealing, and defrauding the orphan of his lawful property. He was a man of few words, and simply saying, 'In the name of Allah, the All-wise, and All-seeing,' he placed the cup on the floor, treating it with much reverence, both in touch and in manner.

He then said to the lookers-on, '*Inshallah*, it will lead us at once to the spot where the money of the deceased Kerbelai Hassan (may God show him mercy!) is or was deposited.'

We all looked at each other, some with expressions of incredulity, others with unfeigned belief, when he bent himself towards the cup, and with little shoves and pats of his hand he impelled it forwards, exclaiming all the time, 'See, see, the road it takes. Nothing can stop it. It will go, in spite of me. *Mashallah, Mashallah!*'

We followed him, until he reached the door of the harem, where we knocked for admittance. After some negotiation it was opened, and there we found a crowd of women (many of whom had only loosely thrown on their veils) waiting with much impatience to witness the feats which this wonderful cup was to perform.

'Make way,' said the diviner to the women who stood in his path, as he took his direction towards a corner of the court, upon which the windows of the room opened—'Make way; nothing can stop my guide.'

A woman, whom I recognized to be my mother, stopped his progress several times, until he was obliged to admonish her, with some bitterness, to keep clear of him.

'Do not you see,' said he, 'we are on the Lord's business? Justice will be done, in spite of the wickedness of man.'

At length he reached a distant corner, where it was plain that the earth had been recently disturbed, and there he stopped.

'*Bismillah*, in the name of Allah,' said he, 'let all present stand around me, and mark what I do.' He dug into the ground with his dagger, clawed the soil away with his hands, and discovered a place in which were the remains of an earthen vessel, and the marks near it of there having been another.

'Here,' said he, 'here the money was, but is no more.' Then taking up his cup, he appeared to caress it, and make much of it, calling it his little uncle and his little soul.

Every one stared. All cried out, '*ajaib*, wonderful'; and the little hump-back was looked upon as a supernatural being.

The capiji, who was accustomed to such discoveries, was the only one who had the readiness to say, 'But where is the thief? You have shown us where the game lay, but we want you to catch it for us:—the thief and the money, or the money without the thief—that is what we want.'

'Softly, my friend,' said the dervish to the capiji, 'don't jump so soon from the crime to the criminal. We have a medicine for every disorder, although it may take some time to work.'

He then cast his eyes upon the company present, twinkling them all the while in quick flashes, and said, 'I am sure every one here will be happy to be clear of suspicion, and will agree to what I shall propose. The operation is simple, and soon over.'

'*Elbetteh*, certainly'; '*Belli*, yes'; '*Een che harf est?* what word is this?' was heard to issue from every mouth, and I requested the dervish to proceed.

He called again to his servant, who produced a small bag, whilst he again took the cup under his charge.

'This bag,' said the diviner, 'contains some old rice. I will put a small handful of it into each person's mouth, which they will forthwith chew. Let those who cannot break it, beware, for Eblis is near at hand.'

Upon this, placing us in a row, he filled each person's mouth with rice, and all immediately began to masticate. Being the complainant, of course I was exempt from the ordeal; and my mother, who chose to make common cause with me, also stood out of the ranks. The quick-sighted dervish would not allow of this, but made her undergo the trial with the rest, saying, 'The property we seek is not yours, but your son's. Had he been your husband, it would be another thing.' She agreed to his request, though with bad grace, and then all the jaws were set to wagging, some looking upon it as a good joke, others thinking it a hard trial to the nerves. As fast as each person had ground his mouthful, he called to the dervish, and showed the contents of his mouth.

All had now proved their innocence excepting the âkhon and my mother. The former, whose face exhibited the picture of an affected cheerfulness with great nervous apprehension, kept mumbling his rice, and turning it over between his jaws, until he cried out in a querulous tone, 'Why do you give me this stuff to chew? I am old, and have no teeth:—it is impossible for me to reduce the grain'; and then he spat it out.—My mother, too, complained of her want of power to break the hard rice, and did the same thing. A silence ensued, which made us all look with more attention than usual upon them, and it was only broken by a time-server of my mother, an old woman, who cried out, 'What child's play is this? Who has ever heard of a son treating his mother with this disrespect, and his old school-master, too? Shame, shame!—let us go—he is probably the thief himself.'

Upon this the dervish said, 'Are we fools and asses, to be dealt with in this manner? Either there was money in that corner, or there was not—either there are thieves in the world, or there are not. This man and this woman,' pointing to the âkhon and my mother, 'have not done that which all the rest have done. Perhaps they say the truth, they are old, and can-not break the hard grain. Nobody says that they stole the money—they themselves know that best,' said he, looking at them through and through; 'but the famous diviner, Hezarfun, he who was truly called the bosom friend to the Great Bear, and the confidant of the planet Saturn,—he who could tell all that a man has ever thought, thinks, or will think,—he hath said that the trial by rice among cowards was the best of all tests of a man's honesty. Now, my friends, from all I have remarked, none of you are slayers of lions, and fear is easily produced among you. However, if you doubt my skill in this instance, I will propose a still easier trial—one which commits nobody, which works like a charm upon the mind, and makes the thief come forward of his own accord, to ease his conscience and purse of its ill-gotten wealth, at one and the same time. I propose the *Hâk reezî*, or the heaping up earth. Here in this corner I will make a mound, and will pray so fervently this very night, that, by the blessing of Allah, the Hajjî,' pointing to me, 'Will find his money buried in it to-mor-row at this hour. Whoever is curious, let them be present, and if some-thing be not discovered, I will give him a miscal of hair from my beard.'

He then set to work, and heaped up earth in a corner, whilst the look-ers on loitered about, discussing what they had just seen; some examining me and the dervish as children of the evil spirit, whilst others again began to think as much of my mother and the schoolmaster. The company then dispersed, most of them promising to return the following morning, at the appointed time, to witness the search into the heap of earth.

CHAPTER LI: OF THE DIVINER'S SUCCESS
IN MAKING DISCOVERIES AND OF THE RESOLUTION
WHICH HAJJI BABA TAKES IN CONSEQUENCE

I MUST own that I began now to look upon the restoration of my property as hopeless. The diviner's skill had certainly discovered that money had been buried in my father's house, and he had succeeded in raising ugly suspicions in my mind against two persons whom I felt it to be a sin to suspect; but I doubted whether he could do more.

However, he appeared again on the following morning, accompanied by the capiji, and by several of those who had been present at the former scene. The âkhon, however, did not appear, and my mother was also absent, upon pretext of being obliged to visit a sick friend. We proceeded in a body to the mound, and the dervish having made a holy invocation, he approached it with a sort of mysterious respect.

'Now we shall see,' said he, 'whether the Gins and the Peris have been at work this night'; and exclaiming *'Bismillah!'* he dug into the earth with his dagger.

Having thrown off some of the soil, a large stone appeared, and having disengaged that, to the astonishment of all, and to my extreme delight, a canvas bag well filled was discovered.

'Oh my soul! oh my heart!' exclaimed the humpback, as he seized upon the bag, 'you see that the Dervish Teez Negah is not a man to lose a hair of his beard. There, there,' said he, putting it into my hand, 'there is your property: go, and give thanks that you have fallen into my hands, and do not forget my *hak sai*, or my commission.'

Everybody crowded round me, whilst I broke open the wax that was affixed to the mouth of the bag, upon which I recognized the impression of my father's seal; and eagerness was marked on all their faces as I untied the twine with which it was fastened. My countenance dropped wofully when I found that it only contained silver, for I had made up my mind to see gold. Five hundred *reals*[1] was the sum of which I became the

---

[1] A real is about two shillings—eight reals one tomaun.

possessor; out of which I counted fifty, and presented them to the ingenious discoverer of them. 'There,' said I, 'may your house prosper! If I
were rich I would give you more: and although this is evidently but a
small part of what my father (God be with him!) must have accumulated,
still again I say, may your house prosper, and many sincere thanks to you.'

The dervish was satisfied with my treatment of him, and took his
leave, and I was soon after left by the rest of the company—the capiji
alone remaining. 'Famous business we have made of it this morning,' said
he. 'Did I not say that these diviners performed wonders?'

'Yes,' said I, 'yes, it is wonderful, for I never thought his operations
would have come to anything.'

Impelled by a spirit of cupidity, now that I had seen money glistening
before me, I began to complain that I had received so little, and again expressed to Ali Mohamed my wish of bringing the case before the Cadi;
'for,' said I, 'if I am entitled to these five hundred reals, I am entitled to
all my father left; and you will acknowledge that this must be but a very
small part of his savings.'

'Friend,' said he, 'listen to the words of an old man. Keep what you
have got, and be content. In going before the Cadi, the first thing you
will have to do will be to give of your certain, to get at that most cursed
of all property, the uncertain. Be assured that after having drained you of
your four hundred and fifty reals, and having got five hundred from your
opponents, you will have the satisfaction to hear him tell you both to "go
in peace, and do not trouble the city with your disputes." Have you not
lived long enough in the world to have learnt this common saying—"Every one's teeth are blunted by acids, except the Cadi's, which are by
sweets"?

'The Cadi who takes five cucumbers as a bribe, will admit any evidence for ten beds of melons.'

After some deliberation, I determined to take the advice of the capiji;
for it was plain that if I intended to prosecute any one, it could only be
my mother and the âkhon; and to do that, I should raise such a host of
enemies, and give rise to such unheard-of-scandal, that perhaps I should
only get stoned by the populace for my pains.

'I will dispose of everything I have at Ispahan,' said I to my adviser,
'and, having done that, will leave it never to return, unless under better

circumstances. It shall never see me more,' exclaimed I, in a vapouring fit, 'unless I come as one having authority.'

Little did I think, when I made this vain speech, how diligently my good stars were at work to realize what it had expressed.

The capiji applauded my intention; the more so, as he took some little interest that my resolutions should be put into practice; for he had a son, a barber, whom he wished to set up in business; and what could be more desirable, in every respect, than to see him installed in the shop in which my poor father had flourished so successfully, close to his post at the caravanserai?

He made proposals that I should dispose of the shop and all its furniture to him, which I agreed to do, upon the evaluation of some well-known brother of the strap, and thus I was relieved of one of my remaining cares.

As for my father's house and furniture, notwithstanding my feelings at the recent conduct of my mother, I determined, by way of acquiring a good name (of which I was very much in want), to leave her in full possession of them, reserving to myself the *temesoûts*, or deeds, which constituted me its lawful owner.

All being settled and agreed upon, I immediately proceeded to work. I received five hundred piastres from the capiji for my shop; for he also had been a great accumulator of his savings, and everybody allowed that money was never laid out to better advantage, since the shop was sure to enjoy a great run of business, owing to its excellent situation. I therefore became worth in all about one hundred and ten tomauns in gold, a coin into which I changed my silver, for the greater facility which it gave me of carrying it about my person. Part of this I laid out in clothes, and part in the purchase of a mule, with its necessary furniture. I gave the preference to a mule, because, after mature deliberation, I had determined to abandon the character of a *sahib shemshir*, or a man of the sword, in which, for the most part, I had hitherto appeared in life, and adopt that of a *sahib calem*, or a man of the pen, for which, after my misfortunes, and the trial which I had in some measure made of it at Kom, I now felt a great predilection.

'It will not suit me, now, to be bestriding a horse,' said I to myself, 'armed, as I used to be, at all points, with sword by my side, pistols in my girdle, and a carbine at my back. I will neither deeply indent my cap, and place it on one side, as before, with my long curls dangling behind my ears, but wind a shawl round it, which will give me a new character; and, moreover, clip the curls, which will inform the world that I have renounced it and its vanities. Instead of pistols, I will stick a roll of papers in my girdle; and, in lieu of a cartouche-box, sling a Koran across my person. Besides, I will neither walk on the tips of my toes, nor twist about my body, nor screw up my waist, nor throw my shoulders forward, nor swing my hands to and fro before me, nor in short take upon myself any of the airs of a *kasheng*, of a beau, in which I indulged when sub-deputy to the chief executioner. No; I will, for the future, walk with my back bent, my head slouching, my eyes looking on the ground, my hands stuck either in front of my girdle, or hanging perpendicular down my sides, and my feet shall drag one after the other, without the smallest indication of a strut. Looking one's character is all in all; for if, perchance, I happen to say a foolish thing, it will be counted as wisdom, when it comes from a mortified looking face, and a head bound round with a mollah's shawl, particularly when it is accompanied with a deep sigh, and an exclamation of *Allah ho Akbar!* or *Allah, Allah il Allah!* and if, perchance, I am brought face to face with a man of real learning, and am called upon to sustain my character, I have only to look wise, shut my lips, and strictly keep my own counsel. Besides, I can read; and, with the practice that I intend to adopt, it will not be long before I shall be able to write a good hand:—that alone, by enabling me to make a copy of the Koran, will entitle me to the respect of the world.'

With reflections such as these I passed my time until it was necessary to decide whither I should bend my steps.—Everything told me that I ought to make the most of the good impression which I had left behind me, on the minds of the mûshtehed of Kom and his disciples, for he was the most likely person to help me in my new career: he might recommend me to some mollah of his acquaintance, who would take me as his scribe or his attendant, and teach me the way that I should go.—Besides, I left him so abruptly when through his means I had been released from my confinement in the sanctuary, that I felt I had a debt of gratitude still to pay. 'I will take him a present,' said I; 'he shall not say that I am unmindful of his goodness.' Accordingly I turned over in my thoughts what I ought to present, when I again determined upon a praying-carpet, which I forthwith purchased; reflecting, at the same time, that it would make a comfortable seat, when duly folded, on the top of my mule's pad.

I had now nearly finished all that I had to do, previous to my departure. I was equipped ready for my journey, and I flattered myself that my outward appearance was that of a rigid mollah. I did not take upon myself the title of one, but rather left that to circumstances; but, in the meanwhile, the epithet of Hajjî, which had been given to me as a pet name when I was a child, now came very opportunely to my assistance, to aid me to sustain my new character.

One duty I still had to accomplish, and that was to pay the expenses of my father's funeral. I do own that, cheated as I had been of my lawful patrimony, I felt it hard that such an expense should fall upon me; and several times had planned a departure from Ispahan unknown to anybody, in order that the burden might fall upon the âkhon and my mother, to whom I had intended the honour of payment; but my better feelings got the mastery, and reflecting that by acting thus I should render myself fully entitled to the odious epithet of *peder sukhtêh*[1] (one whose father is burnt), without further combat, I went round to each of the attendants, namely, mollahs, mourners, and washers of the dead, and paid them their dues.

CHAPTER LII: HAJJI BABA QUITS HIS MOTHER AND BECOMES THE SCRIBE TO A CELEBRATED MAN OF THE LAW

I TOOK leave of my mother without much regret, and she did not increase the tenderness of our parting by any great expression of sorrow. She had her plans, I had mine; and, considering how we stood circumstanced, the less we ran in each other's way the better.

I mounted my mule at break of day, and, ere the sun had past its meridian, was already considerably advanced on my road to Kom. I loitered but little on my journey, notwithstanding the pleasures which a halt at Kashan might have afforded me, and on the ninth day I once again saw the gilded cupola of the tomb of Fatimeh.

Alighting at a small caravanserai in the town, I saw my mule well provided, and then, with my present to the mûshtehed under my arm, I pro-

---

[1] *Peder sukhtêh* is the most common term of abuse in a Persian's mouth. It implies 'one whose father is burning in eternal fires.'

ceeded to his house. His door was open to every one, for he made no parade of servants to keep the stranger in awe, as may be seen at the houses of the great in Persia; and, leaving my carpet at the door with my shoes, I entered the room, in one corner of which I found the good man seated.

He immediately recognized me, and, giving me a welcome reception, he desired me to seat myself, which I did, with all proper respect, at the very edge of the felt carpet.

He asked me to relate the history of my adventures since I left Kom, for he professed himself interested in my fate; and, having made him all the necessary acknowledgments for procuring my release from the sanctuary, I related all that had befallen me. I also told him what a calling I felt within me to devote myself to a holy life, and entreated his help to procure me some situation in which I might show my zeal for the interests of the true faith.

He reflected for a moment, and said, 'that very morning he had received a letter from one of the principal men of the law of Tehran, the Mollah Nadân, who was much in want of one who would act as half scribe and half servant; one, in short, who might be of good materials for a future mollah, and whom he would instruct in all that was necessary in that vocation.'

My heart leaped within me when I heard this, for it was precisely the place that my imagination had created. 'Leave it to me,' thought I, 'to become a whole mollah, when once I have been made half a one.'

Without hesitation I entreated the mûshtehed to continue his good offices in my behalf, which he promised to do; and forthwith addressed a small note, with his own hand, to the Mollah Nadân. This he sealed, and, having duly fashioned it in its proper shape with his scissors, rolled it up and delivered it to me; saying, 'Proceed to Tehran immediately; no doubt you will find the place vacant, and the mollah willing to appoint you to fill it.'

I was so happy that I kissed the good man's hand and the hem of his garment, making him thousands of acknowledgments for his goodness.

'I have one more favour to ask of my master,' said I, 'which is, that he will deign to accept a small *peishkesh*, a present from his humble slave; it is a praying-carpet, and, should he honour him so far as to use it, he hopes that now and then he will not forget the donor in his prayers.'

'May your house prosper, Hajjî,' said he very graciously, 'and I am thankful to you for remembering me, not that there was the least occasion for this present. Be a good Mussulman, wage war against the infidels, and stone the Sûfis,—that is the only return I ask; and be assured that, by so doing, you will always find a place in my memory.'

I then presented my gift, with which he seemed much pleased; and, having received my dismissal, I returned to my caravanserai, in the determination of pursuing my road to the capital as fast as I could. I did not even give myself time to call upon my other friends at Kom, or even to take a look at my former unhappy cell in the sanctuary; but, saddling my mule, I pushed on to the caravanserai of the *Pûl-i-dallâk* that very night.

I reached Tehran in the evening, and, in order not to see the spot in which the unfortunate Zeenab was buried, I made a deviation from my straight road, and entered by the Casbin gate. I was happy to remark that I was not recognized by the guards, who, when I was in office, were accustomed to show themselves on the alert at my approach. But indeed it was not surprising that the active, bustling, imperious nasakchi should not be known under the garb of the would-be humble and insignificant priest; so for the present I felt secure in my disguise, and I boldly took my way through the bazaars and the most public places of the city, where formerly nothing but my face was to be seen; and happy was I to find that no one recollected me. I inquired my way to the house of the Mollah Nadân, which was speedily pointed out, for he was a well-known character; but, on second thoughts, I deemed it more prudent and convenient to put up at a small caravanserai, situated near the house of my new master, than to present myself, late in the day as it then was, to him, upon whom it was my interest, by my looks and appearance, to produce the best possible impression.

Having taken good care of my mule, I slept soundly after the fatigues of the journey; and the next morning I repaired to the bath, where, having given a fresh tinge to my beard, and plentifully used the khena to my hands and feet, I flattered myself that in appearance I was precisely the sort of person likely to meet with success.

The mollah's house was situated between the royal mosque and the quarters of the camel artillerymen, and near to the entrance of the bazaar, which, leading by the gate of the said mosque, opens at its other extremity immediately on the ditch of the Shah's palace. It had a mean front; although, having once passed through the gate, the small court-yard which immediately succeeded was clean, and well watered; and the room which looked into it, though only whitewashed, had a set of carpets, which did not indicate wealth, but still spoke the absence of poverty.

In this room was seated a wan and sickly-looking priest, whom I took to be the master of the house; but I was mistaken—he was in his anderûn, and I was told that he would shortly make his appearance.

In order to make known my pretensions to being something more than a servant, I sat down, and entered into conversation with the priest, who, from what I could pick from him, was a dependent upon the mollah. He, in his turn, endeavoured to discover what my business could be; but he did not so well succeed, although the strange and mysterious questions which he put drew forth my astonishment.

'You are evidently newly arrived in Tehran?' said he.

'Yes, at your service,' said I.

'You intend probably to make some stay?' added he.

'That is not quite certain,' said I.

Then, after a pause, he said, 'It is dull living alone, even for a week, and Tehran is a city full of enjoyment. If there is any service that I can perform, I will do it—upon my eyes, be it.'

'May your kindness never be less! My business is with the Mollah Nadân.'

'There is no difference between him and me,' said he. 'I can facilitate any business you may have; and, praise be to Allah, you will be served to your heart's content. We have at our disposal of all sorts and all prices.'

'I am not a merchant,' said I.

'There is no necessity to be a merchant,' said he; 'it is enough that you are a man and a stranger. You will find, be it for a year, a month, a week, a day, or even an hour, that you will pass your time agreeably; upon my head be it.'

I became more and more puzzled at his meaning, and was on the point of asking him to enlighten my understanding, when the Mollah Nadân, in person, entered the room.

He was a tall handsome man, about forty years of age, with a jet-black beard, glossy with fresh dye, and with fine brilliant eyes, painted with the powder of antimony. He wore on his head an immense turban of white muslin, whilst a *hirkeh*, or Arab cloak, with broad stripes of white and brown alternately, was thrown over his shoulders. Although his athletic person was better suited to the profession of arms than to that of the law, yet his countenance had none of the frankness of the soldier, but on the contrary bespoke cunning and design, while at the same time it announced good humour.

I got up at his approach, and immediately presented my note from the mûshtehed, whilst I did not venture again to sit.—Having unrolled it, he looked at me and then at it, as if to divine what could be my business; but as soon as he had deciphered the seal, his face expanded into a bright smile, and he requested me to be seated.

'You are welcome,' said he; and then he asked me a series of questions concerning the health of the holy man, which I freely answered, as if intimately acquainted with him. He read the note with great attention, but said not a word of its contents. He then began to make apologies for not having a *kalian* (a pipe) to offer me, 'for,' said he, 'I am not a smoker of tobacco. We, who rigidly uphold the true faith, reject all such luxuries, and mortify our senses. Our Holy Prophet (upon whom be blessings and peace!) has forbidden to his followers whatever intoxicates; and although tobacco be almost universally used throughout Persia as well as Turkey, yet it is known sometimes to obscure the understanding, and therefore I abstain from it.'

He continued to talk about himself, his fasts, his penance, and his self-mortification, until I began to think that I should pass my time but so so in his house, nor enjoy the delights the priest had just before promised me; but when I compared his healthy and rubicund face, his portly and well-fed body, to the regimen which he professed to keep, I consoled myself by the hope that he allowed great latitude in his interpretation of the law; and perhaps that I should find, like the house which he inhabited, which had its public and private apartments, that his own exterior was fitted up for the purposes of the world, whilst his interior was devoted to himself and his enjoyments.

CHAPTER LIII: THE MOLLAH NADAN GIVES AN ACCOUNT OF HIS NEW SCHEME FOR RAISING MONEY AND FOR MAKING MEN HAPPY

WHEN left to ourselves (for the priest soon after quitted the room), Mollah Nadân, taking the mûshtehed's note from his breast, said, that he should be happy to receive me in his service upon so good a recommendation; and having questioned me upon my qualifications, I gave such answers, that he expressed himself satisfied.

'I have long been seeking a person of your character,' said he, 'but hitherto without success. He, who has just left us, has assisted me in my several duties; but he is too much of a *napak* (an intriguer) for my purpose. I want one who will look upon my interests as his own, who will eat his bit of bread with me and be satisfied, without taking a larger share than his due.'

In answer to this, I informed the mollah that although I had already seen much of the world, yet he would find in me a faithful servant, and one ready to inbibe his principles; for (as I had already explained to the mûshtehed) my mind was made up to leading a new life, and endeavouring under his direction to become the mirror of a true Mussulman.

'In that,' said the mollah, 'esteem yourself as the most fortunate of men; for I am looked up to as the pattern of the followers of the blessed Mahomed. In short, I may be called a living Koran. None pray more regularly than I. No one goes to the bath more scrupulously, nor abstains more rigidly from everything that is counted unclean. You will find neither silk in my dress, nor gold on my fingers. My ablutions are esteemed the most complete of any man's in the capital, and the mode of my abstersion the most in use. I neither smoke nor drink wine before men; neither do I play at chess, at *gengifeh* (cards), or any game which, as the law ordains, abstracts the mind from holy meditation. I am esteemed the model of fasters;

and during the Ramazan give no quarter to the many hungry fellows who come to me under various pretexts, to beg a remission of the strictness of the law. "No," do I say to them, "die rather than eat, or drink, or smoke. Do like me, who, rather than abate one tittle of the sacred ordinance, would manage to exist from *Jumah* to *Jumah* (Friday) without polluting my lips with unlawful food."'

Although I did not applaud his tenacity about fasting, yet I did not fail to approve all he said, and threw in my exclamations so well in time, that I perceived he became almost as much pleased with me as he appeared to be with himself.

'From the same devotedness to religion,' continued he, 'I have ever abstained from taking to myself a wife, and in that respect I may be looked upon as exceeding even the perfection of our Holy Prophet; who (blessings attend his beard!) had wives and women slaves, more even than *Sûleiman ibn Daoud* himself. But although I do not myself marry, yet I assist others in doing so; and it is in that particular branch of my duty in which I intend more especially to employ you.'

'By my eyes,' said I, 'you must command me; for hitherto I am ignorant as the Turk in the fields.'

'You must know then,' said he, 'that, to the scandal of religion, to the destruction of the law, the commerce of *cowlies*, or courtezans, had acquired such ascendancy in this city, that wives began to be esteemed as useless. Men's houses were ruined, and the ordinances of the Prophet disregarded.

The Shah, who is a pious prince, and respects the Ullemah, and who holds the ceremony of marriage sacred, complained to the head of the law, the Mollah Bashi, of this subversion of all morality in his capital, and, with a reprimand for his remissness, ordered him to provide a remedy for the evil. The Mollah Bashi (between you and me, be it said) is in every degree an ass—one who knows as much of religion and its duties, as of Frangistân and its kings. But I, I, who am the Mollah Nadân,—I suggested a scheme in which the convenience of the public and the ordinances of the law are so well combined, that both may be suited without hindrance to either. You know it is lawful among us to marry for as long or as short a time as may be convenient; and in that case the woman is called *mûtî*. "Why then," said I to the chief priest, "why not have a sufficient number of such-like wives in store, for those who know not where to seek for a companion? The thing is easy to be done, and Nadân the man to do it."

'The Mollah Bashi, who, though the cream of blockheads in all other cases, is very quick-sighted when his interest is concerned, caught at my idea, for he foresaw a great harvest of gain for himself.—He consequently acquired possession of several small houses of little value, in which he has installed a certain number of women, who, through his interference, are married, in the character and with the privileges of mûties, to whoever is ambitious of such a marriage; and as both parties on such occasion pay him a fee, he has thus very considerably increased his revenues. So eagerly do the people marry, that he has several mollahs at work, wholly engaged in

reading the marriage ceremony. He has entirely excluded me from any share in his profits,—I who first suggested the plan; and therefore I am determined to undertake the business myself, and thus add to the public convenience. But we must be secret; for if the Mollah Bashi was to hear of my scheme, he would interpose his authority, overthrow it, and perhaps have me expelled the city.'

During this exposure of the mollah's plans, I began to look at him from head to foot, and to question within myself whether this in fact could be the celebrated pillar of the law, of whom the mûshtehed, good man! had spoken in such high terms. However, I was too new in holy life to permit any scruples against the fitness of such schemes to come across my mind; so I continued to applaud all that Nadân had said, and he continued as follows:

'I have already three women in readiness, established in a small house in the neighbourhood, and it is my intention to employ you in the search of husbands for them. You will frequent the caravanserais, watching the arrival of merchants and other strangers, to whom you will propose marriage, upon easier terms than the chief priest can offer, and according to the riches of the bridegroom you will exact a proportionate fee. I shall not give you any wages, because you will have opportunities of acquiring such knowledge from me, that in time you may become a mollah yourself, and show the road to all true believers in the practices of their duty. You will find everything provided for you in my house; and, now and then, opportunities will offer for putting something honestly into your pocket. Whenever my friends come to see me, and when they take their *shâm* (dinner) with me, you will appear as my servant; on other occasions you may sit before me, and act as my scribe.'

The mollah here finished speaking, in the expectation of hearing what I should say in answer; but I was so bewildered by this vast field of action that he had opened to my view, that it took me some minutes to recollect myself. I, who had expected to lead the life of a recluse, to sit in a corner all the day long, reading my Koran, or mumbling prayers—to frequent lectures in the *medressehs* (schools), and homilies in the mosques,—I, in short, who in my master expected to have found a despiser of this world's goods, and full of no other care than that of preparing for the next,—of a sudden was called upon to engage more deeply in the business of life than before, and to follow the footsteps of a man who seemed to exist for no other purpose than to amass wealth, and acquire consideration. 'However, I can but try,' thought I. My circumstances were too desperate to admit of much hesitation; and, after all, to be the pupil of one of the most celebrated men of the capital, was a situation not to be despised; and so I accepted of the mollah's offer.

He then told me that we should soon have some further conversation, which, for the present, he was obliged to defer, because he was called upon to attend the chief of the law; but, before he went, he mentioned, that as he abstained from worldly pomp, he kept no servants but such as were absolutely necessary. His establishment consisted of a cook, and a servant who acted in the triple capacity of head-servant, valet, and groom; and his stud, for the present, was composed of one ass. 'After considerable trouble,' said he, 'I have managed to procure a white one, which, you know, is an animal that confers consideration on its rider; but, as my business and my dignity increase, I intend to promote myself to a mule.' I did not lose this opportunity of informing him that I had a very good one to dispose of; and, after some negotiation, it was decided that we should keep both mule and ass; he, as the dignitary, riding the former, whilst I should be carried about on the humbler beast.

CHAPTER LIV: HAJJI BABA BECOMES A PROMOTER
OF MATRIMONY AND OF THE REGISTER HE KEEPS

PREPARATORY to the full comprehension of the duties of my office, the Mollah Nadân requested me to introduce myself to the mûties, and gain from them sufficient information to enable me to make a register, in which I should insert their ages, appearance and beauty, tempers, and general qualifications as wives. This I should carry about me, in order to be able to exhibit it to any stranger who might fall in my way.

I first went to the bazaar, and furnished myself with a priest's cloak, with a coat that buttons across the breast, and a long piece of white muslin, which I twisted round my head. Thus accoutred, in the full dress of my new character, I proceeded to the women's house, and found a ready admission, for they had been apprised of my intended visit.

I found them all three seated in a mean and wretched apartment, smoking. Their veils were loosely thrown over their heads, which, upon my appearance, by a habit common to all our women, they drew tight over their faces, merely keeping one eye free.

'Peace be unto you, khanums!' said I (for I knew how an appearance of great respect conciliates)—'I am come, on the part of the Mollah Nadân, to make you a tender of my humble services; and perhaps, as you know the object of my visit, you will not object to lay your veils on one side.'

'May you abide in peace,' said they, 'mollah!' and then gave me to understand, by many flattering speeches, that I was welcome, and that they hoped my presence would bring them good luck.

Two of them immediately unveiled, and discovered faces which had long bade adieu to their lilies and roses; and upon which, notwithstanding the help of the *surmeh* round the eyelids, the blue stars on the forehead and chin, and the rouge on the cheeks, I could, in broad characters, make out a long catalogue of wrinkles. The third lady carefully continued to keep herself veiled.

I did not hesitate to make an exclamation of surprise, as soon as the two charmers had opened their battery of smiles upon me. 'Praises to Allah! *Mashallah!*' said I, 'this is a sight worthy of Ferhad himself. Do not look too intensely upon me, for fear that I consume. What eyes! what noses! what lips! Have pity upon me, and cease looking. But why,' said I, 'does this khanum'—(pointing to the unveiled one)—'why does she hold me so long in suspense? Perhaps she thinks me unworthy of contemplating her charms; and she thinks right, for I am only a poor mollah, whilst doubtless even the sun, in all its majesty, is not entitled to such privilege.'

'Why do you make this *naz* (coyness),' said her companions to her; 'you know he must be able to give an account of us, or else the curse of single life will be our fate, and we shall remain the scorn and reproach of womankind.'

'Be it so,' said the third woman; 'the cat must come from under the blanket'; and, in a sort of pet, she drew off her veil, and, to my great astonishment, exhibited to my view the well-known features of the wife of the Shah's physician, my former master.

'By all that is most sacred! by the beard of the blessed Prophet!' said I, 'how is this? Are the Gins at work, that they should have brought this about?'

'Yes, Hajjî,' said she, very composedly, 'fate is a wonderful thing. But you, you who killed my husband, how came you to be a mollah?'

'Is your husband dead, then,' said I, 'that you talk to me thus? Why do you throw words away in this unguarded manner? What have I to do with your husband's death? He was once my master, and I grieve for his loss. But you might as well say that I killed the martyr Hossein (blessings on his memory!) as that I killed the hakîm. Tell me what has happened; for I am walking round and round in the labyrinth of ignorance.'

'Why do you pretend ignorance,' said she with her usual scream, 'when you must know that it was on your account that the Shah sent Zeenab out of this world—that her death led to the doctor having his beard plucked—that having his beard plucked brought on his disgrace—and his disgrace death?—therefore you are the cause of all the mischief.'

'What ashes are you heaping upon my head, O khanum?' said I with great vehemence; 'why am I to be told that I am the death of a man, when I was a hundred parasangs off at the time? You might as well say, if your husband had died of a surfeit, that the labourer who had planted the rice was the cause of his death.'

We continued to argue for some time, when the other women, fearing that their interests would be neglected, interposed, and put me in mind that we had business to transact; for they were anxious that their charms should no longer lie barren and neglected. The khanum, too, who only talked for talking's sake, and who, to my knowledge, had cherished a more than common hatred for her husband, seemed anxious that I should forget her former more flourishing situation, and requested me to proceed to business.

Still, to carry on the farce of respect, I began first with the doctor's widow, and requested to know some of the particulars of her history; in order, when I came to describe her to some impatient bridegroom, I might be able to do so in the best manner for her interests.

'You know as well as I,' said she, 'that I once enjoyed the favour of that rose in the paradise of sweets, the king of kings; that I was the first beauty in his harem, and the terror of all my rivals. But who can withstand the decrees of destiny? A new woman arrived, who was provided with a more powerful spell than I could possess for securing the Shah's love, and she destroyed my power. She feared my charms so much, that she would not rest until I was expelled; and then, for my misfortune, the Shah made a present of me to his chief physician. Oh, I shall never forget the pangs of my mind, when I was transferred from the glories and delights of the royal palace to the arms of the doctor, and to a residence among physic and galli-pots! I will not repeat all the history of Zeenab. When the hakîm died, I endeavoured to revive the Shah's good feelings towards me; but the ave-nues to his ear were closed; and from one stage of misery to another I, who once could lead the viceregent of Allah by the beard, am reduced to seek a husband in the highway.'

Upon this she began to cry and bemoan her cruel destiny; but I in some measure pacified her, by the assurance that I would do all in my power to procure for her a suitable mate.

'You see', said she, 'that I am still handsome, and that the career of my youth is yet to run. Look at my eyes:—have they lost their brightness? Admire my eyebrows. Where will you meet with a pair that are so com-pletely thrown into one? Then see my waist, it is not a span round.'

She went on in full enumeration of her most minute perfections, upon which I gazed with all my eyes, as she desired; but, instead of youth and beauty, I could make nothing better of her than an old fat and bloated hag, upon whom I longed to revenge myself, for her former ill-treatment to the unfortunate Zeenab.

The other two ladies then gave me a sketch of their lives. One was the widow of a silversmith, who had been blown from a mortar for purloining some gold, which he had received to make a pair of candlesticks for the king; and the other had turned mûti in her own defence, having been aban-doned by her husband, who had fled from the wrath of the Shah, and sought refuge among the Russians.

They also endeavoured to persuade me that they were young and hand-some, to which I agreed with as good a grace as I was able; and, having made the necessary notes in my register, I promised to exert myself to the best for their advantage. 'Recollect', said one, 'that I am only eighteen.' 'Don't forget', said another, 'that I am still a child.' 'Always keep in mind my two eyebrows that look like one,' roared out the hakîm's widow.

'Upon my eyes be it,' exclaimed I, as I left the room; and then I con-soled myself for the sight of such a trio of frights, by giving vent to a peal of anathemas and laughter.

"The cat must come from under the blanket"

CHAPTER LV: OF THE MAN HAJJI BABA
MEETS THINKING HIM DEAD AND OF THE MARRIAGE
WHICH HE BRINGS ABOUT

AVING accomplished this part of my business, I strolled to one of the most frequented caravanserais in the city, to see whether, perchance, some circumstance might not turn up to advance my master's views. As I approached it, I found all the avenues blocked up with mules and camels heavily laden, intermixed with travellers, some of whom wearing a white band, the distinguishing mark of the pilgrims who have visited the tomb of Iman Reza, at Meshed, informed me that the caravan came from the province of Khorassan. I waited to see it gradually unravel from the maze of the narrow streets, and, after a due allowance of wrangling and abuse between the mule and camel drivers, I saw it take up its abode in the square of the building.

'Perhaps', said I, 'my good stars may throw some of my former acquaintance at Meshed into my way'; and I looked at each traveller with great earnestness. It was true that many years had now elapsed since my memorable bastinado, and that time would have made great changes in the appearances of men; but still, I, who knew each face by heart, and had studied its expression as it inhaled my smoke, hoped that my recollection would not fail me.

I had despaired of making a discovery, and was about to walk away, when a certain nose, a certain round back, and a certain projecting paunch, met my eye, and arrested my attention.

'Those forms are familiar to me,' said I; 'they are connected with some of my early ideas; and assuredly are the property of one who is something more than a common acquaintance.' My first master, Osman Aga, came into my mind; but all idea of him I immediately banished, because it was more than certain that he had long since fallen a victim to the horrors of his captivity among the Turcomâns. Still I looked at him, and at every glance I felt convinced it was either he, his brother, or his ghost. I approached to where he was seated, in the hope of hearing him speak; but he seemed to be torpid (which was another characteristic in favour of my suspicion), and I had waited some time in vain, when, to my surprise, I heard him, in a voice well known to my ears, inquire of a merchant who was passing, 'In God's name, what may be the price of lambs' skins at Constantinople?'

'Oh, for once,' said I, 'I cannot be mistaken! You can be no one but Osman,'—and I immediately made myself known to him.

He was as slow to believe that it was Hajjî Baba who accosted him, as I had been to make him out Osman Aga.

After our expressions of mutual astonishment had somewhat subsided, we began to survey each other. I discussed the greyness of his beard, and he complimented me upon the beauty and blackness of mine. He talked with great serenity of the lapse of time, and of the nothingness of this world, from which I perceived that his belief in predestination had rather increased than diminished by his misfortunes, and which alone could account for the equanimity with which he had borne them. In his usual concise manner, he related what had befallen him since we last met. He said, that after the first feelings of misery at his captivity had gone by, his time passed more agreeably than he had expected; for he had nothing to do but to sit with the camels, whose nature being of the same calm and philosophic cast as his own, suited his quiet and sedentary habits. His food was indifferent, but then he had excellent water; and the only privation which he seemed to regret was tobacco—a want which long previous habit rendered infinitely painful. Years had run on in this manner, and he had made up his mind to pass the remainder of his life with the camels, when his destiny took another turn, and he once more had the cheering hope of being restored to liberty. One, who gave himself out for a prophet, appeared among the Turcomâns. According to the custom of such personages, he established his influence by pretending to work two or three miracles, and which were received as such by that credulous people. His word became a law. The most celebrated and experienced marauders freely laid their spoils at his feet, and willingly listed under his banner, in whatever enterprise he chose to propose. Osman Aga presented himself before him, asserted his privileges of a *Suni*, and, moreover, of being an *emir*, and at length succeeded in making the impostor procure his liberty without ransom, which he did, in order to advance the glory of the true faith. Once free, he lost no time in proceeding to Meshed, where, to his great good fortune, he met merchants from Bagdad, one of whom being nearly connected to him by marriage, advanced him a small sum of money to trade with. He received encouraging accounts of the state of the Turkish markets for the produce of Bokhara, and thither he proceeded to make his purchases on the spot. Owing to his long residence among the Turcomâns, he had acquired much useful knowledge concerning their manners and customs—particularly on the subject of buying and selling—and this enabled him to trade, with much success, between Bokhara and Persia, until he had gained a sufficient sum to enable his return to his country with advantage. He was now on the road to Constantinople, with several mules laden with the merchandise of Bokhara, Samarcand, and the east of Persia; and having disposed of it there, it was then his intention to return to his native city, Bagdad. He expressed, however, his intention to remain at Tehran until the spring caravan should assemble, in order to enjoy some of the pleasures of an imperial residence, after having lived so long among savages, as he called the Turcomâns, and he inquired from me how he might most agreeably pass his time. My fair charges immediately came into my mind; and recollecting of old that he was a great advocate for the marriage state, I proposed a wife to him without loss of time.

Certainly, thought I, nothing was ever more strongly pronounced than the doctrine of predestination has been in this instance. Here, one of my masters arrives from regions beyond the rising of the sun, to espouse the widow of another of my masters, who dies just at the very nick of time to produce the meeting, which I, who come from the countries of the south, step in to promote.

The hakîm's widow was the fattest of the three, and therefore I made no scruple in proposing her to Osman, who at once acceded to my offer. Softening down the little asperities of her temper, making much of her two eyebrows in one, and giving a general description of her person, suited to the Ottoman taste, I succeeded in giving a very favourable opinion to the bridegroom of his intended.

I then proceeded to inform the Mollah Nadân of my success, who appeared to listen with delight to the adventures of this couple, which I related to him with scrupulous detail. He directed me how to proceed, and informed me, in order to make the marriage lawful, that a *vakeel*, or trustee, must appear on the part of the woman, and another on that of the man. That the woman's vakeel having beforehand agreed upon the terms of the marriage, proceeded to ask the following question of the man's vakeel, in the Arabic tongue.

'Have you agreed to give your soul to me upon such and such conditions?' to which the other answers, 'I have agreed'; and then the parties are held to be lawfully joined together. Nadân himself proposed to officiate on the part of the hakîm's widow, and I on the part of Osman; and it was left to my ingenuity to obtain as large a fee as possible for ourselves, on this happy occasion.

I forthwith communicated the joyful tidings to the khanum, as I still called her, who did not fail to excite the envy of her other companions, for she immediately laid her success to her superior beauty, and to that never-failing object of her care, her two eyebrows in one. She was, as the reader may be allowed to suppose, in great anxiety at her appearance; for she dreaded not being corpulent enough for her Turk, and from what I could judge, rather doubted the brilliancy of her eye, from the great quantity of black paint which she had daubed on her eyelids.

I left her to return to Osman Aga, who, good man, was also arming himself for conquest; and he seemed to think that, owing to his long residence among camels, he might have imbibed so much of their natures as to have become a fit subject for the perfumes of musk and ambergris. Accordingly, he went to the bath, his grey beard was dyed a glossy black; his hands received a golden tinge; and his mustachios were invited to curl upwards towards the corners of his eyes, instead of downwards into his mouth, as they usually had done.

He then arrayed himself in his best, and followed me to the house of the Mollah Nadân, where owing to this change in his appearance, he very well passed off for a man at least ten years younger than he was in reality.

As soon as the parties came in sight of each other, an unconcerned bystander would have been amused with their first glances—he, the bridegroom, endeavouring to discover what he was about to espouse—she, the bride, making play with her veil in such an artful manner as to induce his belief that it concealed celestial charms. But I was too deeply interested in the game to make it matter of amusement. Besides, more than once, a certain fifty ducats that had formerly belonged to Osman, and which I had appropriated to my own use, came into my mind, and made me fear that it also might have a place in his: 'and if', said I, 'he gets displeased and angry, who knows what ashes may not fall upon my head!'

However, they were married; and I believe most truly that he did not succeed in getting one glimpse of his intended until I had pronounced the awful words, 'I agree'; when in his impatience he partly pulled her veil on one side, and I need not say that he was far from fainting with delight.

As soon as he was well satisfied that his charmer was not a Zuleikha, he called me to him, and said, 'Hajjî, I thought that youth, at least, she would have possessed; but she is more wrinkled than any camel. How is this?'

I got out of the scrape as well as I was able, by assuring him that she had once been the flower of the royal harem, and reminded him that nothing had so much to do with marriage as destiny.

'Ah! that destiny', said he, 'is an answer for everything; but be its effects what it may, it can no more make an old hag a young woman, than it can make one and one three.'

Sorely did I fear that he would return his bargain upon our hands; but when he found that it was impossible to expect anything better in a *mutî*, a class of females, who generally were the refuse of womankind—old widows, and deserted wives; and who, rather than live under the opprobrium that single life entails in our Mohamedan countries, would put up with anything that came under the denomination of husband, he agreed to take

her to his home. I expected, like a hungry hawk, who, the instant he is un-
hooded, pounces upon his prey, that Osman as soon as he had got a sight of
his charmer, would have carried her off with impatience; but I was disappointed. He walked leisurely on to his room in the caravanserai, and told
her that she might follow him whenever it suited her convenience.

CHAPTER LVI: SHOWING HOW THE
AMBITION OF THE MOLLAH NADAN INVOLVES BOTH HIM
AND HIS DISCIPLES IN RUIN

UPON a closer acquaintance with my master, the Mollah Nadân, I
found that, besides his being the most covetous of men, he was also
the most ambitious; and that his great and principal object was to become
the chief priest of Tehran. To that he turned all his thoughts, and left nothing untried which might bring him into notice, either as a zealous practiser
of the ordinances of his religion, or a persecutor of those who might be its
enemies. He was the leader in prayer at the principal mosque; he lectured
at the royal *medresseh*, or college; and whenever he could, he encouraged
litigants to appeal to him for the settlement of their disputes. On every occasion, particularly at the festival of the No Rouz, when the whole corps of
mollahs are drawn up in array before the king, to pray for his prosperity,
he always managed to make himself conspicuous by the over-abundance of
adulation which he exhibited, and by making his sonorous voice predominate over that of others.

By such means, he had acquired considerable celebrity among the people,
although those who knew him better held him in no great estimation. An
opportunity soon occurred which abundantly proved this, and which, as I
will now narrate, gave an entire new turn to my fortunes.

The winter had passed over our heads, and spring was already far advanced, when reports reached the capital, that in the southern provinces
of the kingdom, particularly in Lar and Fars, there had been such a total
want of rain that serious apprehensions of a famine were entertained. As
the year rolled on, the same apprehensions prevailed in the more northern
provinces; and a drought, such as before was never known, gave rise to
the most dismal forebodings. The Shah ordered prayers to be put up at all
the mosques in the city for rain, and the Mollah Bashi was very active in

enforcing the order. My master Nadân had there too good an opportunity of manifesting his religious zeal, and of making himself conspicuous by his exertions, not to take advantage of it; and he lost not a moment in giving himself all the stir in his power. Conscious of the influence he had obtained over the populace, he went a step farther than his rival the chief priest, and invited an immense crowd of the lower orders to follow him to a large open space without the city, where he took the lead in prayer.

The drought still continuing, the Shah ordered all ranks of people to attend him, and join in the supplications which he had first commenced. He accounted this so great a triumph, that his zeal now knew no bounds. He caused all sects, Christians, Jews, and Guebres, as well as Mussulmen, to put up their prayers: still the heavens were inexorable; no rain came, the despair increased, and Nadân redoubled his zeal.

At length, one morning when the weather was more than usually sultry, he addressed a mob which he had purposely gathered round his house, in words something to this purpose:

'Is there nothing more to be done, O men of Tehran! to avert this misfortune which awaits the land of Irâk? 'Tis plain that the heavens have declared against us, and that this city contains some, whose vices and crimes must bring the Almighty vengeance upon us. Who can they be but the Kâfirs, the infidels, those transgressors of our law, those wretches, who defile the purity of our walls by openly drinking wine, that liquor forbidden by the holy Prophet (upon whom be blessing and peace!) and by making our streets the scene of their vices? Let us go; follow me to where these odious wine-bibbers live; let us break their jars, and at least destroy one of the causes of the displeasure of Allah against us.'

Upon this a general stir ensued; and fanaticism, such as I never thought could be excited in the breasts of men, broke out in the most angry expressions, which were only the forerunners of the violence that soon after ensued. Nadân, putting himself at the head of the crowd, haranguing as he pressed onwards, and followed by me—who had become as outrageous a fanatic as the rest—led us to the Armenian quarter of the city.

The peaceable Christians, seeing this body of enraged Mohamedans making for their houses, knew not what to do. Some barricaded their doors, others fled, and others again stood transfixed, like men impaled. But they did not long remain in doubt of our intentions; for first they were assailed with volleys of stones, and then with such shouts of execration and abuse, that they expected nothing less than a general massacre to ensue.

The mollah entered the houses of the principal Armenians, followed by the most violent of the mob, and began an active search for wine. He made no distinction between the women's apartments and the public ones, but broke open every door; and when at length he had found the jars in which the liquor was contained, I leave the reader to imagine what was the havoc which ensued. They were broken into a thousand pieces; the wine flowed in every direction; and the poor owners could do nothing but look on and wring their hands.

By the time that this ceremony had been performed in every house, the fury of the mob had risen to the utmost, and from the houses they proceeded to the church, which be-ing forced open, they demolished everything within — books, cruci-fixes, ornaments, furniture—noth-ing was spared; and as there would not be wanting abundance of rogues  on such occasions, it was soon discovered that whatever valuables the despoiled had possessed were carried away.

The ruin was now complete; and nothing more was left to the fury of the mob but the unfortunate sufferers themselves, who perhaps would next have been attacked, had not a king's *ferash* appeared, accompanied by one of the principal Armenians, and their presence produced an almost instan-taneous return to reason.

Apprehensive of the consequences of their conduct, all Nadân's follow-ers made a precipitate retreat, leaving that revered personage and myself to face the king's officer. I presume our feelings will not be much envied when we heard him inform us, that the King of Kings demanded our im-mediate presence. The mollah looked at me, and I at him; and, perhaps, two bearded men never looked more like raw fools than we did at that moment. He endeavoured to temporize, and requested our conductor to accompany him to his house, in order that he might put on his red cloth stockings.

'There will be no occasion for red cloth stockings,' said the ferash, dryly.

This produced a universal tremor in the mollah, and I must own that it communicated itself to me in no agreeable manner. 'But what have I done, in the name of the Prophet?' exclaimed he: 'the enemies of our faith must be overthrown. Is it not so?' said he to the ferash.

'You will see,' returned the impenetrable man of blows.

We at length reached the palace, and at the entrance found the Grand Vizier, seated with the Mollah Bashi, in the chief executioner's apartment.

As we stood at the window, the Grand Vizier said to the Mollah Nadân, 'In the name of Ali, what is this that we hear? Have your wits forsaken you? Do you forget that there is a king in Tehran?'

Then the Mollah Bashi exclaimed, 'And who am I, that you should presume to take the lead against the infidels?'

'Conduct them before the king,' exclaimed the executioner, as he arose and took his staff of office in hand. 'Do not keep the Centre of the Universe waiting.'

More dead than alive, we were paraded through the avenues of the palace, and then stepped through the small low door, which introduced us into the enclosed garden, where we found the king seated in an upper room.

As we approached, I perceived the august monarch twisting his mustachios, which is always esteemed a sign of wrath. I cast a glance at Nadân, and I saw him streaming from every pore. We took our shoes off, as soon as we had come within sight of him, and advanced to the brink of the marble basin of water. The party who stood before the king consisted of the Mollah Bashi, the chief executioner, the Armenian, Nadân, and myself.

The chief executioner then placed his staff of office on the ground, and making a low prostration, said, with all the prefatory form of words usual in addressing the Shah, 'This is the Mollah Nadân, and this his servant,' pointing to me.

'Say, mollah,' said the king, addressing himself to my master in a very composed tone of voice, 'how long is it since you have undertaken to ruin my subjects? Who gave you the power? Have you become a prophet? or do you perhaps condescend to make yourself the king? Say, fellow, what dirt is this that you have been eating?'

The culprit, who on every other occasion never wanted words, here lost all power of utterance. He stammered out a few incoherent sentences about infidels, wine, and the want of rain, and then remained immovable.

'What does he say?' said the king to the Mollah Bashi. 'I have not learnt from whom he claims his authority.'

'May I be your sacrifice,' said the chief priest; 'he says, that he acted for the benefit of your majesty's subjects who wanted rain, which they could not get so long as the infidels drank wine in Tehran.'

'So you destroy part of my subjects to benefit the remainder! By the king's beard,' said the king to Nadân, 'tell me, do I stand for nothing in my own capital? Are a parcel of poor dogs of infidels to be ruined under my nose, without my being asked a question whether it be my will or not that they should be so? Speak, man; what dream have you been dreaming? Your brain has dried up.' Then raising his voice, he said, 'After all, we are something in our dominions, and the Kâfirs, though such they be, shall know it. Here, ferashes' (calling his officers to him), 'here, tear this wretch's turban from his head and his cloak from his back; pluck the beard from his chin; tie his hands behind him, place him on an ass with his face to the tail, parade him through the streets, and then thrust him neck and shoulders out of the city, and let his hopeful disciple (pointing to me) accompany him.'

Happy was I not to have been recognized for the lover of the unfortunate Zeenab. My fate was paradise compared to that of my master; for never was order more completely executed than that which had passed the Shah's lips.

Nadân's beard was ripped from his chin with as much ease by the ferashes as if they were plucking a fowl; and then, with abundance of blows to hasten our steps, they seized upon the first ass which they met, and mounted the priest, the once proud and ambitious priest, upon it, and paced him slowly through the streets. I walked mournfully behind, having had my mollah's shawl torn from my head, and my *hirkeh* (cloak) from my back.

When we had reached one of the gates Nadân was dismounted, and with scarcely a rag to our backs, we were turned out into the open country; and it is worthy of remark, that no sooner had we left the city than rain began to pour in torrents, as if the heavens had been waiting to witness the disgrace of two of Persia's greatest rogues, and to give the Mollah Nadân the lie in favour of the poor, injured, and ruined Armenians.

CHAPTER LVII: HAJJI BABA MEETS WITH AN ADVENTURE IN THE BATH WHICH MIRACULOUSLY SAVES HIM FROM THE HORRORS OF DESPAIR

 O,' said I to my companion, as soon as we were left to ourselves, 'so I am indebted to you for this piece of happiness. If I had thought that this adventure was to have been the result of the mûshtehed's recommendation, you would never have seen Hajjî Baba in this trim. What could it signify to you whether rain fell or no, or whether the Armenians got drunk or remained sober? This is what we have got by your officiousness.'

The mollah was in too pitiable a condition for me to continue upbraiding him any longer. We walked in silence by the side of each other in the saddest manner possible, until we reached the first village on our road. Here we made a halt, in order to deliberate upon what we should do. My unfortunate companion was expelled the city, therefore it was impossible for him to show himself in it until the storm had blown over; but as we were both very anxious to know what had become of our respective properties—he of his house and effects, I of my clothes, my money, and mule— it was determined that I should return and gain the necessary intelligence.

I entered Tehran in the evening, and, making myself as little recognizable as possible, I slunk through the streets to the mollah's house. At the first glimpse I discovered that we were entirely ruined; for it was in possession of a swarm of harpies who made free property of everything that fell under their hands. One of the first persons whom I met coming from it was the very ferash who had been sent by the Shah to conduct us to his presence; and he was mounted on my mule, with a bundle in his lap before him, doubtless containing my wardrobe, or that of the mollah.

So borne down was I by this sight, and so fearful of being discovered, that I hurried away from the spot; and, scarcely knowing whither I was bending my steps, I strolled into a bath, situated not far from the house of our enemy the chief priest.

I went in, undressed myself, and it being almost dark, I was scarcely perceived by the bathing attendants. Going from the first heated room into the hottest of all, I there took my station in a dark recess, unseen by any one, and gave free course to my thoughts. I considered to what I could now possibly turn my hands for a livelihood: for fortune seemed to have abandoned me for ever, and it appeared that I was marked out for the stricken deer, as the choice game of misfortune.

'I no sooner fall in love,' said I, musing, 'than the king himself becomes my rival, slays my mistress, and degrades me from my employment. I am the lawful heir to a man of undoubted wealth: he lives just long enough to acknowledge me; and although everybody tells me that I ought to be rich, yet I have the mortification to see myself cheated before my face, and I turn out a greater beggar than ever. The most devout and powerful man of the law in Persia takes a fancy to me, and secures to me what I expect will be a happy retreat for life: my master in an evil hour prays for the blessings of heaven to be poured upon us, instead of which we are visited with its vengeance, driven as exiles from the city, and lose all our property.' Never did man count up such a sum of miseries as I did when seated in the corner of the bath. The world seemed for ever gone from me, and I wished for nothing better than to die in the very spot in which I had nestled myself.

The bath had now been almost entirely abandoned by the bathers, when of a sudden a stir ensued, and I perceived a man walk in, with a certain degree of parade, whom, through the glimmering of light that was still left, I recognized to be the Mollah Bashi in person. Neither he nor his attendants perceived me; and as soon as he was left to himself (for so he thought) he immediately got into the reservoir of hot water, or the *hazneh* (the treasury), as it is called in the baths of Persia.

Here I heard him for some time splashing about and puffing with all his might; a sort of playfulness which struck me as remarkable for so grave and sedate a character; and then a most unusual floundering, attended with a gurgling of the throat, struck my ear; I conceived that he might be practising some extraordinary bodily exercise, and curiosity impelled me to rise gently from my corner, and with all the precaution possible, to steal softly on the tips of my toes to the aperture of the reservoir, and look in.

To my horror, I perceived the head of the law at his last gasp, apparently without a struggle left in him. It was evident that he had been seized with a fit, and had been drowned before he could call for help.

All the terrible consequences of this unfortunate event stared me full in the face. 'What can now hinder me,' said I, 'from being taken up as his murderer? Everybody knew how ill-disposed against him was my master, the Mollah Nadân, and I shall be called the vile instrument of his enmity.'

Whilst making these reflections, standing upon the step that leads into the reservoir, the Mollah Bashi's servant, followed by a bathing attendant, came in, with the warm linen that is used on leaving the bath; and seeing a man apparently coming out of the water, naturally took me for the deceased, and without any words proceeded to rub me down and to put on the bathing linen. This gave me time for thought; and as I foresaw an adventure that might perhaps lead me safely out of the scrape into which my destiny had thrown me, I let it take its course, and at once resolved to personify the chief priest.

A dim lamp, suspended from on high, was the only light that shone in the large vault of the dressing-room; and as I happened to be about the size and stature of the deceased, his servants, who were without suspicion, very naturally took me for their master. I had known and seen a great deal of him during my stay with the Mollah Nadân, and, therefore, was sufficiently acquainted with the manners of the man to be able to copy him for the short time it would take to be attended upon by his servants, until we reached his house. The most difficult part of the imposture would be, when I should enter the women's apartments; for I was quite unacquainted with the locality there, and totally ignorant of the sort of footing he was upon with the inmates of his anderûn. Indeed, I once heard that he was a perfect tyrant over the fairer part of the creation; and as much gossip was carried on at my master's, it came to my recollection, that it had been said he waged a continual war with his lawful wife, for certain causes of jealousy which his conduct was said to promote. He was a man of few words, and when he spoke generally expressed himself in short broken sentences; and as he affected to use words of Arabic origin on all occasions, more gutteral sounds obtruded themselves upon the ear than are generally heard from those who talk pure Persian.

I did not permit myself to open my lips during the whole time that I was dressing. I kept my face in shade as much as possible; and when the waterpipe was offered to me, I smoked it in the manner that I had seen the chief priest do; that is, taking two or three long whiffs, and then disgorging a seemingly interminable stream of smoke.

One of the servants appeared to be struck by something unusual, as I pronounced my *Khoda hafiz!* to the owner of the bath upon leaving it; but all suspicion was at an end when they felt the weight which I gave myself, as they helped me to mount the horse that was in waiting.

I deliberately dismounted at the gate of the house of the deceased; and although I bungled about the passages, yet, following the man who seemed to act as the confidential servant, I came to the little door which leads into the anderûn. I permitted him to do what he no doubt was daily accustomed to do, and just as he had opened the door, and I had advanced two or three paces, he shouted out, '*Cheragh biar*, bring lights,' and then retired.

A clatter of slippers and women's voices was then immediately heard, and two young slaves came running towards me with tapers in their hands, apparently striving who should first reach me.

The largest apartment of the building was lighted up, and I could perceive in it more women than one. That I took to be the residence of the principal personage, the now widow of the deceased; and I dreaded lest the slaves should conduct me thither. But, aided by my good stars, I must have fallen upon a most propitious moment, when the Mollah Bashi and his wife had quarrelled; an event which seemed to be understood by my conductors, who, seeing me unwilling to proceed to the lighted apartment, drew me on to a door which led into a small inner court, where I found a *khelwet*, or retiring room, into which they introduced me. How to get rid of them was my next care; for as they had walked before me, they could not have got a sight of my face, and had they entered the room with me, perhaps they would have made a discovery fatal to my safety. I took the light from the hand of one, and dismissed the other, with a sign of the head. Had I been the same inconsiderate youth as at the time of my acquaintance with Zeenab, perhaps I should have committed some act of imprudence that might have led to my discovery; but now I eyed the two young slaves with apprehension and even with terror; and certainly one of the most agreeable moments of my existence was, when I saw them turn their backs upon me and leave me to my own meditations. The change in my fortune, which had taken place during the last hour, was so unexpected, that I felt like one treading between heaven and earth; and my first impulse, upon finding myself in safety, after having got over the most difficult part of the imposture, was at one moment to exult and be joyful, and at another to shiver with apprehension lest my good fortune might abandon me.

CHAPTER LVIII: OF THE CONSEQUENCES
OF THE ADVENTURES WHICH THREATEN DANGER
BUT END IN APPARENT GOOD FORTUNE

I CAREFULLY fastened the inside of my door as soon as I was left to myself, and put my candle in so remote a corner of the room, that if any one was curious to look through the painted glass window, they could never discover that I was not the Mollah Bashi.

Having done this, it then struck me that something more might be elicited from this adventure than I had at first imagined. 'Let me inspect the good man's pockets,' said I, 'and the roll of paper in his girdle; perhaps they may contain the history of my future plans.' In his right-hand pocket were two notes, a rosary, and his seals. In the left his ink-stand, a small looking-glass, and a comb. His watch was kept in the breast of his coat, and in another small pocket, nearly under his arm-pit, was his purse.

The purse first came under inspection, and there I found five tomauns in gold and two pieces of silver. The watch was gold, and of English manufacture. His inkstand, beautifully painted, was also valuable, and contained a penknife, scissors, and pens. All these and the other trinkets I duly looked upon as my own (for I was determined to play the whole game), and I replaced them in their proper places on my person. The notes then came under inspection. One was to this purpose, without a seal.

'O friend! my intimate! my brother!' ('O,' said I, 'this is from an equal!') 'You know the affection that the friend who addresses you entertains for that bright star of the age, the shadow of our blessed Prophet, and his only wish is, that their intimacy should daily increase and strengthen. He sends him six choice Ispahan melons, such as are not to be found every day, and requests him, as he values his beard, to give him an unlimited permission to drink wine; for the doctors assure him if he does not take it in abundance, he will not have long to be the scourge and extirpator of the enemies of the true faith.'

'This can only be from the chief executioner,' said I immediately. 'Who else in Persia could express in such few words his own character, namely, flatterer, drunkard, and braggart? I will make something of this; but let me look at the other note.' I opened it, and read as follows:

'O my lord and master,

'The humble inferior who presumes to address the prop of the true faith, the terror of infidels, and the refuge of the sinner, begs leave to lay before him, that after having encountered a thousand difficulties, he has at length succeeded in getting from the peasantry of his villages one hundred tomauns in ready money, besides the fifty *kherwars*, or ass loads of grain: that the man, Hossein Ali, could or would not pay anything, although he had bastinadoed him twice, and he had in consequence taken possession of his two cows: that he would go on beating and exerting himself to the best of his abilities; and if some one was sent for the money which he had now in hand, he would deliver it over upon receiving a proper order.'

The note then finished with the usual form of words from an inferior to his master, and was sealed with a small seal, upon which was impressed Abdul Kerim, the name of the writer.

'Ah,' said I, 'may my lucky stars still protect me, and I will discover who this Abdul Kerim is, and where the village from whence he writes, and then the hundred tomauns become mine.' However, I let that matter rest for the moment, to think of the good account to which I might turn the note from the chief executioner. After due reflection I wrote as follows:

'O my friend! my soul!

'The note of that friend without compare has been received, and its contents understood. When the sacred standard of Islâm runs the risk of losing that lion of lions, that double-bladed sword, that tower of strength, when he may be saved and preserved, who can doubt what is to be done? Drink, O friend, drink wine, and copiously too; and let the enemies of all true believers tremble. May thy house prosper, for the melons; but add one more favour to the many already conferred; lend thy friend a horse, duly caparisoned, for he has pressing business on hand, and he will return it safe and sound, as soon as the star of his destiny shall direct him home again.'

This I impressed with the seal of the deceased, and determined to present it myself very early in the morning.

To the other note I wrote the following answer:

'To the well-beloved Abdul Kerim.

'We have received your note, and have understood its contents. This will be delivered to you by our confidential Hajjî Baba Beg, to whom you will deliver whatever money you have in hand for us. On other subjects you will hear from us soon; but in the meanwhile go on with the bastinado, and we pray Allah to take you into his holy keeping.'

Having duly accomplished this, I waited for a proper hour to make my escape from a place where I was in momentary danger of a discovery, which perhaps might bring me to an ignominious end. It was past midnight, and I was preparing to issue in great secrecy from my room, when the door was gently pressed as if some one wanted admittance. My fright may better be imagined than described. I expected to see, at least, the *daroga* (police magistrate) and all his officers rush in and seize me; and I waited in agony for the result of the intrusion, when I heard the sound of a female voice whispering words which my agitation prevented my understanding. Whatever might have been the object of the visit, I had but one answer to give, and that was a loud and heavy snore, which sufficiently proclaimed that the occupant of the apartment was in no humour to be disturbed.

I waited for some time until I thought that everything was hushed throughout the mansion, then made my way quietly to the principal entrance, which having easily opened, I fled as if pursued. I watched the best opportunities to steal along the streets without meeting the police, and without being discovered by the sentinels on duty. The day at length dawned, and the bazaars, little by little, began to open. Dressed as I was in the Mollah Bashi's clothes, my first care was to make such alterations in them that they should not hold me up to suspicion, and this I did for a trifling expense at an old clothes' shop, although, at the same time, I took care not to part with any of the valuable articles which had fallen into my possession.

I then proceeded to the house of the chief executioner, where I presented my note to a servant, an utter stranger to me, saying, that the Mollah Bashi requested an immediate answer, as he was about going from the city on important business.

To my delight, I was informed that the great personage was in his anderûn, and that he must for the present delay sending a written answer; but that in the meanwhile he had ordered one of his horses to be delivered to me.

O how I eyed the beast as I saw him led out of the stable, with the gold-pommelled and velvet-seated saddle, with the gold chain dangling over his head, and the bridle inlaid with enamelled knobs. I almost dreaded to think that all this was about to become my property, and that such luck could not last long. So strong was this apprehension that I was about asking for trappings less gaudy and more serviceable; but again, I thought that any delay might be my ruin; so without mincing the matter I mounted him, and in a very short time had passed the gates of the city, and was far advanced into the country.

I rode on, without stopping or once looking behind, until I had got among some of the broken ground produced by the large and undefined bed of the river Caraj, and there I made a halt. I recollected to have heard that the village of the Mollah Bashi lay somewhere in the direction of Hamadan, and consequently I directed my course thither. But, to say the truth, when pausing to breathe, I was so alarmed at the extraordinary turn which my fortunes had taken, that, like one dizzy on the brink of a precipice, invaded by a sort of impulse to precipitate himself, it was with some difficulty that I could persuade myself not to return and deliver up my person to justice. 'I am,' said I, 'nothing more nor less than a thief, and, if caught, should duly be blown from the mouth of a mortar. But then, on the other hand, who made me so? Surely, if *takdeer* (destiny) will work such wonderful effects, it can be no fault of mine. I sought not the death of the Mollah Bashi; but if he chooses to come and breathe his last in my lap, and if, whether I will or no, I am to be taken for him, then it is plain that fate has made me his *vakeel*, his representative; and whatever I do so long as I remain in that character is lawful—then his clothes are my clothes, his hundred tomauns are my hundred tomauns, and whatever I have written in his name is lawfully written.'

Revived by these conclusions, I again mounted and proceeded to the nearest village, to inquire where the property of the chief priest was situated, and if a person of the name of Abdul Kerim was known in the neighbourhood. As if the dice were determined to keep turning up in my favour, I found that the very next village, about one parasang distant, was the one in question, and Abdul Kerim a priest of that name who superintended the interests and collected the revenues of his deceased master. 'Ho,' said I, 'a priest! I must change the tone of the letter and insert his proper titles.' I immediately sat down on the ground, taking the inkstand from my pocket, and cutting off a slip of paper from the roll in my girdle I framed my note anew, and then proceeded on my errand, determined, if I obtained possession of the hundred tomauns, to take the shortest road to the nearest Persian frontier.

CHAPTER LIX: HAJJI BABA DOES NOT SHINE IN HONESTY
THE LIFE AND ADVENTURES OF THE MOLLAH NADAN

I PUT on an air of consequence suited to the fine horse which I bestrode as soon as I reached Seidabad (for that was the name of the village), and rode through its gates with such a look of authority that the peasants who saw me did not fail to make very low inclinations of the head.

'Where is Abdul Kerim?' said I, as I dismounted, and gave my horse to one of the bystanders.

In a moment every one was in motion to find him, and he very soon appeared.

'I am come,' said I (after the usual salutations), 'on the part of the chief priest, upon certain business well known to you'; and straight I delivered him my note.

Abdul Kerim had a piercing eye, which did not at all suit me, particularly as he kept conning me over through a corner of it; but I was relieved as soon as he had read the note to hear him say, '*Be cheshm!* By my eyes! the money is ready. But you must refresh yourself. In the name of God, come in.'

I pretended great hurry, not at all liking to remain under the fire of his sharp eyes; but by way of not exciting suspicion, I consented to eat some fruit and sour milk.

'I do not remember to have seen you at the chief priest's,' said he to me, as I was opening wide my mouth to swallow a piece of melon; 'and yet I am acquainted with every one of his servants perfectly.'

'No,' said I, half choked at the question, 'no, I do not belong to him. I am an attendant upon the chief executioner, with whom the Mollah Bashi, I believe, has some money transactions.'

This seemed to settle every difficulty which I saw had been rising in the mind of my entertainer; and thus the fine horse, the gold-pommelled saddle, and the brilliant bridle, were at once accounted for.

Having received the one hundred tomauns, I safely deposited them in my breast; and then, apparently taking the road back to the city, I left the village with a heart much lighter than I had brought. But as soon as I was fairly out of sight I turned my horse's bridle in the contrary direction, and clapping the stirrups into his flanks galloped on without stopping, until the foam fairly ran down his sides.

I determined to proceed direct to Kermanshah, there sell horse, saddle, and bridle, and then make my way to Bagdad, where I should be safe from all danger of molestation.

Having proceeded some five parasangs on my road I saw a strange figure walking before me at a good pace, singing with all his throat. He was lightly dressed, having only a skull-cap on his head, his face bound round with a piece of linen, a pair of slippers on his feet, and nothing to indicate that he was a wayfaring man. As I drew near I thought that I had seen his form before; he was tall and well-shaped, with broad shoulders, and a narrow waist. I should immediately have taken him for the Mollah Nadân but for his singing; for it never struck me as possible that one of his grave character and manners could ever lower himself by so ignoble an act. But little by little I saw so much of him, although he had not yet discovered me, that I could not be mistaken; it was the mollah himself.

I stopped my horse to deliberate whether I should notice or make myself known to him. To pass him would be the height of cruelty, but to recognize him would of necessity burden me with an inconvenient companion. But then, should he discern who I was, and find that I had shunned him, he would very probably denounce me as a thief on the very first occasion; and if I escaped him now I should have the fear ever after of knowing him to be my enemy.

We were both approaching a village where we must pass the night, therefore there was no retreating on my part; for it was necessary to see that proper care was taken of my horse, considering the long journey it had to travel, and to push him on farther was impossible.

I took a middle line. Should he recognize me I would speak to him; if not, I would pass him unheeded. I urged my horse on, and as I approached he turned round and surveyed me from head to foot, but apparently without making me out.

'O Aga, for pity's sake,' exclaimed he, 'have compassion on an unfortunate man, who has no other refuge in this world than God and you!'

I could not resist such an appeal to my feelings, and, keeping silence for some little while by way of hearing what more he would say, I at length burst into an immoderate fit of laughter. My laughter seemed to be as much out of season as his singing, for he was extremely puzzled what to make of me: but when I began to speak, all doubts were removed, and he ran up to me with a sort of joy and ecstasy that bordered upon madness.

'Ay, Hajjî, my soul, my uncle, light of my eyes!' said he, as he kissed my knee. 'From what heaven have you dropped? What means this finery, this horse, this gold, these trappings? Do you deal with the *Gins* and the *Dives* or has fortune fallen in love, and adopted you its heir?'

I continued laughing, so amused was I at these sallies, and he went on, saying: 'How comes it that you have so soon turned your mule into this fine horse? And my property, what is become of it? Have you not even saved my ass, for I am sorely tired of going on foot? Tell me, tell me all: by the beard of the Prophet, tell me all.'

I soon found that had I refused to give him a full account of my adventures, he would suspect me of having got possession of his property, and turned it into the finery which had just drawn forth his admiration; so I promised faithfully to relate everything, but I entreated him at the same time to prepare a large quantity of credulity, for what I had to say was so marvellous that he would very probably conceive it was my intention to impose upon him.

We then proceeded to the village, where we took up our quarters at the *mehman khaneh*, or strangers' house, a convenience generally to be found in every hamlet throughout Persia, and there established ourselves for the night.

A person of my appearance could not long remain unnoticed, and I was duly waited upon by the *ked khoda*, who supplied us with a good supper; and during the time required for its preparation I related my adventures to my companion. Their singularity was in no manner thrown away upon him; and he seemed to die away with delight when he found that all my present prosperity was at the cost of his old enemy the Mollah Bashi. As we sat communicating to each other in the full confidence of our hearts (for the miserable are ever greatly relieved by talking of themselves), I discovered that never before had I acquired an insight into the real character of my associate. 'There must have been an assumed importance in you,' said I to him, 'as long as I was in your service; for how could one really proud be so amiable as you appear now?'

'Ah, Hajjî!' said he, 'adversity is a great alterative. My life has been one eternal up and down. I have often compared it to those whirligigs set up by louts in our market-places on the No Rouz, which keep one dangling between heaven and earth. Unfortunately, I am one of those who has never adopted the maxim of "spread not your carpet in a wet place."'

'Tell me,' said I, 'the history of your adventures. We cannot better pass our time, and I hope that you know me well enough now not to refuse me your confidence.'

'You will hear nothing in my history but what is common to many Persians, who one day are princes and the next beggars; but since you are curious to know, I will relate it with pleasure'; and he began in the following words:

'I am a native of Hamadan. My father was a mollah of such eminence that he was ambitious of becoming the mûshtehed of Persia; but his controversies upon particular points of faith unfortunately carried him so far that a party was created against him, which deprived him of the elevation he sought. His most prominent quality was the hatred he bore to the Osmanlies, and to Sûnis in general. One of our ancestors is said to have first introduced into Persia a more universal hatred against them than ever before existed, by a simple innovation in the education of the Shiah children, by which means their very first ideas were trained to be inimical to the race of Omar. I mean,' said the mollah, 'that which you no doubt very well remember: when a little boy in schooltime is pressed upon certain occasions to ask his master's leave to retire, the form of words in which he is enjoined to make his request is "*Lahnet beh Omar*, curse be upon Omar." I dare say you have through life, as I have, never omitted to unite the name of Omar with everything that is unclean, and at least once a day to repeat the curse which you were taught at school.'

I fully assented to this, and then he proceeded with his story.

'My father's hatred for the secretaries of Omar extended itself to all sorts of infidels. Jews, Christians, fire-worshippers, and worshippers of images, all came within the scope of his execration; and what at first he had practised from motives of ambition, at length became the ruling principle of his nature. His family, and I among the number, were brought up in his tenets, and imbibed all his violent prejudices; and so much did we hang together by them that we formed as it were a distinct sect—the terror of infidels, and the most zealous upholders of the Shiah faith.

'After this you will not be surprised at the part I lately took in the destruction of the Armenian wine-jars at Tehran. But that is not the only scrape my zeal has led me into. Very early in life, when still a student at Hamadan, I was involved in a terrible disturbance, of which I was the principal promoter.

'An ambassador from the Pasha of Bagdad, with his suite, was quietly taking his road through our city, having sojourned there two or three days on his way to the court of the Shah, when burning to put into practice my father's lessons, I collected a band of young fanatics like myself, and, making them an appropriate address, I so excited their passions that we resolved to perform some feat worthy of our principles. We determined to attack our Turkish guests, inform them of the curses we denounced against Omar, and invite them to become adherents to the doctrine of Ali. Heedless, and, perhaps, ignorant of what is due to the character of *Elchi*, or ambassador, we only saw in Suleiman Effendi an enemy to the Shiahs, and one calling himself a Sûni. One day, as he was setting forth from his house to visit the governor of Hamadan, we gathered ourselves into a body and greeted him by loud cries of "Curses be upon Omar!" This enraged his domestics, who retorted the insult by blows. Showers of stones ensued from our party, and this led to a general fray, in which the Pasha's representative had his turban knocked from his head, his beard spit upon, and his clothes nearly torn from his back.

'Such an outrage of course could not be overlooked. The ambassador was furious; he threatened to send off couriers to the Shah, and was even on the point of returning to his own master when the governor, frightened at the consequences if his wrath was not appeased, promised that he should have all satisfaction, and that the ringleaders of the disturbance should immediately be delivered up to him.

'Trusting to my father's consequence in the city, and full of vapouring pride at what we had achieved, I at first made light of the vows of vengeance which the Turks breathed against us; but the governor, who only contemplated the loss of his place if the news of this event reached Tehran; and caring little whether Ali was the true successor to the Prophet, or whether Osman, Omar, and Abubekr were usurpers or not, he at once ordered me to be seized, as well as two others of my companions, and forthwith we were placed at the disposal of the enraged Osmanlies.

'I shall never forget the contending emotions of my mind when brought face to face before these objects of my hatred. I did not at all relish the sound beating which they had it in contemplation to inflict upon me; and, at the same time, I groaned under the necessity of keeping to myself that stream of abuse which was ready to flow against them upon the smallest provocation.

'They seemed, however, quite ready to return all our hatred with interest, and did not lose this opportunity of letting us know its full extent. They were not generous enough to let us off, but ordered the administration of the bastinado with a degree of religious zest that I thought could never have existed in any breast except my own. To be short, our feet were beat into a jelly, and our only consolation during the operation was the opportunity afforded us of giving vent to our pent-up rage. The Turk, however, was revenged, and we were set free.

'This adventure cooled my zeal for many years; although, in the pursuit of the distinctions which my father sought, I continued to addict myself to controversy. When about twenty-five years old, and my beard had acquired a respectable consistency, I went to Ispahan in order to improve myself by associating with our celebrated doctors, and to make my own abilities known by the part which I might take in their disputations. I succeeded to the utmost of my wishes, and acquired considerable reputation. I only wanted an opportunity of distinguishing myself, and that was soon afforded me by the following circumstance.

'In the time of our famous Shah Seffi, who was himself half a heretic, the Franks (a sect of the Christians) had considerable establishments at Ispahan for the purposes of commerce, and were much patronized and encouraged by him. He allowed them free exercise of their religion, permitted them to build churches, to import priests, and, to the scandal of the true faith, even allowed them the use of bells to call them to prayer. These Franks have a supreme head of their church—a sort of caliph, whom they call *Papa*—part of whose duty, like that of our own blessed Prophet, is to propagate his religion throughout the world. Under different pretexts, convents of his dervishes were established, some in Ispahan itself, and some in Julfa among the Armenians. Most of these have been abandoned, and the buildings fallen into decay; but one whose object more particularly was the propagation of the Christian faith still existed, and to its destruction my endeavours and those of some of our most zealous mollahs were directed, notwithstanding the opposite views of the government, who are anxious to encourage the Christians to settle in Persia, owing to the riches which they introduce by their trade.

'This convent was served by two dervishes, one of whom was in himself a calamity!—one who understood the world—a man of deep design—and of a wit so sharp that the *shaitan* in person was not fit to be his father. He was tall, thin, and strong. His eyes were like live charcoal, and his voice like a high wind. He never lost an opportunity of entering into argument with our most learned men upon points of religion, and would boldly assert, with the heart of a lion, that our holy Prophet, "the chief of created beings, the sealed intercessor, Mohammed Mustapha," (upon whom be eternal blessings!) was a cheat and an impostor. In short, he embarked in the sea of controversy, as if he had Noah for a pilot; and, not content with words, he even wrote a book, in which he pretended to prove the truth of his mad assertions. This book was unfortunately attempted to be answered by one of our divines, who did not recollect that it is folly to play with fire, unless there be plenty of water at hand to extinguish it. His book said anything but what it ought, and tended more to throw ridicule upon Islamism than to uphold its glory and perfection. Ispahan was full of this subject when I arrived there; and, being anxious to bring myself forwards, I proposed that an invitation should be made to the Frank dervish to meet the mollahs of the city in person, on an appointed day, in the Medresseh Jedeed, when they would argue every point of their respective faiths, and when they would either make the dervish turn Mohammedan, by producing conviction in his mind, or they would become Christians, if his arguments prevailed. To this he immediately assented; but we determined beforehand, amongst ourselves, that such a thorn in the side of our *Ullemah* should no longer exist in Persia, and that the overwhelming truth of our belief should not be left to the chances of vain words and uplifted voices, but show itself in the zeal and numbers of its adherents. Accordingly every turbaned head, and every beard that wagged, were secretly invited to appear on the appointed day; and never was attendance more complete— never did the children of Islam make such a show of their irresistible force, as they did on that memorable occasion.

'The Medresseh was already filled; for, besides the mollahs, a great crowd, all anxious to witness the triumph of the true faith, had taken possession of the courts. Head over head and turban over turban were piled upon each other, in thick array, along the walls and in the utmost corners of the hall, when the Frank dervish, alone, unsupported, and unfriended, appeared before us. He looked around in dismay, and appeared appalled by our numbers. Two or three of the principal mollahs, who were to carry on the controversy, were seated in front of their body, and I was close at hand. We had prepared questions which were to be proposed to him, and according to the answers he gave so were we to act. He appeared to be provided with no other weapon of defence save his tongue; and he sat down opposite to us, evidently much alarmed at the hostility which he remarked on the countenances of all present.

'Without giving him any time for reflection, we immediately began:

'"Do you believe," said one, "that the God in heaven put himself into a human form?" "Do you," said another, "acknowledge that God is composed of three persons, and still is only one?" "Are you convinced," said a third, "that what you call the Holy Ghost came down from heaven in the body of a dove?"

'These questions were put so quickly that he knew not which way to turn, until, collecting within himself all the powers of his voice, he exclaimed, "If your intention is to kill me, be it so; but what good will that do your argument? If your intention be to argue, attacking me in this manner by numbers and personal violence will prove that you can only oppose passion to argument; and show the world, that by me you have been overcome."

'Seeing that we were likely to fare ill, and observing that his words were producing an effect in his favour, I was the first to exclaim to the surrounding mob, and to the assembly present: "O Mussulmans! Mussulmans! come to our help—our religion is attacked—the infidel is trying to subvert our faith—vengeance! help!"

'These words produced an immediate effect, and a thousand voices were lifted up against him. "Seize him!" said some; "kill him!" said others. The mob was agitated to and fro, like the waves of the sea; when the dervish, seeing himself in danger, made an attempt to escape, which was seconded by one of the mollahs, whose compassion was moved towards him. He threw his own cloak over the infidel's shoulders, and just as violent hands were about to be laid upon him, he pushed vigorously through the crowd, and succeeded in reaching the house of an Armenian in safety.

'We, the mollahs, being disappointed of our prey, proceeded in a body to the house of the governor of the city, followed by an immense crowd of the people. A great fermentation had been excited, and we promoted it all in our power.

'The governor himself was a strict and pious Mussulman, and we expected that he would without hesitation join in the cry we had raised. We accused the Frank dervish of preaching false doctrine, with a view to subvert our religion.

'"This fellow," said we, "calls our Prophet cheat, and talks abomination. We demand that he be delivered over to us."

'The governor was perplexed how to act; for he knew how dangerous it was to interfere in matters in which the subjects of Europe were concerned; and he was far from seconding our disposition to violence.

'"Why invite the dervish to an argument," said he, "if you will not hear what he has to say? If you have no arguments to oppose to his, violence only makes your cause worse, and you do more harm than good to our religion. But if on the other hand your arguments are better than his, and he can bring no answer to them, then indeed he is a kafir, an infidel; and according to our law is worthy of death."

'Finding ourselves balked again, we departed breathing vengeance; and I verily believe, had we met the dervish at that moment, he would have been torn into a thousand pieces. He was so well aware of this, we soon heard that he had left the city in secret; and so far our endeavours were successful, for it was long before he ventured again to show himself.

'I had put myself so much forward on this occasion, and had shown my zeal in so many different ways, that I had become a prominent character.

But hitherto I had got nothing by it. The capital I felt, after all, was the place where I ought to endeavour to gain some permanent and lucrative situation; and to that I turned my views. To gain this end, I took myself to Kom, with a view of ingratiating myself with the mûshtehed, whose recommendation I knew would do me more good than ten years of prayer and fasting. I succeeded perfectly; for with the character I had acquired of being the scourge of infidels, I was received by him with great favour, and he was delighted to acknowledge me for one of his most diligent disciples. I soon took up his cause against the Sûfies with all the ardour that he could wish; and it was not long before I ventured to solicit his recommendation to the body of the Ullemah at Tehran, and to the principal men in office at court. He professed to be sorry to part with me, but acceded to my request; and I was soon after counted one of the holy fraternity at the seat of empire.

'I confess to you, although I enjoy as good an opinion of myself as most men, that I was much less successful in making my way at court than I had expected. My competitors for advancement were numerous, and more versed in the ways of the world than I. Like them, I was obliged to begin by paying a most assiduous attention to men in office. Having once gained the privilege of being seated in the *mejlis* (assembly) of the head of the law, who was in fact my chief, I little by little became noticed by the grand vizier, the lord high treasurer, the secretary of state, the chief executioner, and others. I was constantly to be seen at their uprisings, and at their evening meetings; but after all, I was nothing but a poor mollah, and I longed for some opportunity of distinguishing myself from the common herd. The prime vizier first noticed me owing to my once having succeeded in making him shed tears, at the commemoration of the death of the blessed Hossein, which he held at his house, and where I preached and chanted the service in a manner that drew forth his approbation, and that of all the assembly. Since then I have made great progress, particularly in the eyes of the people, whose good opinion I look upon as the first of acquisitions to an ambitious man.

'But you have had an opportunity of judging how little their assistance is to be depended upon, when opposed to the will of an absolute king. Trusting too much to my influence over them, I have lost myself; and I am now what you see, a miserable wanderer, returning to my native city, as penniless as when I first left it.'

CHAPTER LX: HAJJI AND THE MOLLAH MAKE PLANS
SUITED TO THEIR CRITICAL SITUATION, SHOWING THAT
NO CONFIDENCE CAN EXIST BETWEEN ROGUES

THE Mollah Nadân having finished his narrative, I endeavoured to persuade him that the same destiny which had presided over his success in life, and afterwards over his misfortunes, would no doubt serve him again, and restore him to his lost situation: 'for,' said I, 'we both of us have seen enough of life in Persia to have ascertained its extreme instability. When events depend upon the will of one man, he may with as much consistency order you back from exile, as he did the plucking your beard and the thrusting you forth from the city. There is a reaction in misfortune which frequently produces increased prosperity. Thus when the smith sprinkles water upon his burning charcoal, it is extinguished for a moment, and smoke takes the place of flame; but again, at the slighest blast of his bellows, the fire breaks out with redoubled brilliancy.'

'That is precisely the thought with which I was consoling myself,' said my companion, 'and which set me singing, when you overtook me on the road. The Shah most probably thought it necessary to make an exhibition

of justice, by way of ingratiating himself with the Christian merchants;
but the day will come when he will feel the necessity of making friends of
the upholders of the Mohamedan religion, and then the good opinion of
such a man as I, who am beloved by my people, will be of consequence to
him. I had some thoughts, I confess, of relinquishing priestcraft, and becoming a merchant; but, all things considered, I shall continue to follow
my original destiny. I have now an opportunity of setting up for a martyr,
and *that*, now I recollect it, is worth more than the loss of my worldly
goods, my house, my furniture, my white ass, and even my mûties.'

'Then what do you propose doing?' said I. 'Will you accompany me to
Bagdad, or will you wait the tide of events in Persia?'

'My plan,' said he, 'is to proceed to my native place, Hamadan, where
my father, who is still alive, enjoys considerable reputation: through his
means I will set negotiations on foot for my readmission to the capital,
and ultimately for my restoration to the situations of which I have been
deprived. But you—what road do you intend to pursue? When, *inshallah*,
please God, I am restored, I shall require your talents to make my mûtî
establishment prosper. You had better remain at Hamadan with me, and
follow my fortunes.'

'Ah, my friend,' said I, 'with all my present apparent prosperity, I am
more of an exile than you. Events have played wickedly into my lap, and
here am I (God knows how unwillingly) an avowed thief. I could not do
otherwise than follow my destiny, which has clothed me with the garments
of the chief priest, enriched me with his money, and mounted me upon the
finely caparisoned steed of the executioner in chief. That same destiny
compels me to fly my country: I cannot remain in it to run the chance of
being discovered and cut into quarters, to grace the gates of the city. No,
before many days are expired, I hope to have reached the Turkish frontier,
and then only shall I call myself in safety.'

Upon this I made him an offer of part of my acquired spoils, by which
I hoped to secure his secrecy, and happy was I to find him nothing loth.
He accepted of ten tomauns (leaving me ninety-five in hand), which he
said would be enough for present purposes, and which he promised to repay whenever his fortunes should be reestablished. But upon taking them
from me, he again urged me to proceed with him to Hamadan. He represented in the strongest colours the danger I ran of being seized before I

could escape from the Shah's territories, and even when I should have quitted them. 'For,' said he, 'the moment the death of the Mollah Bashi is known, and as soon as the chief executioner shall have discovered the loss of his horse, he will not fail to dispatch officers throughout the country in search of you, and you are too conspicuous a character now not to be easily traced. It will be much better for you to take refuge with me, who will not fail to avert any inquiries, until the event has blown over, when you will be at liberty to follow your plans in safety. My father owns a village at some distance from Hamadan, where you can live unsuspected; and as for your horse and trappings, we may dispose of them in such a manner that they cannot lead to your discovery. Hamadan is not very far distant. If you depart hence at midnight, we shall reach it early to-morrow; and this we can easily do by making your horse carry us both. Consider that the journey is long to the Turkish frontier; and should the beast fail you, what is to hinder your being taken?'

His words gave a new turn to my thoughts, and I saw that he spoke the language of reason. Totally ignorant of this part of Persia, and feeling how necessary it was for my safety not only to be acquainted with the high roads, but also with the unfrequented paths, I looked upon a rapid flight to the frontier as an undertaking not so easily performed as imagined. If the mollah was inclined to betray me, he would as easily do so whether I fled or whether I adopted his plan; and of the two, it appeared to me a safer line of conduct to confide in than to distrust him: and accordingly I agreed to accompany him.

Refreshed both by food and rest, we departed at midnight, and made great progress on the road to Hamadan ere the sun rose. Having reached a rising ground which gave us a view of the city, we made a halt, in order to decide upon our present operations. Nadân pointed with his hand to a village about a parasang distant, and said, 'That is the village in which you must take up your quarters, until the story of the Mollah Bashi's extraordinary death be blown over; but you cannot present yourself in this magnificent garb, and mounted on this fine horse, without creating suspicion. I propose that we exchange dresses, and that you surrender the horse up to me. By this means you will appear in the character of a dependant of my father at his village, and I shall keep up the respectability of mine, by returning to the paternal roof properly equipped. This arrangement will advance our mutual as well as our combined interests. You will be safe from suspicion, and I shall not look the pauper that I do now. The history of my disgrace will no doubt soon reach the ears of my family, and perhaps lower them in the eyes of the world; but in this country, where so much depends upon the effect of outward show, as soon as it is known that I returned to them mounted on a horse with an enamelled bridle, a gold-pommelled saddle, and with a Cashmerian shawl round my waist, they as well as I will be restored to our proper places again. After I have enjoyed the advantage of these things a few days, it will be easy to sell them under some plausible pretext, and then you shall duly receive their amount.'

I was rather startled by this proposal, for certainly my companion had not inspired me with sufficient confidence to encourage me trusting him with so much property without any other security than his word. But I felt the truth of all he said. It was impossible for me to keep my incognito at the village for ten days or a fortnight dressed as I was, and the possessor of a fine horse, without creating suspicion. I was now, 'tis true, completely in the power of the mollah; but by his proposed arrangement he would have become such an accomplice in my guilt, that he could never denounce me without at the same time involving himself.

'But,' said I, 'suppose a nasakchi discovers the horse, what becomes of us then? You will be seized as well as I.'

'God is great,' answered the mollah; 'no one can have travelled as fast as we, and before any officer can arrive at Hamadan I shall have reached my father's house, and produced all the sensation I require in the city. It will be easy after that to secrete both the horse and his trappings. I take all the risk upon myself.'

Nothing more after this was to be said on my part. We immediately stripped, and made an exchange of clothes. He got from me the deceased Mollah Bashi's under garment, his *caba*, or coat, his Cashmerian girdle, and his outward cloak, made of a dark green broad cloth; and I, in return, received his old clothes, which had been torn on his person the day he had been thrust out of Tehran. I gave him my black cap, round which he wound the chief priest's head-shawl, which I had still preserved; and, in return, he delivered over to me his skull-cap. I preserved the Mollah Bashi's purse, the remaining money, the watch and seals; whilst I permitted him the use of the inkstand, the rosary, the pocket looking-glass, and the comb.

He then stuck the roll of paper in his girdle; and when completely made up and mounted, he looked so much like the deceased chief priest himself, that I quite started at the resemblance.

We parted with great apparent affection: he promised that I should hear from him immediately, and in the meanwhile gave me every necessary information concerning his father's village, leaving it to my own ingenuity to make out as plausible a story for myself as I might be able.

He then rode away, leaving me with no very agreeable feelings, on finding myself alone in the world, uncertain of the future, and suspicious of my present fate.

I made the best of my road to the village; but was extremely puzzled in what character to introduce myself to the inhabitants. In fact, I looked like one dropped from the skies; for what could be possibly said for a man of good appearance, without a shawl to his waist, or an outer coat to his back, with a pair of slippers to his feet, and a skull-cap on his head? After much hesitation I determined to call myself a merchant, who had been robbed and plundered by the Cûrds, and then sham a sickness, which might be a pretext for remaining in the village until I could hear from the mollah, who would no doubt furnish me with intelligence which might enable me to determine how long I ought to remain in my hiding-place.

In this I succeeded perfectly. The good people of the village, whom Heaven for my good luck had endowed with a considerable share of dullness, believed my story, and took me in. The only inconvenience I had to endure was the necessity of swallowing prescriptions of an old woman, the doctor of the community, who was called to show her skill upon me.

CHAPTER LXI: THE PUNISHMENT DUE TO HAJJI BABA
FALLS UPON NADAN, WHICH MAKES THE FORMER
A STANCH PREDESTINARIAN

I HAD passed ten long and tedious days in my hiding-place without the smallest tidings from the Mollah Nadân. I was suspicious that his star was still glancing obliquely at him, and that matters had not gone quite so well as he had expected. Little communication existed between the city and the village; and I began to despair of ever again hearing of my horse, my rich trappings and clothes, when, one evening a peasant, who had gone to the market-place of Hamadan for the purpose of hiring himself as a labourer in the fields, and who had returned disappointed, by his discourse threw some light upon my apprehension.

He said that a great stir had been excited by the arrival of a nasakchi, who had seized the son of their Aga (the owner of the village), taken away his horse, and carried him off prisoner to the capital, under the accusation of being the murderer of the Mollah Bashi of Tehran.

I leave the gentle reader to judge of my feelings upon hearing this intelligence. I soon became satisfied of the reason of the mollah's silence; and although I felt myself secure for the present, yet I was far from certain how long I might remain so. I immediately declared that I was perfectly restored to health, and taking a hasty leave of my hospitable villagers, made the best of my way to Hamadan, in order to ascertain the truth of the peasant's intelligence.

Nadân's father was well known in the city, and I found no difficulty in discovering where he lived. I abstained from entering his house, and making any direct inquiries concerning the fate of my friend; but I stopped at the shop of a barber in the neighbourhood, both because I wanted his assistance in giving a decent appearance to my head and face, and because I knew that he would be the most likely person to inform me of the real state of the case.

I found him as talkative and as officious as I could wish. When I had asked him the news of the day, and had pleaded my ignorance of the recent occurrence that had filled everybody with astonishment, he stepped back two paces, and exclaimed, 'Whence do you come, that the iniquities of that dog the Mollah Nadân are unknown to you? He was not satisfied with killing the chief priest, but he must needs dress himself in his very clothes; and, not content with that, he also has stolen one of the chief executioner's best horses and furniture. Wondrous dirt has he been eating!'

I entreated my informant to relate all the particulars of a story of which I pretended to be totally ignorant; and without waiting for a second request, he spoke as follows:

'About ten days ago this Nadân arrived at the gate of his father's house, mounted on a superb horse, caparisoned in a style more fitting a khan and a man of the sword than a poor servant of God. He was dressed in shawls of the finest quality, and looked indeed like the high priest himself. His appearance in this fashion of dress and equipage created an extraordinary sensation; because a very short time before it was reported that he had incurred the Shah's displeasure, and had been turned out of Tehran in the most ignominious manner. He gave himself all sorts of airs upon alighting; and when questioned concerning his expulsion from the capital, he appeared to make very light of it, and said that he had been made to understand, in a secret manner, that his disgrace was only temporary; and that, by way of softening it, he had been presented with the horse which he then rode.

'This tale was believed by every one, and he was received at his father's house with great honours; but most unfortunately, the next day, when about mounting his horse to show himself in the city, a nasakchi passed the gate of the house, having just arrived from Tehran. He stopped, and looked at the animal very earnestly; inspected the bridle and gold-pommelled saddle, and then cried out, *La Allah il Allah!* there is but one God! He inquired of the bystanders to whom the horse belonged, and was informed that it was the property of the Mollah Nadân.

'"The Mollah Nadân!" exclaimed he in a great rage: "whose dog is he? That horse is the property of my master, the chief executioner; and whoever says it is not is a liar, whoever he may be, mollah or no mollah!"

'At this interval appeared the delinquent himself, who, upon seeing what was going on, endeavoured to hide himself from the observation of the nasakchi; for it so happened that he was one of the officers who had paraded him through the capital on the day of his disgrace.

'Wearing the garments and turbaned cap of the deceased chief priest, the dangers of his situation immediately stared him in the face, and he would have decamped on the spot, had he not been recognized by the nasakchi, who as soon as he saw him cried out, "Seize him, take his soul, that is he—the very man. Well done, my happy stars! By the head of Ali, by the beard of the Prophet, that is the bankrupt rogue who killed the chief priest and stole my master's horse."

'By this time the nasakchi had dismounted, and, with the assistance of his own attendant, and of the bystanders (who soon discovered that he was acting under authority), he secured the mollah, who, in his defence, made oath upon oath that he was neither thief nor murderer, and that he was ready to swear his innocence upon the Koran.'

The barber related very faithfully the whole conversation which took place between Nadân and the nasakchi, the result of which was that the latter took the former with him to Tehran, notwithstanding all the interest made in his favour by the mollah's father and friends.

Never was breast torn by so many contending feelings as mine, upon hearing the fate that had befallen my companion, as related to me by the barber. In the first place, I bemoaned the loss of my horse and his rich trappings, and of my fine shawl dresses; but in the next I enjoyed a feeling of security when I considered, that if poor Nadân should happen to lose his head, no account would ever be asked from me of my late iniquities. I still could not help looking upon myself as one under the protection of a good star, whilst the mollah, I concluded, was inevitably doomed to be unfortunate: else why should we have exchanged clothes, and he taken my horse from me at a time when I was in no way inclined to accede to his proposals? But, notwithstanding there was every likelihood that he would suffer the punishment due to me, still, for the present, I could not feel myself secure so long as I remained in Persia, and therefore determined to proceed upon my original intention, and quit it without further delay. I consoled myself for the loss of the horse and clothes, by the possession of the remaining ninety-five tomauns, which would be sufficient for my present wants; and then those powerful words, *Khoda buzurg est!* God is great, stood me in lieu (as they do many a poor wretch besides) of a provision for the future, and of protection against all the unforeseen misfortunes preparing for us by the hand of fate.

CHAPTER LXII: HAJJI BABA HEARS AN EXTRAORDINARY SEQUEL TO HIS ADVENTURE IN THE BATH, AND FEELS ALL THE ALARMS OF GUILT

HAVING equipped myself as a merchant, for I had long since determined to abandon the character of a priest, considering how ill I had succeeded in it, I sought out the conductor of a caravan, which was on its road to Kermanshah, and bargained with him for the hire of a mule. He had a spare one, that had run unloaded from Tehran, and which he let me have for a trifle; and as I had no baggage but what I carried on my back, my beast and I agreed very well together.

We reached our destination on the seventh day, and here I was obliged to look out for a fresh conveyance. I was informed that none was likely to offer under a month, because, owing to the Cûrdish robbers, who infested the frontier, no caravan ventured on the road unless its numbers were considerable, and it would take some time to collect them; but I was told that a caravan of pilgrims and dead bodies had set off for Kerbelah only the day before, and that, with a little exertion, I might easily overtake them before they had reached the dangerous passes.

Constantly apprehensive of being discovered and detained, I did not hesitate upon the course to adopt, and forthwith set off on foot. My money was safely deposited in my girdle; and without any other baggage than a good staff in my hand, I left Kermanshah, and proceeded on my road.

On the evening of the third day, when nearly exhausted with fatigue, my eyes were cheered by the sight of fires at a distance, the smoke of which curled up over the brow of a hill; and approaching them, I discovered cattle spread over the plain grazing, and thus was not mistaken in supposing that the caravan was nigh at hand. As I advanced towards the baggage, which was piled up in a hollow square, and where I knew that I should find the conductor, I observed a small white tent, pitched at some little distance, which indicated that pilgrims of consequence were of the party; and, moreover, that women were amongst them, for a *takhteravan* (a litter) and a *kejaweh* (panniers) were seen near the tent.

I gave myself out for a pilgrim, and found the conductor very ready to furnish me with a mule for my conveyance. I was anxious to pass unnoticed, considering the predicament in which I stood; but still the conscious dignity which the ninety-five pieces of gold in my girdle gave me made it difficult for me to restrain that vanity of display so common to all my countrymen.

Among the baggage, at a small distance from the square in which I was seated, were several long and narrow packages sewn up in thick felts, which were spread in pairs upon the ground, apparently having been unloaded there from the backs of camels. I inquired what they might be, for the sight of them was new to me, and was informed that they contained dead bodies bound to Kerbelah.

'It is evident you are a stranger,' said the conductor, who appeared to be as loquacious and mother-witted as those of his profession generally are, 'or otherwise you would have been better informed. We are carrying rare things to Kerbelah!'

'Yes,' said I, 'I am a stranger; I come from afar, and am like one descended from the mountains. In God's name, what are you carrying to Kerbelah?'

'What!' answered he, 'have you heard nothing of the extraordinary death of the Mollah Bashi of Tehran; how he died in the bath; and how his ghost was seen on horseback, and then in his harem; and how it afterwards ran off with one of the chief executioner's best horses? Where have you been living all this while?' added he, shaking both his hands before him as he spoke, and shrugging up his shoulders.

Alarmed at what he had said, I pretended ignorance; and requested him to satisfy my curiosity concerning the story in question, which he did in a manner that, but for my being so deeply implicated in it, would have afforded me much amusement.

'You must know then,' said the muleteer, 'that what I am about to relate is true, because I was on the spot in person, at the time it happened.

'The chief priest having gone to the bath at the close of day, just after the evening prayer, returned to his house surrounded by his servants, and retired to bed for the night in the *khelwet* of his women's apartments.

'You need not be told that most of the public baths in Persia are open to the women the first thing in the morning, to a certain hour in the day, and are then appropriated to the men. The wife of the Mollah Bashi, attended by her servants and slaves, the morning after her husband had bathed, at the earliest sound of the cow horn, proceeded to the same bath, and she and her suite were the first party who entered it on that day. Out of respect to their mistress, none of her attendants ventured to get into the reservoir of hot water before her. The cupola of the bath was but very dimly lighted by the dawn; and the chief priest's wife was almost in utter darkness when she entered the water. Guess at her horror, when scarcely having proceeded two steps, her extended hand fell upon a large mass of floating flesh.

'Her first impulse was to utter an amazing shriek; her second to tumble headlong out as if she had been pursued, and straight to faint away.

'The consternation which she produced amongst her women may easily be conceived. One after the other, with the lamp in their hand, they looked in, shrieked, and then ran back, not one among them having yet discovered what was the object of their terror.

'At length the old duenna taking courage, looked boldly into the reservoir, and to her surprise she there found a dead man. More screams and cries ensued, which having brought the chief priest's wife to her senses, caused her to join the inspecting party. Little could be recognized of a floating corpse inflated with water, presenting various odd surfaces to the eye, and giving but little clue to discovery. At length the head and face appeared to view; and, as soon as the old duenna had applied her lamp to it, one and all cried out, "O Ali! it is the Mollah Bashi; it is the Mollah Bashi!"

'The wife again fell into a trance; the slaves made their cries; in short, there was that stir amongst them, that one would have thought they had heard the "blast of consternation from the trumpets of the resurrection."

'But amidst all the wailing, which by this time had attracted every woman in the building, one of the slaves cried out, "But it cannot be our Aga, for I saw him return from the bath, I made his bed, and I am sure he was soon asleep. It is impossible he can be in bed and asleep, and in the bath, drowned, at one and the same time. It must be somebody else."

'This observation threw them all into greater consternation than ever, because they immediately felt that what the slave had seen must have been her master's ghost. "See," said the wife—who had again come to life—pointing to the face of the corpse, "I am sure this was my husband; there is the scratch I gave him but yesterday." "And there," said one of her servants, "that is the place in his beard from which you plucked a handful of hairs."

'These tender recollections threw the poor widow into a violent flood of tears, which were only stopped by her slaves assuring her that the Mollah Bashi was still alive. "How else could he have taken the lamp from my hand?" said the slave—"how could he have shut the door? how dismissed me? how snored?" So persuaded was she of the truth of what she said, that she forthwith dressed herself, and volunteered to go to her master's bed-room, where no doubt she would find him asleep.

'"But if he is there," said one of the women, "then what can this be?" (pointing to the corpse.)

More screams and cries ensued

'"Why, this must be his ghost," said another; "for surely no man can possess two bodies—one in which he lives, and the other by way of a change."

'"No," said a third in a waggish tone, "that would be quite new. He might then make the same use of them as he would of a town and country house."

'All this time (many additional bathers having poured in) whilst those who were indifferent were speculating after this fashion, the chief priest's women were uttering loud and piercing shrieks, particularly when the slave returned and informed them that no Mollah Bashi had she found, and that he had left no trace behind except the print of his body in the bed.

'The story had now got abroad, the bath was surrounded by a crowd, who pressed to gain admittance; and ere the women had had time to dress themselves, the place was full of men. Such a scene of confusion as then ensued had never before been witnessed in a public bath at Tehran. What with the wailing and lamentations of the women of the chief priest—what with the noise and cries of those who inveighed against the intrusion of the men—the clamour was excessive.

'At length the friends and relations of the deceased appeared, and, with them, the washers of the dead, who immediately bore the corpse to the place of ablution, where it was embalmed, and prepared for its journey to Kerbelah, for thither it was judged expedient to send it for burial.

'His widow at once avowed her intention of accompanying the body; and my mules,' added my informant, 'were hired on the occasion. The tent you see yonder is occupied by her and her slaves; and there,' pointing to the packages, 'lies the carcass of her husband. The accompanying dead bodies are the remains of those who, both at Tehran and on our road hither, died about the time that this event took place, and are now sent to Kerbelah to be buried in the suite and under the protection of one who at the day of resurrection, it is hoped, may lend them a helping hand into paradise.'

Here the conductor stopped, whilst I, who had been struck by the latter part of his speech, became almost mute from fear. I felt that having endeavoured to escape danger, I had fallen into its very mouth. Were I to be recognized by the chief priest's servants, some of whom I had known intimately, their knowledge of my person would lead to my discovery.

'But what happened after the corpse was carried out of the bath?' said I, anxious to know whether the clothes which I had left in one of its corners had been noticed.

'By the head of Ali!' said the man, 'I do not very well recollect. This I know, that many stories were in circulation; and every person had a different one. Some said that the chief priest, after being drowned, was seen in his anderûn and went to bed. Others that he appeared the next morning at the chief executioner's, and rode away with one of his best horses. The chief executioner himself shows a note of his, sealed with his seal, giving him permission to drink wine. In short, so many and so contradictory were the reports, that no one knew what to believe. All were puzzled to find out how he managed to get alive out of the bath (for that is attested by his servants, and by the master of the bath), and still remain in the reservoir. Difficulties continued to increase as fast as people argued, until a discovery took place which threw a marvellous light upon the subject. Some clothes were found in a dark corner of the bath. They were torn and in bad case; but without much difficulty they were known to have belonged to one Hajjî Baba, a drivelling priest, and an attendant upon that famous breeder of disturbance, the Mollah Nadân, the open and avowed enemy of the head of the law. Then everybody exclaimed, "Hajjî Baba is the murderer! without doubt he is the murderer of the holy man, he must pay the price of blood!" and all the city was in full search for Hajjî Baba. Many said, that Nadân was the culprit; in short, messengers have been sent all over the country to seize them both, and carry them dead or alive to Tehran. I only wish that my fate may be sufficiently on the ascent, to throw either of them into my hands; such a prize would be worth my whole mule-hire to Kerbelah.'

I leave every one to guess my feelings upon hearing this language; I who was never famous for facing difficulties with courage, and who would always rather as a preliminary to safety make use of the swiftness of my heels, in preference to adopting any other measure. But here to retreat was more dangerous than to proceed; for in a very short time I should be in the territory of another government, until when I promised faithfully to wrap myself up in the folds of my own counsel; and to continue my road with all the wariness of one who is surrounded by imminent danger.

CHAPTER LXIII: HE IS DISCOVERED
AND SEIZED, BUT HIS GOOD STARS AGAIN BEFRIEND
AND SET HIM FREE

THE caravan pursued its march early the next morning, and I took my station among the muleteers and the hangers on (many of whom are always at hand), in order to screen myself from notice. The litter with the chief priest's widow, and her attendants, preceded the line of march, the camels with the bodies followed, and the remainder of the caravan, consisting principally of loaded mules, spread itself in a long straggling line over the road.

I envied every fellow who had a more ruffian-like face, or a more ragged coat than my own; so fearful was I of being thought good-looking enough to be noticed. More particularly I dreaded the approach of the widow's servants, for although I was dying to know if any of them were of my acquaintance, yet I carefully turned my head on one side, as soon as there was the smallest likelihood of their looking towards me.

The first day's march had passed over in safety; and I laid my head on a projecting part of the baggage, where I slept sound through the night. I was equally fortunate on the second day, and with so much confidence did this success inspire me, that I began to be ambitious of associating with something better than a common mule-driver.

I had opened a conversation with one, who I was informed was an Armenian bishop; and had already made him understand how thankful he ought to be for being thus noticed by a true believer, when one of the much dreaded attendants rode by us, and in him I recognized the man who had endeavoured to palm off a *mûtî* upon me, upon my first introduction to the Mollah Nadân. My heart leapt into my mouth at the sight of him. The chief priest's ghost, had it appeared, could not have frightened me more. I turned my head quickly on one side, but he passed on without heeding me; so for this time I was let off only with the fright; but I resolved to return to my humble station again, and forthwith left the bishop to his own meditations.

On the following day we were to pass through the defiles infested by the Cûrdish banditti, when every one would be too much taken up with his own safety to think of me. Once having passed them, we should no longer be in the Persian territory, and I might then claim protection of the Turks, in case I were discovered and seized.

On that eventful day, a day well remembered in the annals of my adventurous life, the caravan wore a military appearance. All those who possessed anything in the form of a weapon brought it forth and made a display. The whole scene put me in mind of a similar one which I have recorded in the first pages of my history; when, in company with Osman Aga, we encountered an attack from the Turcomans. The same symptoms of fear showed themselves on this occasion as on that; and I am honest enough to own that time had not strengthened my nerves, nor given me any right to the title of lion-eater.

The whole caravan marched in compact order, marshalled by a chaoush and by the conductor, who, with the servants of the chief priest's wife, formed a sort of vanguard to the main body. I, who had my own safety to consult for more reasons than one, huddled myself among the crowd, and enjoyed the idea that I was encumbered with no other property than the money in my girdle.

We were proceeding in silence; nothing was heard save the bells of the caravan, and I was deep in thought in what manner I might dispose of my ninety-five tomauns, on our arrival at Bagdad; when, turning up my eyes, I perceived the conductor and a well-equipped Persian riding towards me.

The conductor pointed with his hand to me, and said to his companions, '*hem een est*, this is even he!'

'By the beard of Ali!' thought I, 'my good fortune has turned its back upon me.'

I looked at the conductor's companion, whom I instantly discovered to be the very Abdul Kerim, from whom I had extracted the one hundred tomauns, at the village of Seidabad, by means of the letter which I had written in the name of the deceased chief priest.

I was about giving myself up for lost, when the conductor relieved me a little, by saying, 'You are the last man who joined our caravan: perhaps you can tell us upon what part of the frontier Kelb Ali Khan, the robber, is said to be at present.'

I answered him in a great state of perturbation; but kept my eyes fixed upon Abdul all the while, who also began to stare at me with those penetrating eyes of his, which almost turned my heart inside out. He continued looking at me like one in doubt, whilst I endeavoured to skulk away; but at length appearing to recollect himself, he exclaimed, 'I have it, I have it! it is the very man; he it was who laughed at my beard and stole the hundred tomauns.' Then addressing himself to the bystanders, he said, 'If you want a thief, there is one. Seize him in the name of the Prophet!'

I began to expostulate, and to deny the accusation, and probably should have succeeded to convince those who surrounded us that I was wrongly accused, when, to my consternation, the promoter of matrimony came up, at once recognized me, and called me by my name. Then my whole history came to light. I was denounced as the murderer of the chief priest, and this event produced so general a bustle throughout the caravan, that fear of the robbers was for a while suspended, and every one came to gaze upon me.

I was seized, my hands were pinioned behind my back, I was about

being dragged before the chief priest's widow to be exhibited, when my
good planet came to my help and showed its ascendant. Of a sudden a great
cry was heard at a distance, and to my delight I beheld a body of cavaliers
rushing down the slope of an adjacent hill. These were the very Cûrds so
much dreaded. The consternation was universal, the whole caravan was
thrown into confusion, and resistance was unavailing when both heart and
hand were wanting. Those who were mounted ran away; the muleteers,
anxious for the safety of their cattle, cut the ropes of their loads, which fell
and were left spread on the plain to the mercy of the marauders. The
camels were also disencumbered of their burdens, and coffins were to be
seen in all parts of the road. I remarked that the one containing the chief
priest had fallen into a rivulet, as if fate was not tired of drowning him. In
short, the rout was universal and complete.

I soon was left to myself, and easily found means to disengage my
bonds. I perceived that the Cûrds had directed their attention principally
to the litter and its attendants, where they naturally expected to find prisoners of consequence; and it rejoiced me to observe, that those whom but
a few minutes before I had looked upon as destined to be the perpetrators
of my ruin, and very possibly of my death, were now themselves thrown
into a dilemma nearly equally disastrous with the one from which I was
now relieved.

In vain the widow's attendants threatened, swore, and bade defiance;
nothing would soften their wild and barbarous assailants, who, under some
lawless pretext of fees to be paid, began a regular pillage of such parts of
the caravan as had not fled their attack. I again had an opportunity of
ascertaining that my good star was
prevailing; for now, whilst those who
possessed any article of dress which
might give respectability to their appearance became the object of the robbers' attention, I and my solitary
mule had the satisfaction to find ourselves so totally unworthy of notice,
that we proceeded without molestation on the original object of our journey. I owned no corpse—I was not

called upon to pay duty upon a dead relation—I was free as air; and as soon as I once found myself released from the thousand miseries which had arisen all around me, and which, as if by magic, had been as quickly dispelled, I went on my way, exclaiming, 'Barikallah, ai talleh mun! Well done, oh my good fortune!'

CHAPTER LXIV: HE REACHES BAGDAD, MEETS HIS FIRST MASTER AND TURNS HIS VIEWS TO COMMERCE

LEAVING the Mollah Bashi's widow, her slaves, and attendants in the hands of the Cûrds, I made the best of my way to my destination; and caring little to hold converse with any one, after what had so recently taken place, I shaped my course in such a manner as not to attract observation.

Many stragglers, flying from the Cûrds, were to be seen on the road; but as they all, more or less, had interest in the fate of the caravan, they did not proceed far, but hovered about the scene of action, in the hopes of reclaiming either their friends or their property. I alone seemed to be totally independent, and by the time I had travelled two or three parasangs from the danger, I had the road to myself. Everything that had befallen me was turned over and over again in my mind, and I came to this conclusion, that powerfully protected as I seemed to be by fate, I might again turn my steps towards the paths of ambition, and hope that my last failure in the pursuits of advancement was to be made up by realizing a speedy and ample fortune.

'Ninety-five tomauns in my girdle, and all the world before me,' said I, 'is no insignificant prospect. And if Nadân be but blown from a mortar, and the chief priest's widow detained and ruined by the Cûrds, I do not see why I may not put my cap on one side as well as the best man in Persia.'

At length the walls and turrets of Bagdad appeared in view, and I entered the city a total stranger, and ignorant of its localities. Caravanserais I knew that I should find at every turn, and indifferent whither I bent my steps, or where I alighted, I let my mule take the road it liked best. Well acquainted with every street, the animal took me to a large caravanserai, where it no doubt had long been accustomed to resort, and there stopping, gave several loud grunts as it entered the porch, in the expectation of meeting its companions of the caravan. Although disappointed, yet I was more fortunate (if fortunate I could call myself), in seeing some of my countrymen in the square, and I soon found out that this was their usual rendezvous.

My person, I flattered myself, could attract no notice, go where I might: but I was sorry to find it otherwise. Upon alighting I was assailed by a thousand questions—the caravan was hourly expected, the merchants were eager for the reception of their goods, and I might possibly give them some intelligence respecting it. I made such answers as were necessary for the occasion; but resolved within myself very soon to quit so inquisitive a society, and bury myself in obscurity. I accordingly left my mule to its fate, reflecting that its owner would very soon arrive and take possession of it, and straightway settled myself in another part of the city.

As a first step towards preserving my incognito, I exchanged my dusty and weather-beaten sheep's-skin cap for a head-dress of the country, namely, a long red cloth bag, which fell down in a flap behind, and fastened to my head with a parti-coloured silk. I also bought a second-hand *beniche*, or cloak, usually worn by the Turks, which, going over my Persian garments, gave me the general appearance of an Osmanli; and finished my adjustment by a pair of bright crimson leather slippers.

Having done this, it came into my head that much good might accrue if I made myself known to the family of my first master, Osman Aga, for through them I might make acquaintance in the city, and promote my views in trade.

I accordingly sallied forth, and took my road through the principal bazaars and bezestens, in order to make inquiries, and particularly stopped where lambskins were sold, for I well recollected that they were his favourite article of trade. I also recollected many particulars concerning Bagdad, which he used to take pleasure in relating during our journeys, and I fancied that I could almost find my way to his very door without inquiry.

However, my trouble was soon at an end, for in putting my head into the shop of one of the principal Bokhara merchants, and inquiring if any news had reached Bagdad of one Osman Aga, I heard a well-known voice, in answer, say, 'Who wants me? In the name of the Prophet, I am he!'

Guess at my joy and surprise—it was the old man himself. I was almost as much astonished to see him at Bagdad, as I had before been to meet him at Tehran, and his surprise was equal to mine. I related as much of my history as I thought it necessary for him to know, and he told me his in return, which in two words was as follows.

He had left Tehran in the determination of proceeding to Constantinople, there to dispose of his merchandise, but hearing that great danger of being robbed existed on the road between Erivan and Arz Roum, he had deemed it a safer plan to visit Bagdad; and here he was, restored to his native city after an absence of many years. He had found his son grown up to man's estate, who, having gone through all the ceremony of mourning for his loss, had duly taken possession of his patrimony, which, according to the law, he had shared in the prescribed portions between his mother and sister. But as soon as his father was restored to him, he made no wry faces, but, like a good Mussulman, put into practice that precept of the Koran which ordaineth man to show kindness to his parents—but not to say unto them 'Fie upon you!' The old man added, that he had found his wife alive, and that his daughter was old enough to be married.

But having thus disburthened himself of this short history of his adventures, he turned round upon me in a sharper manner than he had even done before, and said, 'But Hajjî, my friend, in the name of the blessed Mohammed, what could have possessed you to join me to that female Satan at Tehran, by way of making me pass my time agreeably? By the salt which we have so often ate together, the few days that I passed in her company were filled with more misery than was the whole time I spent among the Turcomans! Was it right to treat an old friend thus?'

I assured him that I had no object in view but his happiness, taking it for granted that she, who had been the favourite of the monarch of Persia, must, even in her later days, have had charms more than enough for one who had passed some of the best years of his life with camels.

'Camels!' exclaimed Osman, 'camels, indeed! they are angels compared to this fury. Would to Heaven that you had married me to a camel instead, for it, at least, poor animal, would have sat quiet, with calm and thoughtful gravity, and let me have my own way; whereas your dragon, she, the viper, she passed her whole time in telling me how vastly honoured I was in having taken to wife one who had led the Shah by the beard, and enforced each word with either a slap or a scratch. *Amân! Amân!'* said the old man, rubbing his hand on his cheek, 'I think I feel them now.'

He at length ceded to my assurances that I had no other object in view than his happiness, and then very kindly asked me to take up my abode at his house during my stay at Bagdad, to which, of course, I acceded with all manner of pleasure.

This conversation had taken place in the back room of the Bokhara merchant's shop, during which the old man had treated me to five paras' worth of coffee, brought from a neighbouring coffee-house; and when it was over, he proposed going to his son's shop, situated in the same bazaar, some few doors farther on. His son's name was Suleiman. Having set himself up in the cloth trade during his father's long absence, he had acquired an easy livelihood, and passed the greatest part of the day (except when necessary to go to his prayers) seated in the little platform in the front of his shop, surrounded by his merchandise, neatly arranged on shelves fixed in the wall. He was a fat, squat little man, very like his father; and when he was informed that I was Hajjî Baba, he said that I was welcome, and taking the pipe which he was smoking from his own mouth, he immediately transferred it to mine.

These preliminaries of mutual good-will being established, I enjoyed the prospect of an easy and quiet sojourn at Bagdad, in the company of these good people; but in order to show that I did not intend wholly to be a dependant upon them, I made it known that I was possessed of ninety-five tomauns, and asked their opinion upon the mode of laying them out to the best advantage in trade. I gave them to understand that, tired of the buffetings of an adventurer's life, it was my intention for the future to devote my time to securing an independence by my own industry. Many had acquired wealth from beginnings much smaller than mine, said I; to which they both agreed: and, as we anticipated the fortune that I was to make, Osman Aga gravely let off the only bit of Persian poetry which he had picked up during his travels—'Drop by drop water distilleth from the rock, till at length it becometh a sea.'

Upon this conclusion we, that is, the father and I, proceeded to his house, which was situated at a convenient distance from the bazaars.

CHAPTER LXV: HE PURCHASES PIPE-STICKS
AND INSPIRES A HOPELESS PASSION IN THE BREAST OF
HIS OLD MASTER'S DAUGHTER

OSMAN AGA'S house was situated in a narrow lane, leading out of the street which leads into one of the principal bazaars. Immediately in front of the door was a heap of rubbish, upon which a litter of kittens had just been thrown, making an essay of their young voices as we passed; and a little farther, on a similar mound, a colony of puppies had been planted, guarded by a mangy mother, which, by their united cries, left us nothing to desire in the way of discord. Between these was situated the gate of Osman Aga's house, into which we entered. It was a small building, consisting of some crazy rooms, which neither indicated riches nor cleanliness. As I had no baggage belonging to me, except a small carpet, my removal here from the caravanserai was soon accomplished, and I took up my future abode in a corner of mine host's principal room, where he also spread his bed and slept.

By way of celebrating my arrival, he treated me with roasted lamb, and an abundant dish of rice, to which were added dates, cheese, and onions. The dishes were cooked in the harem, by the hands of his wife and daughter, aided by a female slave, the only domestic in the establishment. Neither of these had I yet seen, for it was dusk when we reached the house; nor, from good manners, did I ask more about them than Osman was inclined to tell me.

Besides myself and his son, the old man had invited a brother dealer in lambskins to the entertainment, with whom he had formed a close intimacy during his travels in Bokhara. The conversation turned exclusively upon commerce, about which I was so ignorant, that I took very little share in it, although, considering that it was my intention to enter it myself, I was very happy to open my ears to all that was said.

They entered deeply into the subject and discussed the relative merits of each article of trade. To hear them talk, one might have inferred that the end of the world was at hand, because it was rumoured that the price of their favourite commodity had fallen at Constantinople. They dissuaded me from embarking my capital in that article, but recommended in preference that I should invest it in pipe-sticks, which, they remarked, were subject to no decay, and for which there was a constant demand in the market of Constantinople.

The entertainment being over, and the guests having parted, I ruminated deeply upon what I had heard, and forthwith turned the whole weight of my thoughts to pipe-sticks. There, in a corner, I sat all day calculating what number of pipes I might acquire for my tomauns, and what would be my profit when sold at Constantinople; and when my imagination was heated by the hopes of the ultimate fortune that might be realized, I gave myself up to the most extravagant expectations. The plan of the merchant, whom Saadi relates he met in the island of Kish, was trifling when compared to the one which I formed. 'With the produce of my pipe-sticks,' said I, 'I will buy figs at Smyrna, which I will take to Europe, and having made great profit by them there, my money shall then be invested in skull-caps, which I will carry to Grand Cairo; these being sold in detail, for ready cash, I will carefully pack my money in sacks, and proceed to Ethiopia, where I will purchase slaves, each of whom I will sell for great profit at Moccha, and thence I will make the pilgrimage to the tomb of the Prophet. From Moccha I will transport coffee to Persia, which will fetch an amazing price; and then I will repose in my native city, until I can purchase a high situation at court, which may in time lead me to become the grand vizier to the King of Kings.'

Having thus disposed of the future in my favour, I set myself actively to work in laying in my merchandise. According to the most approved method, I made a bargain with a wood-cutter, who was to proceed to the mountains of Lour and Bakhtiari, where he would find forests of the wild cherry-tree, from which he would make his selections, according to the sizes with which I should furnish him. He was then to return to Bagdad, where the sticks would be bored, and made up into appropriate parcels for the markets of Turkey.

All this was duly executed; but during the time that I was waiting for the return of the wood-cutter, I was attacked by a disorder, from which few residents, as well as strangers at Bagdad are exempt, which terminating by a large pimple, as it dries up, leaves an indelible mark on the skin. To my great mortification, it broke out upon the middle of my right cheek, immediately upon the confines of the beard, and there left its baleful print, destroying some of the most favourite of my hairs, and making that appear a broken and irregular waste, which before might be likened to a highly cultivated slope.

I bore this calamity as well as I was able, although I could not help frequently quarrelling with fate, for having chosen so conspicuous a spot to place that which might have been so conveniently settled anywhere else.

'So be it,' said I, heaving a sigh at the same time; 'the wise man said true when he remarked, "if every stone was left to choose what it would be, most probably it would be a diamond;" and if every man might choose whereabouts he would have his pimple, there would be no ugly faces in Bagdad.'

However, by way of consolation, I recollected the Osman Aga's face was the mirror of deformity, although his pimple had budded elsewhere. He, instead of condoling with me on my misfortune, rather seemed to enjoy it.

'Hajjî,' said he to me, 'if you are not afflicted with any greater calamity than this in life, look upon it as a blessing: although one side of your face be deformed, still the other is perfect. The turquoise is the perfection of colour on one side, but is black and dirty on the other; still it is a turquoise, and a precious stone.'

'Ah,' said I to myself, 'the ugly man cannot endure the sight of the handsome, no more than the vicious can the virtuous: in the same manner as curs of the market howl at a hunting dog, but dare not approach him.'

Notwithstanding the deformity of my cheek, I found, as I continued to be an inmate in the house of my old master, that I had made no small impression upon the heart of his daughter, the fair Dilaram, who, by a thou-sand little arts, did not fail to make me acquainted with the state of her af-fections. Her mother and she were both experienced in the mode of curing the Bagdad disorder, and they undertook to superintend mine. My pimple and Dilaram's love appear to have risen at about the same time; their progress was mutual, and by the time that the former had risen to its full height, the latter had become quite inconvenient.

I, 'tis true, had not caught the infection; for my charmer was the very image of her father, whose face and that of an old camel's were so entirely identified in my mind, that I never could lose that ugly association of ideas when I gazed upon her. It was, therefore, a considerable relief to me when the season for travelling approached, and when the caravan for Constanti-nople was about to assemble. My pipe-sticks were collected and packed into their proper bundles, my accounts with my creditors regularly dis-charged, my wardrobe complete, and I was all delight when it was an-nounced, that at the very next favourable conjunction of the planets the caravan was to take its departure. But as for poor Dilaram, she hovered about my cheek with looks of despair; and as fast as the swelling subsided, she appeared to lose the only tie which kept her united to this world and its vanities.

CHAPTER LXVI: HE BECOMES A MERCHANT, LEAVES BAGDAD AND ACCOMPANIES A CARAVAN TO CONSTANTINOPLE

IT WAS a fine spring morning when the caravan took its departure from the Constantinople gate of the city. Mounted on the top of one of my loads, with my bed tied on the pad by way of a soft seat, and my bags surrounding me, I contemplated the scene with pleasure, listened to the bells of the mules as I would to music, and surveyed myself as a merchant of no small consequence.

My more immediate companions were Osman Aga, and his associate in lambskins (he of whom I have already made honourable mention at the entertainment), and one or two other Bagdad merchants; but besides, there were many of my own countrymen, natives of different cities of

Persia, all bound upon purposes of trade to Constantinople, and with whom I was more or less acquainted. My adventure with the chief priest of Tehran had in great measure blown over; and indeed the dress I had adopted, with the scar on my cheek, made me look so entirely like a native of Bagdad, that I retained little in my appearance to remind the world that I was in fact a Persian.

I will not tire the reader with a recital of our adventures through Turkey, which consisted of the usual fear of robbers, squabbles with muleteers, and frays at caravanserais. It will be sufficient to say, that we reached our destination in safety; but I cannot omit the expression of my first emotions upon seeing Constantinople.

I, a Persian, and an Ispahani, had ever been accustomed to hold my native city as the first in the world: never had it crossed my mind that any other could, in the smallest degree, enter into competition with it, and when the capital of Roum was described to me as finer, I always laughed the describer to scorn. But what was my astonishment, and I may add mortification, on beholding, for the first time, this magnificent city! I had always looked upon the royal mosque, in the great square at Ispahan, as the most superb building in the world; but here were a hundred finer, each surpassing the other in beauty and in splendour. Nothing did I ever conceive could equal the extent of my native place; but here my eyes became tired with wandering over the numerous hills and creeks thickly covered with buildings, which seemed to bid defiance to calculation. If Ispahan was half the world, this indeed was the whole. And then this gem of cities possesses this great advantage over Ispahan, that it is situated on the borders of a beautiful succession of waters, instead of being surrounded by arid and craggy mountains; and in addition to its own extent and beauty, enjoys the advantage of being reflected in one never-failing mirror, ever at hand to multiply them. But where should I stop, if I attempted to describe the numerous moving objects which attracted my attention? Thousands of boats, of all forms and sizes, skimmed along in every direction, whilst the larger vessels, whose masts looked like forests, more numerous than those of Mazanderan, lined the shores of the intricate and widely extended harbour.

'O, this is a paradise,' said I to those around me; 'and may I never leave it!' But when I recollected in whose hands it was, possessed by a race of the most accursed of heretics, whose beards were not fit to be brooms to our dust-holes, then I thought myself too condescending in allowing them to possess me amongst them. One consolation, however, I did not fail to derive from reflection, which was, that if they were allowed the possession of so choice a spot for their use in this world, they would doubly feel the horror of that which was doubtless preparing for them in the next.

After undergoing the necessary forms and examinations at the custom-house, I and my companions took boat at Scutari, crossed over to Constantinople, and established ourselves and merchandise in a large caravan-serai, the resort of Persian traders, situated in a very central part of the city, near the principal bazaars. I felt myself a slender personage indeed, when I considered that I was only one among the crowd of the immense population that was continually floating through the great thoroughfares. And when I saw the riches displayed in the shops, the magnificence of dress of almost every inhabitant, and the constant succession of great lords and agas, riding about on the finest and most richly caparisoned horses, I could not help exclaiming, in a secret whisper to myself, 'Where is Constantinople and her splendours, and where Persia and her poverty?'

I, in conjunction with old Osman, hired a room in the caravanserai, in which we deposited our merchandise. During the daytime I displayed my pipe-sticks in goodly rows on a platform; and as my assortments were good, I began my sales with great vigour, and reaped considerable profit. In proportion as I found money returning to my purse, so did I launch out into luxuries which I little heeded before. I increased the beauty and conveniences of my dress; I bought a handsome amber-headed chibouk; I girded my waist with a lively-coloured shawl; my tobacco pouch was made of silk, covered with spangles; my slippers were of bright yellow, and I treated myself to a glittering dagger. Temptations to expense surrounded me everywhere, and I began to think that there was something worth living for in this world. So numerous were the places in which I might exhibit my person in public, that I could not refrain from visiting the most frequented coffee-houses, where, mounted on a high bench, with soft cushions to recline upon, I smoked my pipe and sipped my coffee like one of the highest degree.

Implicated as I had been in disagreeable adventures in Persia, I was mistrustful of my own countrymen, and rather shunned them, whilst I sought the acquaintance of the Turks. But they, my countrymen, who are always so inquisitive, and who feel themselves slighted upon the least inattention, they discovered who and what I was, and eyed me with no great feelings of approbation. However, I endeavoured to live upon good terms with them; and as long as we did not enter into competition in matters of trade, they left me unmolested.

In places of public resort I gave myself out for a rich Bagdad merchant; and now my scar, which I had before esteemed a great misfortune, was conveniently conspicuous to attest the truth of my assertions. Nothing, I found, was so easy as to deceive the Turks by outward appearance. Their taciturnity, the dignity and composure of their manner and deportment, their slow walk, their set phrases, were all so easy to acquire, that in the course of a very short time I managed to imitate them so well, that I could at pleasure make myself one of the dullest and most solemn of their species. So perfect a hearer had I become, so well did I sigh out, every now and then, in soft accents, my sacred ejaculations of 'Allah! and there is but one Allah!' and so steady was I in counting my beads, that I was received at the coffee-house, which I frequented, with distinguished attention. The owner of it himself made my coffee, and as he poured it out with a high flourish of his arm, he never failed to welcome me by the friendly epithets of 'my Aga, my Sultan.' Such influence had the respectability of my appearance secured for me, that in every trifling dispute which might take place in the coffee-room, either upon the subjects of horses, dogs, arms, or tobacco (the principal topics of conversation), I was ever referred to, and any low growl from my lips, of either *belli* (yes), or *yok* (no), was sure to set the matter at rest.

CHAPTER LXVII: HAJJI BABA MAKES A CONQUEST OF THE WIDOW OF AN EMIR

I HAD lived in this manner for some time, when for three successive evenings, towards the dusk, retiring from my coffee-house, I remarked an old woman standing at the corner of a small street that nearly faced it. She always gazed intensely at me, seemed desirous to speak, looked up every now and then at the latticed windows of the house, at the foot of which she had taken post, and then allowed me to pass on.

The first time I scarcely took notice of her, an old woman standing at the corner of a street being nothing remarkable; but, on the second, I became surprised, and was on my guard; the third roused all my curiosity; and on the fourth evening I determined, if she appeared again, to discover what could be her meaning.

Accordingly I dressed myself rather better than usual, having taken it for granted that my good looks, added to the protection of my good planet, were at work for me; and issuing forth from the coffee-house, I walked with a slow and sauntering step towards the mysterious woman. I was about accosting her, when, as I turned the angle of the street that screened me from the windows of the coffee-house, of a sudden a lattice of the house before mentioned was thrown open, and an unveiled female presented herself to my sight, whose face and form appeared to me of the most dazzling beauty. A flower was in her hand, which she first held out to my notice, then placed it on her heart, threw it to me, and then shut the lattice in such haste, that the whole scene was like an apparition which had shown itself, and then suddenly disappeared. I stood with my mouth open, and my eyes directed upwards, until I was gently pulled by the sleeve by the old woman, who had picked up the flower, and was presenting it to me as I looked round upon her.

'What is this,' said I, 'in the name of the Prophet? Are there Gins and Peris in this land?'

'Are you such a novice,' answered the old woman, 'not to know what that flower means? Your beard is long enough, you are not a child, and your dress proclaims that you have travelled; but you have travelled to little purpose, if you know not what a lady means when she gives you an almond flower.

'O yes,' said I, 'I know that *fistek* (almond) rhymes to *yastek* (pillow); and I also know that two heads upon one pillow have frequently been compared to two kernels in one almond; but my beard is long enough to remind me also, that such things do not happen without danger, and that the heads may be cut off, as well as the kernels swallowed up.'

'Fear nothing,' said my companion with great emotion, 'by the holy Mohamed, we are clean ones, and you despise fortune, if you reject us. Are you an ass, that you should start at a shadow? for such are your fears.'

'Tell me then,' said I, 'who is the lady I have just seen, and what am I to do?'

'Be not in such a hurry,' answered she; 'nothing can be done to-night, and you must have patience. Time and place are not now convenient; but meet me to-morrow at noon, at the cemetery of Eyúb, and you will hear all that you wish to know. I shall be seated at the foot of the tomb of the first emir on your right hand, and you will recognize me from any other woman by a red shawl, thrown over my left shoulder. Go, and Allah go with you!'

Upon this we parted, and I returned to my room in the caravanserai to ruminate over what had happened. I did not doubt that something good was in store for me; but I had heard terrible accounts of the jealousy of Turkish husbands, and could not help imagining that I might fall a victim to the fury of some much-injured man. Zeenab and her tower, Mariam and her Yûsuf, Dilaram and her pimple, all the instances of unfortunate loves, came across my mind in succession, and damped any desire that I might at first have felt in prosecuting this adventure. However, my blood was yet young and warm enough to carry me forwards, and I determined, though reluctantly, to proceed.

On the noon of the ensuing day I faithfully kept my engagement, looked for the first green-turbaned tomb, which I duly found on my right hand, where I discovered the old woman with her red shawl over her left shoulder. We retired from the roadside, and retreated to the shade of some of the loftiest cypress trees in the burial-ground; where, seated on the ground, with the magnificent view of the harbour of Constantinople before us, we calmly entered upon the subject of our conference.

She first complimented me upon my punctuality, and then again assured me, that I had nothing to fear from what she was about to propose. She had all the garrulity of her age, and spoke for some time but to little purpose, making professions of her attachment, and of her desire to serve me; all of which I foresaw would ultimately diminish the profits of my pipe-sticks, and I therefore stopped her progress, and requested her at once to let me know the history of the fair lady at the window.

Divesting her narrative of all her repetitions and circumlocutions, she spoke nearly to the following effect:

'The lady whom you saw, and whose servant I am, is the only daughter of a rich Aleppo merchant, who, besides her, had two sons. The father died not long ago, and was succeeded in his business by his sons, who are now wealthy merchants, and reside in this city. My mistress, whose name is *Shekerleb*, or Sugar-lips, was married when very young to an old but rich Emir, who scrupulously refrained from having more than one wife at a time, because from experience he knew that he could have no peace at home if he took advantage of the permissions of his law in multiplying to himself his female companions. He was very fond of domestic quiet, and therefore hoped, by taking one so young, he might be able to mould her to his wishes, and that she would never thwart him in his inclinations. In that he was fortunate, for a more gentle and docile creature than my mistress does not exist. There was only one point upon which they could never agree, which proved indeed one of the causes of the Emir's death, which happened soon after. She liked tarts made with cream, and he preferred his with cheese. On this subject, regularly for five years they daily at break-fast had a dispute, until, about six months ago, the old man, having ate over much of his favourite cheese-tarts, had an indigestion and died. He bequeathed one-fourth of his wealth, the house which you saw, his furni-ture, his slaves, in short, all that he could leave according to the Mo-hamedan law, to the fair Shekerleb, now his disconsolate widow. With the advantages of youth, beauty, and riches, you may be certain that she has not lived without admirers; but she has wisdom and discretion beyond most young women of her age, and hitherto has resisted forming any new tie, resolving to wait until some good opportunity, to marry one whom she might really love, and who would neither be swayed by interest nor ambition. Living opposite to one of the most fashionable coffee-houses in the city, she has had an opportunity of watching those who frequent it; and without a compliment, I need not say that she soon distinguished you as the handsomest amongst them, and indeed, as the man most to her fancy whom she had ever seen. My brother,' said the old woman, 'is the owner of the coffee-house, and as the opportunities of seeing him are frequent, I requested him to inquire who you were; and to let me know what sort of a character you bore. His report was such as highly pleased my mistress; and we resolved to endeavour to make you notice us, and if possible to get acquainted with you. You best know how we have succeeded, and now will be able to judge whether I have rendered you a service or not.'

Little did I expect to hear such a result when first the old woman began her tale. I now felt like one who had received his reprieve after condemnation. Instead of the mysteries, disguises, scaling of walls and windows, drawn scimitars, and bloody wounds attendant on a Turkish intrigue, I saw nothing before me but riches, ease, and repose from all future care. I blessed my star; in short, I held my fortune to be made. I was so transported at what I heard, that I made use of a thousand incoherent expressions to my companion; I protested and vowed eternal love to her mistress, and promised the most liberal remuneration to herself.

'But there is one circumstance,' said she, 'which my mistress has ordered me to ascertain before she can receive you; which is, the respectability of your family and the extent of your fortune. You must know that her brothers and relations are very proud; and if she were to make an unworthy alliance, they would treat her with the greatest harshness, and not fail to ill-treat if not to make away with her husband.'

Although I was not prepared for this, yet such was the quickness with which I had seized the whole extent of the good fortune awaiting me, that with the same quickness I without hesitation said, 'Family? Family, did you say? Who is there that does not know Hajjî Baba? Let him inquire from the confines of Yemen to those of Irâk, and from the seas of Hind to the shores of the Caspian, and his name will be well known.'

'But who was your father?' said the old woman.

'My father?' said I, after a pause; 'he was a man of great power. More heads came under his thumb, and he took more men with impunity by the beard, than even the chief of the Wahabi himself.'

I had now gained sufficient time to arrange a little off-hand genealogy for myself; and as the old woman's countenance expanded at what I had said, I continued to speak to her after this manner:

'If your mistress wants high blood, then let her look to me. Be assured, that she and her brothers, be they who they may, will never exceed me in descent. Arab blood flows in my veins, and that of the purest kind. My ancestor was a Mansouri Arab, from the province of Nejd in Arabia Felix, who with the whole of his tribe was established by Shah Ismael of Persia in some of the finest pastures of Irâk, and where they have lived ever since. My great ancestor, *Kâtir, ben Khur, ben Asp, ben Al Madian*, was of the tribe of Koreish, and that brought him in direct relationship with the family of our blessed Prophet, from whom all the best blood of Islam flows.'

'Allah, Allah!' exclaimed the old woman, 'enough, enough. If you are all this, my mistress wants no more. And if your riches are equal to your birth, we shall be entirely satisfied.'

'As for my riches,' said I, 'I cannot boast of much cash; but what merchant ever has cash at command? You must know as well as myself, that it is always laid out in merchandise, which is dispersed over different parts of the world, and which in due time returns back to him with increase. My Persian silks and velvets are now travelling into Khorassan, and will bring me back the lambskins of Bokhara. My agents, provided with gold and otter skins, are ready at Meshed to buy the shawls of Cashmere, and the precious stones of India. At Astrakan, my cotton stuffs are to be bartered against sables, cloth and glass ware; and the Indian goods which I buy at Bassorah and send to Aleppo are to return to me in the shape of skull-caps and shalli stuffs. In short, to say precisely what I am worth, would be as difficult as to count the ears in a field of wheat; but you may safely tell your mistress that the man of her choice, whenever he gathers his wealth together, will astonish her and her family by its extent.'

'Praise be to Allah!' said the confidant, 'all is now as it should be, and it only remains to make you acquainted with each other. You must not fail to be at the corner of the street at night-fall, when, with all the necessary precautions you will be introduced to the divine Shekerleb; and if she approves of you, nothing will interpose to defer your marriage and your happiness. There is only one piece of advice which I have to give; that is, be sure to like cream-tarts, and to disapprove of cheese ones. Upon every other topic she is liberal and without prejudice. May Allah keep you in peace and safety!'

So saying, she drew up the lower part of her veil over her mouth; and receiving two pieces of gold without a struggle, which I put into her hand, she walked away, and left me again to my meditations.

CHAPTER LXVIII: HE OBTAINS AN INTERVIEW
WITH THE FAIR SHEKERLEB, MAKES A SETTLEMENT
UPON HER AND BECOMES HER HUSBAND

I DID not long remain at the foot of the tree, for I felt that much was to be done before the time of assignation. It would be necessary to put on an appearance of wealth, to have a purse well furnished, and a dress suited to my character; and moreover, it quite behoved me to make my person as acceptable as possible by going to the bath, and using all the requisite perfumes. Frequently as I walked along did I apostrophize myself in terms of the highest approbation. 'Ahi Hajjî, friend Hajjî,' would I exclaim, 'by the beard of your father, and by your own soul, for this once you have shown the difference between a fool and a sage. Well done, thou descendant from the Mansouris! thou scion of the root of Koreish!'

Deeply pondering over my future destinies, at length I reached my caravanserai. I saw the old Osman seated in one corner of our apartment, calculating the profits of his merchandise, and in the other I observed my bundle of pipe-sticks. The contrast which these ignoble objects formed to the great schemes then planning in my mind struck me so forcibly, that it affected my ordinary deportment, and gave a certain tone of superiority to my manner which I had never before felt. I know not whether it was noticed by Osman; but he seemed rather startled when I asked him immediately to advance me fifty gold pieces, for which I offered to deliver over my merchandise as security.

'My son,' said he, 'what news is this? what can you want with so much money, and in such haste? Are you mad, or are you become a gambler?'

'God forgive me,' answered I, 'I am neither a madman nor a gambler. My brain is in good order, and the world has taken me into favour; but give me the money, and you will hear the rest hereafter.'

He did not longer hesitate to accede to my wishes, for he well knew the value of my goods, and that the transaction could not fail to be safe and profitable. So without further hesitation he counted out the money, and I forthwith left him.

I immediately bought some very handsome additions to my wardrobe, and proceeded without delay to the bath, where I went through all the necessary lustrations, and attired myself like a man of the highest fashion.

By the time that my new arrangements were complete, the hour of assignation had arrived, and with a beating heart I proceeded to the place appointed.

I found the old woman waiting, and having looked well round to see that nobody remarked us, she introduced me into the house through a door situated in a remote corner.

I was charmed at the great ease and comfort which appeared to exist throughout the whole establishment; for I now looked upon myself as lord and master of all I saw. We had entered at once into the apartments kept sacred for the use of the women, because it seems that the principal entrance of the house had been but little used since the Emir's death, out of reverence to his memory; and the same sort of mystery and precaution in entering here was kept up as if the good man was still in existence. Having passed through the small street-door, we entered into a court-yard, in which was a fountain. We then ascended a wooden flight of steps, at the top of which we found a cloth curtain, composed of various colours, which being lifted up, I was introduced into an ante-room, the only furniture of which consisted of women's slippers and a lamp. Four doors, which were now closed, opened upon this, and here I was left to myself, whilst my old conductress shuffled off to prepare her mistress for my reception. I heard voices in the different apartments, the owners of which I presumed belonged to the slippers; and imagined that many eyes were directed at me, for I could distinguish them through the crannies. At length the door at the farthest angle was opened, and I was beckoned to approach.

My heart beat within me as I stepped forwards, and covering myself close with the flaps of my cloak, in order to show my respect, I entered a room that was lighted up by only one lamp, which shed a soft and dubious light over the objects within it.

It was surrounded by a divan, covered with the richest light blue satins fringed with gold, in one angle of which, near the window, was seated the object of all my desires. She was carefully veiled from head to foot, and all I could then distinguish of her person was a pair of brilliant black eyes, that seemed to delight in the anxious curiosity which they had roused in my features.

She pointed to me with her hand to be seated; but this I obstinately refused, so anxious was I to show the depth of my respect and gratitude. At length, when further resistance was useless, I took off my slippers, and seated myself with a corner of my hip just resting upon the edge of the sofa, keeping my hands covered with the sleeves of my garment, and affecting a coyness and a backwardness, at which, now that I recollect myself, I cannot help laughing.

After we had sat facing each other for some few minutes, little, except commonplace compliments, having passed, my fair mistress ordered the old Ayesha (for that was the name of my conductress) to leave the room, and then leaning forwards, as if to take up her fan of peacock's feathers, which was on the cushion, she permitted her veil to fall, and exhibited to my impatient eyes the most beautiful face that nature had ever formed.

This was the signal for laying by all reserve, and I prostrated myself before this divinity with all the adoration of a profound devotee, and poured out such a rhapsody of love and admiration, as to leave no doubt in her mind of the tenderness of my heart, the acuteness of my wit, and the excellence of my taste. In short, the Emir's widow had every reason to be satisfied with the choice she had made; and she very soon showed the confidence which she intended to place in me, by making me at once the depository of her secrets.

'I am in a difficult situation,' said she, 'and the evil eye which many cast upon me hath embittered my soul. You may conceive, that, owing to the wealth with which I have been endowed by my late husband (upon whom be eternal blessings!) and to my own dower besides, which was considerable, I have been tormented with many persecutions, and they have almost driven me mad. My relations all claim a right to me, as if I were part of the family estate. My brothers have their own interest in view when they would negotiate a husband for me, as if they would barter a sack of wool against bags of rice. A nephew of my husband, a man of the law, pretends to claim an old custom, by which, when a man died, one of his relations had a right to his widow, which he might assert by throwing his cloak over her. Another relation again pretends, that, according to the law, I am not entitled to the whole of what I now possess, and threatens to dispute it. In short, so sadly perplexed have I been under these circumstances, I only saw one way to set the matter at rest, which was to marry again. Fate has thrown you in my way, and I am no longer at a loss.'

She then informed me of the arrangements she had made for our immediate union, in case I was not averse to it, and referred me to a man of the law, whom she had secured to act in her behalf, who would make out all the proper papers, and whom she informed me was now in the house ready to officiate. I was not prepared for quite so much dispatch, and felt my heart misgive me, as if it were hovering between heaven and earth; but I did not hesitate to reiterate my protestations of eternal love and devotion, and said nothing to my intended but what seemed to overwhelm her with delight.

So impatient was she of any delay, that she immediately ordered the old Ayesha to conduct me to the man of the law, who was in attendance in a small apartment, in a more distant part of the house. Besides himself he had brought another, who, he informed me, would act as my *vakeel* or trustee, such an intervention being necessary on the part of the man as well as the woman; and then he exhibited before me the *akdnameh* or marriage deed, in which he had already inscribed the dower of my intended, consisting of her own property, and demanded from me what additions it was my intention to make thereto.

I was again thrown back upon my ingenuity, and as the best answer I could give, repeated what I had before said to Ayesha, namely, that a merchant was uncertain of his wealth, which was dispersed in trade in different parts of the world; but I did not hesitate to settle all that I possessed upon my wife, provided such engagement were mutual.

'That is very liberal,' replied my wily scribe; 'but we require something more specific. As for instance, what do you possess here at Constantinople? You cannot have come thus far, except for important purposes. Settle the wealth which you can command upon the spot, be it in cash, merchandise, or houses, and that will suffice for the present.'

'Be it so,' said I, putting the best face possible upon the demand. 'Be it so—let us see.' Then appearing to calculate within myself what I could command, I boldly said, 'You may insert that I give twenty purses in money and ten in clothes.'

Upon this, a communication took place between the Emir's widow and her agent, for the purpose of informing her what were my proposals, and for gaining her consent to them. After some little negotiation, the whole was arranged to the apparent satisfaction of both parties, and our different seals having been affixed to the documents, and the necessary forms of speech having been pronounced by our different vakeels, the marriage was declared lawful, and I received the compliments of all present.

I did not fail to reward the scribes before they were dismissed, and also to send a very liberal donation to be distributed throughout the household of my fair bride. Then instead of returning to old Osman, and my pillow of pipe-sticks, I retired, with all the dignity and consequence of the gravest Turk, into the inmost recesses of my harem.

CHAPTER LXIX: FROM A VENDER OF PIPE-STICKS HE BECOMES A RICH AGA, BUT FEELS ALL THE INCONVENIENCE OF SUPPORTING A FALSE CHARACTER

I SOON found that I had a very difficult part to perform. A Chinese philosopher is said to have remarked, that if the operation of eating was confined to what takes place between the mouth and the palate, then nothing could be more pleasant, and one might eat for ever; but it is the stomach, the digestive organs, and, in fact, the rest of the body, which decide ultimately whether the said operation has been prejudicial or healthful. So it is in marriage. If it were confined to what takes place between man and wife, nothing more simple; but then come the ties of relationship and the interests of families, and they decide much upon its happiness or misery.

My fair spouse entertained me for several successive days after our marriage with such manifold and intricate stories of her family, of their quarrels and their makings-up, of their jealousies and their hatreds, and particularly of their interested motives in their conduct towards her, that she made me feel as if I might have got into a nest of scorpions. She recommended that we should use the greatest circumspection in the manner of informing her brothers of our marriage; and remarked that although we were so far secure in being lawful man and wife, still as much of our future happiness depended upon their goodwill towards us (they being men of wealth, and consequently of influence in the city), we ought to do everything in our power to conciliate them. As a precautionary measure, she had spread a report that she was on the point of being married to one of the richest and most respectable of the Bagdad merchants, and in a conversation with one of her brothers, had not denied, although she had abstained from confessing it to be the case. She now requested that our marriage might be proclaimed, and to that effect recommended that we should give an entertainment to all her relations, and that no expense should be spared in making it as magnificent as possible, in order that they might be convinced she had not thrown herself away upon an adventurer, but, in fact, had made an alliance worthy of them and of herself.

She found me ready in seconding her wishes, and I was delighted to have so early an opportunity to make a display of our wealth. I began by hiring a suite of servants, each of whom had their appropriate situation and title. I exchanged the deceased Emir's family of pipes for others of greater value, and of the newest fashion. In the same manner I provided myself with a new set of coffee-cups, the saucers of which were fashioned in the most expensive manner; some of filigreed gold, others of enamel, and one or two, for my own particular use, inlaid with precious stones. Then, as I had stepped into the emir's shoes, I determined to slip on his pelisses also. He was curious in the luxuries of dress, for his wardrobe consisted of robes and furs of great value, which his widow informed me had existed in his family for many years, and which I did not now blush to adjust to my own shoulders. In short, before the day of the entertainment came, I had time to set up an establishment worthy of a great Aga; and I do believe, although born a barber, yet in look, manner, and deportment, no one could have acted a part truer to my new character than I did.

But I must not omit to mention, that previously to the feast, I had not failed to visit my new relations in all due form; and although I was greatly anxious respecting the result of our meeting, yet when I rode through the streets mounted on one of the emir's fat horses, caparisoned in velvet housings that swept the ground, and surrounded by a crowd of well-dressed servants, my delight and exultation exceeded any feeling that I had ever before experienced. To see the crowd make way, look up, and lay their hands on their breast as I passed—to feel and hear the fretting and champing of my horse's bit as he moved under me, apparently proud of the burden he bore—to enjoy the luxury of a soft and easy seat, whilst others were on foot—in fine, to revel in those feelings of consequence and consideration which my appearance procured, and not to have been intoxicated, was more than mere humanity could withstand, and accordingly I was completely beside myself. But what added most to the zest of this my first exhibition, was meeting some of my own needy countrymen in the streets, who had been my companions in the caravan from Bagdad, and who, in their sheepskin caps and thin scanty cotton garments, made but a sorry figure among the gaily dressed Osmanlies, and seemed to stand forth expressly to make me relish in the highest degree the good fortune with which I had been visited. Whether or no they recognized me, I know not; but this I recollect, that I turned my head on one side as I passed, and buried my face as well as I could in the combined shade of my beard, great turban, and furred pelisse.

My visits succeeded better than I could have expected. Whatever might have been the motives of my wife's brothers, they behaved to me with marked civility, and indeed flattered me into the belief that I had conferred an honour on their family in taking their sister off their hands. Merchants as they were, their conversation turned principally upon trade, and I made my best endeavours to talk up to the character I had assumed, and convinced them of the extent of my undertakings in commerce. But, at the same time, great was my circumspection not to commit myself; for when they began to question and cross-examine me upon the trade of Bagdad and Bassorah, the relations of those cities and of Arabia in general with India

and China, and to propose joint concerns in their various articles and produce, I immediately reduced my speech to monosyllables, entrenched myself in general terms, and assented to proposals which led to nothing.

Having completed my visits, I felt that one duty was still left, which
was, to make the good old Osman a partaker of my happiness, to inform
him of my marriage, and to invite him to our ensuing entertainment. But,
shall I own it? so much did I feel that I was acting a false part, and so fearful was I of being detected, that I dared not trust even him, taciturn as he
naturally was, with my secret, and therefore determined for the present to
have no communication with him, or, in fact, with any of my countrymen,
until I could feel myself so securely fixed in my new situation as to be
fearless of being displaced.

CHAPTER LXX: HIS DESIRE TO EXCITE ENVY
LAYS THE FOUNDATION OF HIS DISGRACE
HE QUARRELS WITH HIS WIFE

THE entertainment went off with the greatest success, and there was
every reason to suppose that I fully succeeded in making my guests
believe I was really the personage whom I pretended to be. I therefore began to feel secure in my new possessions, and gave myself up to enjoyment, associating with men of pleasure, dressing in the gayest attire, and,
in short, keeping a house that was the talk and envy of the city. 'Tis true
that I almost daily felt the inconvenience of being indebted to my wife for
such good fortune; for, notwithstanding the previous assurances of the
old Ayesha, I soon found that differences of opinion would arise on many
other subjects besides the comparative delicacy of cream and cheese tarts.
'Excellent man must that old emir have been,' frequently did I exclaim,
'who could go through life with only one subject of dispute with his wife!
For my part, if there happens to be two sides to a question, we are sure to
appropriate them one in opposition to the other.'

I had long promised to myself the enjoyment of one of the principal
pleasures arising from my good fortune; I mean, the exhibition of myself
in all my splendour before my countrymen in the caravanserai, and enjoying the astonishment which I should excite in the old Osman, my former
master.

Now, that all was safe, as I fully hoped, I could no longer resist the temptation, and accordingly dressed myself in my best attire, mounted the finest horse in my stable, gathered my whole suite of servants about me, and in the very busiest hour of the day proceeded to the caravanserai, in which, on my first arrival at Constantinople, I had appeared as a vender of pipe-sticks. Upon entering the gate, no one seemed to know me, but all were anxious to do me honour, hoping that in me they might find a purchaser of their merchandise. I inquired for Osman Aga, whilst my servants spread a beautiful Persian carpet for my seat, and at the same time offered me one of my most costly amber-headed chibouks to smoke. He came and seated himself, with all due respect, on the edge of my carpet, without recognizing me. I talked to him without reserve for some time, and remarked that he eyed me with looks of peculiar interest, when at length, unable to restrain himself any longer, he exclaimed, 'By the beard of the blessed Mohammed, you are either Hajjî Baba, or you are nobody!'

I laughed with all my heart at his exclamation, and when we had mutually explained, very soon related how I was situated, and to what profit I had turned the fifty pieces of gold which he had lent me. His philosophic mind did not appear so much elated with my change of fortune as I had anticipated; but my countrymen, the Persians, as soon as they heard that under that large turban and that heavy pelisse was seated Hajjî Baba, the once vender of little wares like themselves, and that all that splendour and circumstance of horse, servants, and rich pipes was attendant upon his person, their national feelings were awakened, and they could neither contain their envy nor their malevolence.

I now, too late, discovered the mistake I had committed in showing myself off in this manner, and would willingly have sneaked away without further triumph.

'What! is this Hajjî Baba?' said one, 'the son of the Ispahan barber? May his father's grave be polluted, and his mother abused!'

'Well acted, true child of Irân!' said another; 'you have done your utmost with the Turk's beard, and may others do the same with yours!'

'Look at his great turban, and his large trousers, and his long pipe,' said a third: 'his father never saw such things, not even in a dream!'

In this manner did my envious countrymen taunt me, until, asserting all my dignity, I rose from my seat, mounted my horse, and left the place amidst their scoffs and expressions of contempt. My first sensation was that of indignation at them, my second of anger at myself.

'You have been rightly served,' said I to myself, 'by the soul of Kerbelaif Hassan, the barber! What well-fed hound ever went among wolves without being torn to pieces? What fool of a townsman ever risked himself amongst the wild Arabs of the desert without being robbed and beaten? Perhaps Hajjî may one day become a wise man, but plentiful is the vexation he must eat first! Of what use is a beard,' said I, taking mine into my hand, 'when an empty sconce is tied to the end of it? about as much as a handle is to a basket without dates. Great wisdom had the sage who declared that no man was ever pleased with the elevation of his fellow, except perhaps when he saw him dangling on a gibbet!'

In this manner did I soliloquize until I reached my house, where, having retired to the harem, I endeavoured to seek repose for the remainder of the day, in order to chew the cud of my bitter reflections. But I was mistaken; for, to add to my misery, Shekerleb, my wife, as if impelled by some wicked demon, demanded that I should immediately advance her the money inserted in the marriage settlement for clothes, and so worked upon me by her very unreasonable entreaties, that, involving her in the ill-humour in which I had continued against my own countrymen, I poured forth the current of my feelings in language and gestures the most violent. Curses upon them and maledictions upon her came from my lips in horrid succession, until I, the once mild and patient Hajjî, had become more furious than a Mazanderan lion.

My wife at first was all astonishment, and, as she drew herself up at the head of her slaves and handmaids, seconded by the old Ayesha, waited with impatient silence for an opportunity to speak. At length, when she had found utterance, her mouth appeared too small for the volume of words which flowed from it. Her volubility unloosed the tongue of Ayesha, and the old woman's those of all the other women, until there arose such a tempest of words and screams, all of which were directed against me, that I was nearly overwhelmed.

I would have resisted, but I found it impossible. It raged with such fury, that the room in which we all stood was not large enough to contain us. I was the first to seek shelter, and made a retreat from my harem amid the groans, the revilings, and the clapping of hands of the beings within

"Seize him in the name of the Prophet!"

it, who, with my wife at their head, looked more like maniacs than those fair creatures, in paradise, promised by our Prophet to all true believers.

Tired, jaded, and distressed by my day's adventures, I retired into my own apartment, locked the door, and there, though surrounded by and master of every luxury that man can enjoy, I felt myself the most miserable of beings, detesting myself for my idiotical conduct in the present posture of my affairs, and full of evil forebodings for the future. The inconveniences of lying now stared me full in the face. I felt that I was caught in my own snare; for if I endeavoured to extricate myself from my present dilemma by telling more lies, it was evident that at the end I should not fail to be entirely entangled.

'Would to Heaven,' did I exclaim, 'that I had been fair and candid at first; for now I should be free as air, and my wife might have stormed until the day of judgement, without being a single shift the better for it; but I am bound by writings, sealed and doubly sealed, and I must ever and shall stand before the world a liar both by word and deed.'

CHAPTER LXXI: HE IS DISCOVERED
TO BE AN IMPOSTER, LOSES HIS WIFE AND
THE WIDE WORLD IS AGAIN BEFORE HIM

I PASSED a feverish night, and did not fall asleep until the muezzins from the minarets had announced the break of day. Scarcely had an hour elapsed, ere I was awoke by an unusual stir, and then was informed by one of my servants that my wife's brothers, attended by several other persons, were in the house.

Involuntarily, upon hearing this, I was seized with a trembling, which at first deprived me of all power of action, and the consequences of lying now spoke for themselves. Fifty horrors, one more hideous than the other, rose in my mind, and I began to feel a tingling in the soles of my feet, which the lapse of years had not been able to dispel, so impressive had been the lesson received at Meshed. 'But, after all,' I reflected, 'Shekerleb is my wife, happen what may; and if I have pretended to be richer than is really the case, I have only done what thousands before me have done also.' I then turned to my servant, and said, 'In the name of the Prophet let them come in,—and make ready the pipes and coffee.'

My bed was then rolled up and carried out of the room, and my visitors one after the other in silent procession walked in, and seated themselves on my divan. They consisted of my wife's two brothers, of her late father's brother, and his son, and of a stern-looking man whom I had never before seen. These were seated; but, besides, a numerous train of servants followed, who stood in a row at the end of the room, amongst whom, standing foremost, were two ruffian-like looking fellows armed with heavy canes, eyeing me as I thought with peculiar fierceness.

I endeavoured to appear as innocent and undisturbed as possible, and pretended the greatest delight at seeing them. Having made them every civil speech which I could devise, to which indeed I received nothing but monosyllables for answers, I ordered pipes and coffee, at the partaking of which I hoped to acquire some insight into the object of their visit.

'May your hours be fortunate!' said I to the elder brother. 'Is there anything at this early time of the day in which I can be of use? If there is, command me.'

'Hajjî,' said he, after an ominous pause, 'look at me! Do you take us for animals, without understanding, without common sense? or do you look upon yourself as the man of his day without compare, specially privileged to take the beards of humankind into your hand, and to do what you like with them?'

'What is this that you say?' I replied. 'O my Aga! I am nobody and nothing; I am less than an ounce of dust.'

'Man!' said the second brother, in a warmer tone of voice, 'nobody and nothing, do you say? then what have you made of us? Are we nothing, that you should come all this distance from Bagdad to make us dance like apes at your bidding?'

'Oh, Allah, great and good!' exclaimed I, 'what is all this? Why do
you speak after this manner? What
have I done? Speak, and speak truth!'

'Ah, Hajjî, Hajjî!' said my wife's
uncle, shaking his head and grey
beard at the same time, 'you have
been eating much abomination! Could
a man who has seen the world like

you, suppose that others will eat it with you, and say, thanks be to Allah! No, no—we may eat, but will not digest your insolence.'

'But what have I done, O my uncle?' said I to him; 'by my soul, speak!'

'What have you done?' said my wife's cousin. 'Is lying nothing? is stealing nothing? is marrying a wife under false pretences nothing? You must be a rare man without shame to call such acts nothing!'

'Perhaps,' said the eldest brother, 'you think it a great honour which the son of an Ispahan barber confers upon one of the richest families of Constantinople, when he marries their daughter!'

'And perhaps,' said the other, 'you may look upon a beggarly vender of pipe-sticks in the light of a merchant, and think him worthy of any alliance!'

'But Hajjî, praise be to Allah! is a great merchant,' said the uncle ironically: 'his silks and velvets are now on their way to bring us lamb-skins from Bokhara; his shawls are travelling to us from Cashmere, and his ships are blackening the surface of the seas between China and Bassorah!'

'And his parentage,' continued his son in the same strain, 'a barber's son did you say? forbid it, Allah! No, no; he dates from the Koreish. He is not even the descendant, but, by the blessing of God, of the ancestry of the Prophet; and who can come in competition with a Mansouri Arab?'

'What is all this?' again and again did I exclaim, as I saw the storm gathering about my ears. 'If you want to kill me, do so; but do not pull off my skin by inches.'

'I tell you what is it, man without faith,' said the stern man, who hitherto had remained immovable; 'you are a wretch who deserves not to live! and if you do not immediately give up all pretensions to your wife, and leave this house and everything that belongs to it, without a moment's delay, do you see those men' (pointing to the two ruffians before mentioned); 'they will just make your soul take leave of your body as easy as they would knock the tobacco out of their pipes. I have spoken, and you are master to act as you please.'

Then the whole of the assembly, as if excited by this speech, unloosed their tongues at once, and, without reserve of words or action, told me a great number of disagreeable truths.

This storm, which I permitted to rage without opening my lips, gave me time for reflection, and I determined to try what a little resistance would do.

'And who are you,' said I to the stern man, 'who dares come into my house, and treat me as your dog? As for these,' pointing to my wife's relations, 'the house is theirs, and they are welcome; but you, who are neither her father, her brother, nor her uncle, what have you to do here? I neither married your daughter, nor your sister, and therefore what can it be to you who I am?'

All this while he seemed swelling with rage. He and his ruffians were curling up their mustachios to the corners of their eyes, and eyeing me, as the lion does the hind, before he pounces upon it.

'Who am I?' said he with a voice of anger. 'If you want to know, ask those who brought me here. I and my men act from authority, which if you dispute, it will be the worse for you.'

'But,' said I, softening my tone, for I now found that they were officers of the police, 'but if you insist upon separating me from my wife, to whom I have been lawfully married, give me time to consult the men of the law. Every son of Islâm has the blessed Koran as his refuge, and ye would not be such infidels as to deprive me of that? Besides, I have not been told yet that she agrees to what you propose. She first sought me out; I did not seek her. She wooed me for my own sake, not for any worldly interest; and when I accepted her I knew her not, neither had I any tidings of either her wealth or her family. The whole has been the business of predestination, and if ye are Mussulmans, will ye dare to oppose that?'

'As to the wishes of Shekerleb upon the subject,' said the eldest brother, 'make your mind easy. She desires a separation more even than we do.'

'Yes, yes, in the name of the Prophet, yes, let him go in peace. For the sake of Allah, let us be free,' and fifty other such exclamations, all at once struck my ear; and on looking to the door which led into the women's apartments, from whence the sound came, I beheld my women veiled, headed by my wife, who had been conducted there on purpose to give evidence against me, and who all seemed possessed by so many evil spirits, shouting and wailing out their lamentations and entreaties for my dismissal, as if I were the wicked one in person to be exorcised from the house.

Finding that all was over with me, that it was in vain to contend against a power I could not withstand, stranger and unprotected as I was in a foreign land, I put the best face I could upon my forlorn situation, and getting up from my seat, I exclaimed, 'If it is so, be it so. I neither want Shekerleb nor her money, nor her brothers, nor her uncle, nor anything that belongs to them, since they do not want me; but this I will say, that they have treated me in a manner unworthy of the creed and name of Mussulmans. Had I been a dog among the unbelievers, I should have been treated better. From the bottom of my heart I believe that the same punishment which shall be inflicted, on the last day, upon those who reject our Holy Prophet, shall be inflicted upon my oppressors.' I then, with great emphasis, pronounced the following sentence against them, as near as my memory would serve me, from the blessed Koran: 'They shall have garments of living fire, fitted tight upon them; boiling water shall be poured over them; their bowels and skins shall be dissolved, and, in this state, they be beaten with red hot maces of iron, and flogged with whips, whose lashes are made of lightnings, and the noise of which shall be claps of thunder.'

Upon this, roused and excited as I was with the speech I had made, I stood in the middle of the room, and divested myself of every part of my dress which had belonged to my wife, or which I might have purchased with her money. Throwing down every article from me, as if it had been abomination, and then calling for an old cloak which had originally belonged to me, I threw it over my shoulders and made my exit, denouncing a curse upon the staring assembly I left behind me.

CHAPTER LXXII: AN INCIDENT IN THE STREET
DIVERTS HIS DESPAIR; HE SEEKS CONSOLATION
IN THE ADVICE OF OLD OSMAN

WHEN I had got into the street I walked hastily on without, for some time, heeding whither I was bending my steps. My breast was convulsed by a thousand contending passions; and so nearly had I lost possession of my reason, that, when in sight of the sea, I began seriously to consider whether it would not be wisdom to throw myself headlong in.

But, crossing a large open space, an occurrence happened which, however trifling it may appear, was of great consequence to me, inasmuch as it turned the current of my thoughts into a new channel, and saved me from destruction. I was witness to one of those dog fights so frequently seen in the streets of Constantinople. A dog had strayed into the territory of another community, had infringed their rights, and stolen a bone. Immediately an immense uproar ensued; all were on foot, and in full cry, and the strange dog was chased across the border into his own territory. Here, meeting some of his own friends, he called them about him, returned to the attack, and a general engagement ensued as I was passing.

While I stood by, intent upon the scene, a thought struck me, and I exclaimed, 'Allah, oh Allah, how inscrutable are thy designs! and how little ought man, narrow-minded, short-sighted man, ever to repine at thy decrees! Thou throwest into my path a lesson, which teaches me the way that I should go, and that assistance is ever at hand to those who will seek it; and, though given by a dog, let me not despise it. No, am I to be surprised at anything, when I see animals, without reason, acting like men, with it? Let me not be cast down, but rather retreat to where I may still find a friend, and seek consolation in his advice and experience!'

Upon this, I turned almost mechanically to where I knew I should find my faithful friend and adviser, the old Osman, who, although a Turk and a Sûni, had always behaved to me as if he had been my countryman, and one of my own religious persuasion. He received me in his usual quiet manner; and when I had related all my misfortunes, he puffed out a long volume of smoke from his never-failing chibouk, and exclaimed, with a deep sigh, '*Allah kerim!* (God is merciful!)'

'My friend,' said he, 'when you appeared here in all your magnificence before the Persians, from that moment I was apprehensive that some evil would befall you. You perhaps are yet not old enough to have learnt how odious are comparisons. Could you for a moment suppose, that men, in your own station in life, who are drudging on, day after day, intent upon the sale of a pipestick or a bag of Shiraz tobacco, that they could bear to be bearded by an appearance of greatness and prosperity, so much beyond anything which they could ever expect to attain? Had you appeared with a better coat or a richer cap than they, or had you been mounted on a horse, when they could only afford an ass, then, perhaps, nothing more would have been said, but that you were more expert in making your fortune, and a better retailer of your wares. But to crush, to beat them down, with your magnificent dress, your amber-headed pipes, your train of servants, your richly caparisoned horse, and, above all, the airs of grandeur and protection which you took upon yourself, was more than they could allow, and they immediately rose in hostility, and determined to bring you down to their own level again, if possible. Evidently, it is they who have whispered into the ear of your wife's brothers that you were not a Bagdad merchant, but only the son of an Ispahan barber, and a sorry vender of little wares. They, doubtless, soon undeceived them respecting the possibility of fulfilling the stipulations to which you have bound yourself in your wife's marriage contract; and they, it is plain, have commented freely upon your pretensions to noble birth, and upon the flourishing account which you gave of your mercantile concerns, of your transactions in Bokhara, and of your ships sailing to China. Had you first visited me in a quiet way, as Hajjî Baba, the Ispahani, and not as Hajjî Baba, the Turkish Aga, I would have warned you against making an undue exhibition of yourself and your prosperity before your countrymen; but the mischief was done as soon as the deed was over, and now all that can be recommended is, that from the past you gain experience for the future.' After this speech he took to his pipe again, and puffed away with redoubled vigour.

'This may be very true,' said I. 'What is done, is done, and peace abide with it: but, after all, I am a Mussulman, and justice is due to me as well as to another. I never heard of a woman putting away her husband, although the contrary frequently happens; and it has not yet reached my understanding why I should be the only true believer who is called into the house, and thrust out of it again, in a manner that would even disgrace a dog, merely because it suits a capricious woman one morning to like, and the evening after to dislike, me. Cadies, mufties, sheikh-el-islams, abound here as well as in other Mohamedan cities, and why should I not have recourse to them? They are paid to administer justice, and wherefore should they sit, with their hands across, counting their beads, when such injustice as that, with which I have been visited, is going about the land seeking for redress?'

'Are you mad, Hajjî', rejoined the old man, 'to think of redress from the widow and relations of one of the most powerful emirs of Islam, and that, too, when she is supported by her brothers, two of the richest merchants in Constantinople?—Where have you lived all your lifetime, not to know, that he who hath most gold hath most justice? and that, if such a man as you were to appear before the tribunal of the mufti, with every word, line, leaf, and surai of the Koran in your favour, and one as rich and powerful as your wife's brother were to appear on the other side against you, as long as he had gold in his favour, you might appeal to your sacred book until you and it were tired of walking round each other, for justice you would never obtain.'

'O, Ali! O, Mohamed!' exclaimed I, 'if the world is indeed as iniquitous as this, then Hajjî Baba, truly, has made a bad bargain, and I wish he were again in possession of his pipesticks: but I cannot, and will not, lose all and everything in this easy manner,—I will go and proclaim my misfortunes from the housetop, rather.'

Upon which, in utter despair, I began to cry and moan, and pulled out some of my beard by the roots.

Osman Aga endeavoured to comfort me—made me look back upon my past life, and brought to my recollection our mutual adventures while prisoners among the Turcomans.

'God is all-powerful and all-merciful,' said he. 'Our destinies are written in the book, and therefore what is there left, but to submit?'

'But I am a Persian,' exclaimed I (a new thought having crossed my mind), 'as well as a Mussulman; why, therefore, should I submit to injustice from a Turk?—We are, after all, a nation, and have had our Jinghizs, our Timours, and our Nadirs, who made our name respected throughout the world, and who burnt the fathers of the Turks wherever they could find them. I will seek our ambassador, and, if he be a man, he will insist upon justice being done me. Yes, yes! the ambassador shall get back my wife; (oh, lucky thought!) and then we shall see who will take her from me again.'

So elated was I by this idea, that I did not stop to hear what Osman might have to say on the subject, but immediately sallied forth, full of fresh spirits and vigour, to seek out the representative of our King of Kings, who, at the best of all fortunate hours, had very recently arrived on a mission to the Sublime Porte.

CHAPTER LXXIII: ENDEAVOURING TO GAIN SATISFACTION
FROM HIS ENEMIES HE ACQUIRES A FRIEND
SOME ACCOUNT OF MIRZA FIROUZ

UPON inquiry I found that the ambassador had been provided with a residence at Scutari, and thither I immediately bent my course, happy to have the time which I should pass in the boat at my disposal, in order to arrange my ideas for the purpose of making out a clear and strong case of complaint.

Having landed, I inquired the way to his house, the avenues of which were thronged by his numerous servants, who reminded me of my country (so different from that in which we were), by their loquaciousness and quick gesticulation.

They soon found by my discourse, that I was one of them, although disguised by a Turkish dress, and without any difficulty I was promised immediately to be ushered into the presence of their master. But previously to this, I was anxious to acquire some little insight into his character, in order that I might shape my discourse accordingly; and therefore entered into conversation with one of his valets, who did not scruple to talk fully and unreservedly upon every topic upon which I required information.

The result of my inquiries was as follows: The ambassador, by name Mirza Firouz, was by birth a Shirazi, of respectable though not of high parentage, excepting in the instance of his mother, who was sister to a former grand vizier of great power, who, in fact, had been the means of placing the Shah upon his throne. The Mirza married his cousin, a daughter of the said vizier; and this led to his being employed in the government, though he had previously undergone many vicissitudes, which had caused him to travel into various countries. This circumstance, however, was one of the reasons of his being selected by the Shah to transact his business at foreign courts. 'He is a man of a quick and penetrating mind,' said my informant: 'irascible, but easy to soothe, of a tender and forgiving nature, although in his first anger led to commit acts of violence. He is gifted with the most overwhelming powers of speech, which always are sure to get him out of the scrapes into which his indiscreet use of them very frequently leads him. To his servants and followers he is kind and the contrary, by turns. Sometimes he permits them to do and say everything which they choose, at others, he keeps them at a most chilling distance. But, on the whole, he is easy of access, of agreeable commerce, of most fascinating manners, and of a joyous and sociable nature.'

Such was the man into whose presence I was conducted. He was seated in a corner, after the manner of Persia; therefore I could not ascertain what his height might be, but his bust was extremely fine. His head was symmetrically placed on his shoulders, which were blended in an easy curve with his neck; whilst his tight dress helped to give great breadth to his breast. His face was one of the handsomest I had ever seen amongst my countrymen, his nose aquiline, his eyes large and sparkling, his teeth and mouth exquisite, and his beard the envy of all beholders. In short, as a specimen of the country he respresented, none could have been better selected.

When we had interchanged our greetings as true believers, he said to me, 'Are you an Irani?'

'Yes,' said I, 'so please you.'

'Then why in looks an Osmanli?' said he. 'Praise be to Allah, that we have a king and a country of whom no one need be ashamed.'

'Yes,' answered I, 'your ordonnances are truth, and I am become less than a dog, since I have put on the airs of a Turk. My days have been passed in bitterness, and my liver has melted into water, since I have entangled myself by a connexion with this hated people; and my only refuge is in God and you.'

'How is this?' said he: 'speak.—Has a child of Ispahan (for such you are by your accent) been taken in by a Turk? This is wonderful indeed! We travel all this way to make them feed upon our abomination, not to learn to eat theirs.'

I then related the whole of my adventures from the beginning to the end. As I proceeded he seemed wonderfully interested. When I got to my marriage he became much amused, and roared with laughter at the settlements I had made on my wife. The account I gave of the entertainment, the respect with which I was treated, my magnificence and grandeur, afforded him great delight; and the more I descanted upon the deception which I had practised upon the cows of Turks, as he called them, the more interest he took in my narrative, which he constantly interrupted by his exclamations, 'Aye, well done, oh Ispahani!—Oh! thou bankrupt!—By Allah! You did well!—If I had been there, I could not have done better.'

But when I informed him of the manner I had been served by my envious countrymen, of the finishing scene in my own house, of the screams of my women, of the speeches of my wife's relations,—and when I represented the very words, look, and attitude with which I made my exit, far from having produced the sympathy I expected, his mirth was excited to such a degree, that I thought the veins in his forehead would have burst; and he actually rolled himself on his sofa in the convulsions of laughter.

'But may it please you to consider,' said I, 'oh my Aga! the situation in which I am now placed. Instead of the bed of roses upon which I slept, I have not even a pillow whereon to lay my head. As for the horses and velvet which I used to bestride, happy should I now be could I claim even an ass for my own. And when I call to mind the luxuries in which I revelled, my rich dresses, my splendid horses, my train of servants, my marble baths, my pipes, my coffee-cups—in short, what shall I say, my everything a man could wish for, and now find myself a beggar—conceive the bitter recollections which prey upon me, and which excite anything but laughter in my breast, whatever they may do in yours.'

'But those Turks, those heavy buffaloes of Turks,' roared he, still screaming with laughter; 'praise be to Allah! I can see them now with their long beards, their great caps, and their empty heads, believing all that the sharp-witted madman of Persia chose to tell them, and they would have gone on believing, had they not been undeceived by a similar species of madman.

'But what have I to do in the business?' said he to me. 'I am neither your father nor your uncle, to interfere and make it up with your wife's relations; nor am I a cadi, or a mufti, who can judge the case between you.'

'No,' answered I; 'but you are my refuge here, and the representative of God's vicegerent upon earth; and you can see justice done me, and not let a poor unfriended stranger be oppressed.'

'But would you get back possession of your wife,' said he, 'and stand a chance of being murdered? Of what good would all your riches be, if the day after repossessing them you were found dead in your bed? No, no; lend me your ear, and hearken to good council. Throw off your Turkish clothes, and be a Persian again; and when in your proper character, I will keep you in mind, and see what may be done for you. Your story has interested me, your wit and manner are agreeable, and believe me that many better things are to be done in the world than to smoke a long pipe all day, with no other object in life than to sleep upon a bed of roses, and to ride a fat horse. In the meanwhile, take up your quarters here; look upon yourself as one of my suite for the present, and whenever I wish to be merry you shall come and relate your story over again.'

Upon this I went up to him, kissed his knee in token of acknowledgement, and retired, scarcely knowing what steps to take in this unsettled posture of my affairs.

CHAPTER LXXIV: HE BECOMES USEFUL TO AN AMBASSADOR, WHO MAKES HIM PARTAKER OF HIS CONFIDENCE

NECESSITY,' so the poet sayeth, 'is as a strong rider with sharp stirrups, who maketh the sorry jade do that which the strong horse sometimes will not do.'

I was disappointed, vexed, and mortified. My hopes of living a life of ease and enjoyment had disappeared, and I once more saw myself obliged to have recourse to my own ingenuity to keep me from starvation.

'If I have lost a home,' said I, 'see I have found a friend. Let me not reject his proffered protection; and the same powerful destiny which has led me on step by step through the labyrinth of life will doubtless again take me by the hand, and perhaps at length safely land me where I shall no longer be perplexed respecting the path I ought to pursue.'

I determined to make the most of my access to the ambassador; and happy was I to find, that the liking which he had taken to me at first sensibly, though gradually, increased during our succeeding interviews. He made use of me to acquire information, and conversed freely upon the business of his government, and upon matters connected with his mission.

Having all my life been taken up in making my own fortune, I had turned my mind but little to public events. Of the nations of the world I scarcely knew any but my own and the Turks. By name only the Chinese, the Indians, the Affghans, the Tartars, the Cûrds, and the Arabs were known to me; and of the Africans I had some knowledge, having seen different specimens of them as slaves in our houses. Of the Franks—the Russians (if such they may be called) were those of whom we had the most knowledge in Persia, and I had also heard of the Ingliz and the Franciz.

When I reached Constantinople, I was surprised to hear that many more Frank nations existed besides the three above mentioned; but still occupied with my own affairs, I acquired but little knowledge concerning them.

Now that I was thrown into the ambassador's society, my ideas took a new turn, and hearing matters discussed which had never even reached my understanding, I became more inquisitive. He seemed pleased to have found in me one who took interest in his views, and at length let me entirely into his confidence.

One morning, having received letters from his court, he called me to him, said that he wished for some private conversation, and accordingly ordered every one to depart from before him except myself.

He made me sit, and then in a low voice said, 'Hajjî, I have long wished to speak to you. Those who compose my suite, between you and me, do not possess the sort of understanding I require. 'Tis true, they are Persians, and are endowed with more wit than all the world beside; but in affairs of the *dowlet* (the state), they are nothing, and rather impede than forward the business upon which I have been sent. Now, praise be to Allah! I see that you are not one of them. You are much of a man, one who has seen the world and its business, and something may come from out of your hands. You are a man who can make play under another's beard, and suck the marrow out of an affair without touching its outside. Such I am in want of, and if you will devote yourself to me, and to our Shah, the King of Kings, both my face as well as your own will be duly whitewashed; and, by the blessings of our good destinies, both our heads will touch the skies.'

'Whatever is of my strength,' replied I, 'is at your service. I am your slave and your servant, and I myself will place my own ear into your hand. Order and command me: by my head and eyes, I am ready.'

'Perhaps you have heard it reported in the world,' said he, 'that the object of my mission is to buy women slaves for the Shah, to see them instructed in dancing, music, and embroidery, and to purchase spangled silks and other luxuries for the royal harem; but that is of course a blind for the multitude. I am not an ambassador for such miserable purposes: no, my business is of greater import; and our king, whose penetration is as searching as lightning itself, does not select men to transact his affairs without very substantial reasons. He has chosen me, and that's enough. Now hearken to what I shall tell you.

'But a few months ago an ambassador from Europe arrived at the Gate of Empire, Tehran, and said he was sent by a certain Boonapoort, calling himself Emperor of the French nation, to bring a letter and presents to the Shah. He exhibited full powers, by which his words were to be looked upon as his master's, and his actions as his actions; and he also affirmed, that he had full instructions to make a treaty. He held himself very high indeed, and talked of all other nations of Franks as dirt under his feet, and not worth even a name. He promised to make the Russians restore their conquests in Georgia to us, to put the Shah in possession of Teflis, Baadkoo, Derbent, and of all which belonged to Persia in former times. He said, that he would conquer India for us, and drive the English from it; and, in short, whatever we asked he promised to be ready to grant.

'Now, 'tis true, we had heard of the French before, and knew that they made good cloth and rich brocades; but we never heard that they could do all this ambassador proclaimed.

'Something we had heard also of their attacking Egypt, for coffee and khenna had become dear in consequence; and it was in the recollection of one of our old khans of the Seffi family, that an ambassador from a certain Shah Louis of France had been seen at the court of Shah Sultan Hosein; but how this Boonapoort had become Shah, not a single man in Persia could explain. The Armenian merchants, who travel into all countries, affirmed, that to their knowledge such a person in fact did exist, and that he was a great breeder of disturbance; and it was from what they said and from other circumstances, that the Shah agreed to receive his ambassador; but whether the papers which he exhibited, written in characters that no one could read, were true or false, or whether all he said was to the purpose or not, who was to say? Our viziers, great and small, knew nothing of the matter; our Shah, who (may Allah preserve him) knows everything under the sun, he had no knowledge of it; and excepting one Coja Obed, an Armenian, who had been to Marsilia, a town in France, where he had been shut up in a prison for forty days,[1] and one Narses, a priest of that nation, who had studied in a convent of dervishes somewhere in those countries, we had no one at the gate of the King of Kings who could let any light into the chambers of our brain, or who could in the least explain whether this Boonapoort or his representative were impostors or not—

[1] Quarantine, we presume, is here meant.

whether they were come to take our caps from off our heads, or to clothe us with the kalaats of good fortune.

'However, we were not very long in doubt; for when the English infidels who trade between India and Persia, some of whom reside at Abusheher, heard of the arrival of this ambassador, they immediately sent off messengers, letters, and an agent, to endeavour to impede the reception of this Frenchman, and made such extraordinary efforts to prevent his success, that we soon discovered much was to be got between the rival dogs.

'"By my crown," exclaimed the Shah, "all this cometh from the ascendant of my good stars. Here sit I upon my throne, whilst the curs of uncleanness come from the north and the south, from the east and west, bringing me vast presents for the liberty of fighting and quarrelling at the foot of it. In the name of the Prophet, let them approach!"

'When I left the imperial gate, an ambassador from the English was expected, and the letters which I have just received are full of the circumstances of his proposed reception, and the negotiations on foot concerning it, but the Shah cannot well enter upon them before he hears from me; because, having been informed that specimens of all the different European nations were to be seen at Constantinople, each of whom had an ambas-

sador, there, he, in his wisdom, has judged it expedient to dispatch me hither, to obtain all the information of which we are so much in want, to clear up every doubt that exists in Persia about the French and English, and if possible to find out whether all they say of themselves be true or false.

'Now, Hajjî,' said the ambassador, 'I am only one man, and this is a business, as I have found out, sufficient for fifty. The Franks are composed of many, many nations. As fast as I hear of one hog, another begins to grunt, and then another and another, until I find that there is a whole herd of them. As I told you before, those who compose my suite are not men to help me in research, and I have cast my eyes upon you. From your exertions I expect much. You must become acquainted with some infidels; you understand the Turkish language, and they will be able to inform you of much that we want to know. I will furnish you with a copy of the Shah's instructions to me upon that head, which you will lock up of course in the secret corners of your brain, and which will be your guide upon what we wish to acquire. And until that be done, go, sit in a corner, and make one long and deep thought upon the plan of operations that we ought to pursue.' Upon this he dismissed me, and I left him with new prospects of advancement in the career of life.

CHAPTER LXXV: HIS FIRST ESSAYS IN PUBLIC LIFE
AND THE USE HE WAS OF TO HIS EMPLOYER

AS soon as the ambassador had furnished me with an extract of his *vakayeh nameh*, or his instructions, I walked out to an adjacent cemetery to read it over undisturbed. I kept the paper carefully folded in the lining of my cap, and as it was my first initiation into public business, the principal contents of it have remained in my memory through life.

The ambassador was, in the first place, enjoined to discover, in truth, what was the extent of that country called Frangistan; and if the Shah, known in Persia by the name of the *Shahi Frank*, or king of the Franks, actually existed, and which was his capital.

In the second place, he was ordered to discover how many *Ils*, or tribes of Franks, there were; whether they were divided into *Shehernisheens* and *Sahranisheens*, inhabitants of towns and dwellers in the desert, as in Persia, who were their khans, and how governed.

Thirdly, to inquire what was the extent of France, whether it was a tribe of the Franks or a separate kingdom, and who was the infidel Boona-poort, calling himself emperor of that country.

In the fourth place, his attention was to be turned particularly to what regarded the Ingliz, who had long been known in Persia, by means of their broadcloth, watches, and penknives. He was to inquire what description of infidels they were, whether they lived in an island all the year round, without possessing any *kishlak* (warm region) to migrate to in the summer, and whether most of them did not inhabit ships and eat fish; and if they did live there, how it happened that they had obtained possession of India; and he was to clear up that question so long agitated in Persia, how England and London were connected, whether England was part of London, or London part of England?

In the fifth place, he was commanded to bring positive intelligence of who and what the *Coompani* was, of whom so much was said—how connected with England—whether an old woman, as sometimes reported, or whether it consisted of many old women; and whether the account which was credited of its never dying, like the Lama of Thibet, were not a fable. He was also enjoined to clear up certain unintelligible accounts of the manner in which England was governed.

In the sixth place, some positive information concerning *Yengi duniah*, or the New World, was much wanted, and he was to devote part of his attention to that subject.

Lastly, he was ordered to write a general history of the Franks, and to inquire what would be the easiest method of making them renounce pork and wine, and converting them to the true and holy faith, that is, to the religion of Islâm.

Having well pondered over this paper, I considered that it would be easy to get it answered through the means of a *katib*, or scribe, attached to the then Reis Effendi, and with whom, during the short gleam of splendour and riches which had shone upon me, I had formed a great intimacy. I knew the coffee-house he frequented, and the hour he was most likely to be found there; and although he was not much addicted to talking, yet I hoped, as he sipped his coffee and smoked his pipe (particularly if I treated him), his heart might expand, and I might obtain his real opinion.

Full of this idea, I immediately imparted it to the ambassador, who seemed so delighted, that he at once did me the honour to take all the merit of it to himself.

'Did not I tell you so?' exclaimed he; 'did I not say that you were a man of ingenuity? Acknowledge, then, that I am not without penetration; own, that it requires a sharp discernment to discover at once where abilities lie; and that had it not been for me, we should never have discovered this katib, who is to tell us everything, and thus fulfil the instructions of the Asylum of the Universe.'

He then empowered me, if I found it necessary, to promise him a present, by which means, should there be any deficiency in his information, he might perhaps succeed in obtaining it from the fountain head, namely, the Reis Effendi himself.

I went to the coffee-house at the proper time, and there found my friend. I approached him with great demonstrations of friendship; and calling to the waiting man, ordered some best Yemen coffee, which was served up as we sat one opposite the other. In the course of conversation he pulled out his watch, when I seized the opportunity of introducing my subject.

'That is an European watch,' said I, 'is it not?'

'Yes, truly,' said he; 'there are none in the world beside.'

'Wonderful,' answered I, 'those Franks must be an extraordinary people.'

'Yes,' said he, 'but they are kafirs' (infidels).

'In the name of Allah,' taking my pipe from my mouth and putting it into his, 'tell me something respecting them. This Frangistan, is it a large country? Where does its king reside?'

'What say you, friend?' answered he; 'a large country, do you ask? A large country indeed, not governed by one king alone, but by many kings.'

'But I have heard,' said I, 'it is composed of many tribes, all having different names and different chiefs; still begin, in fact, but one nation.'

'You may call them one nation if you choose,' said he, 'and perhaps such is the case, for they all shave their chins, let their hair grow, and wear hats—they all wear tight clothes—they all drink wine, eat pork, and do not believe in the blessed Mahomed. But it is plain they are governed by many kings; see the numerous ambassadors who flock here to rub their foreheads against the threshold of our Imperial Gate. So many of these dogs are here that it is necessary to put one's trust in the mercies of Allah, such is the pollution they create.'

'In the name of the Prophet speak on,' said I, 'and I will write. Praise be to Allah! you are a man of wisdom.' Upon which, whilst I took out my inkstand from my girdle, and composed myself to write, he stroked his beard, and curled the tips of his moustachios, recollecting within himself which were the principal nations of Europe.

He prefaced his information by saying, 'But why trouble yourself? They all are dogs alike—all sprung from one dunghill; and if there be truth in Heaven, and we believe our blessed Koran, all will burn hereafter in one common furnace. But stop,' said he, counting his fingers: 'in the first place, there is the *Nemsé Giaour*, the Austrian infidel, our neighbours; a quiet, smoking race, who send us cloth, steel, and glassware; and are governed by a Shah springing from the most ancient race of unbelievers: he sends us a representative to be fed and clothed.

'Then come those heretics of Muscovites, a most unclean and accursed generation. Their country is so large, that one extremity is said to be buried in eternal snows, whilst its other is raging with heat. They are truly our enemy; and when we kill them, we cry *Mashallah*, praise be to God! Men and women govern there by turns; but they resemble us inasmuch as they put their sovereigns to death almost as frequently as we do.

'Again, there is a Prussian infidel, who sends us an ambassador, Allah only knows why; for we are in no need of such vermin: but, you well know, that the Imperial Gate is open to the dog as well as the true believer; for the rain of Providence descends equally upon both.

'Who shall I say next, in the name of the Prophet? Let us see: there are two northern unbelievers, living at the extremity of all things—the Danes and Swedes. They are small tribes, scarcely to be accounted among men, although it is said the Shah of Denmark is the most despotic of the kings of Franks, not having even janissaries to dispute his will; whilst the Swedes are famous for a madman, who once waged a desperate war in Europe; caring little in what country he fought, provided only that he did fight; and who, in one of his acts of desperation, made his way into our borders, where, like a wild beast, he was at length brought to bay, and taken prisoner. Owing to this circumstance we were introduced to the knowledge of his nation; or otherwise, by the blessing of Allah, we should never have known that it even existed.

'I will mention one more, called Flemengs, infidels, dull, heavy, and boorish; who are amongst the Franks what the Armenians are amongst us —having no ideas beyond those of thrift, and no ambition beyond that of riches. They used to send us a sleepy ambassador to negotiate the introduction of their cheeses, butter, and salt-fish; but their government has been destroyed since the appearance of a certain Boonapoort, who (let them and the patron of all unbelief have their due) is in truth a man; one whom we need not be ashamed to class with the Persian Nadir, and with our own Suleiman.'

Here I stopped the Katib in his narrative, and catching at the name, I exclaimed, 'Boonapoort, Boonapoort—that is the word I wanted! Say something concerning him. I have heard he is a rare and daring infidel.'

'What can I say,' said my companion, 'except that he once was a man of nothing, a mere soldier; and now he is the Sultan of an immense nation, and gives the law to all the Franks? He did his best endeavours to molest us also, by taking Egypt, and sent innumerable armies to conquer it; but he had omitted to try the edge of a true believer's sword ere he set out, and was obliged to retreat, after having frightened a few Mamalukes, and driven the Bedouins into their deserts.'

'But is there not a certain tribe of infidels called Ingliz?' said I, 'the most unaccountable people on earth, who live in an island, and make pen-knives?'

'Yes, truly,' said the Katib, 'they, amongst the Franks, are those who for centuries have most rubbed their heads against the imperial threshold, and who have found most favour in the sight of our great and magnanimous Sultan. They are powerful in ships; and in watches and broadcloth unrivalled.'

'But what have you heard of their government?' said I: 'is it not composed of something besides a king?'

'Yes,' returned he, 'you have been rightly informed; but how can you and I understand the humours of such madmen? They have a Shah, 'tis true; but it is a farce to call him by that title. They feed, clothe, and lodge him; give him a yearly income, surround him by all the state and form of a throne; and mock him with as fine words and with as high-sounding titles as we give our sovereigns; but a common Aga of the Janissaries has more power than he; he does not dare even to give the bastinado to one of his own viziers, be his fault what it may; whereas the Aga, if expedient, would crop the ears of half the city, and still receive nothing but reward and encouragement.

'Then they have certain houses full of madmen, who meet half the year round for the purposes of quarrelling. If one set says white, the other cries black; and they throw more words away in settling a common question than would suffice one of our muftis during a whole reign. In short, nothing can be settled in the state, be it only whether a rebellious Aga is to have his head cut off and his property confiscated, or some

such trifle, until these people have wrangled. Then what are we to believe? Allah, the Almighty and Allwise, to some nations giveth wisdom,
and to others folly! Let us bless Him and our Prophet, that we are not
born to eat the miseries of the poor English infidels, but can smoke our
pipes in quiet on the shores of our own peaceful Bosphorus!'

'Strange, strange things you tell me,' said I, 'and had I not heard them,
I could not believe something more, which is, that all India belongs to
them, and that it is governed by old women. Do you know that fact?'

'I shall not be surprised to hear of anything they do,' answered he, 'so
mad are they generally reported to be; but that India is governed by infidel old women, that has never yet reached our ears. Perhaps it is so. God
knows,' continued he, musing, 'for mad people do wonderful things.'

After a pause, 'Now,' said I, 'have I learnt all, or are there more unbelievers? By your beard, tell me; for who would have thought that the
world was so composed?'

He reflected for some time, and
said, 'O yes, I forgot to mention
two or three nations; but, in truth,

they are not worthy of notice. There are Spanish, Portuguese, and Italian
infidels, who eat their swine, and worship their image after their own
manner; but who, in fact, are nothing even amongst the Franks. The first
is known to us by their *patakas* (dollars); the second sends us some Jews;
and the third imports different sorts of dervishes, who pay considerable
sums into the imperial treasury for building churches, and for the privilege

of ringing bells. I must also mention the *papa* (pope), the Caliph of the Franks, who lives in Italia, and does not cease his endeavours to make converts to his faith; but we are more than even with him, for we convert infidels in greater proportion than they, notwithstanding all the previous pain which man must suffer before he is accepted for a true believer.'

'One more question I must ask,' said I, 'and then I am satisfied. Can you tell me anything positive about *Yengi duniah*, the New World; for I have heard so many contradictory reports that my brain is bewildered? How do they get at it, underground, or how?'

'We have not had many dealings with it,' said the Katib, 'and, therefore, know not much of the matter; but this is true, that one can get there by ship, because ships belonging to the New World have actually been seen here. They are all infidels, my friend,' exclaimed he, with a sigh; 'all infidels, as much as those of the old world, and, by the blessing of Allah, the Allwise, they will all grill in the same furnace.'

Finding that upon this subject the Katib was deficient, I ceased questioning; and our conversation having now lasted a long time, I released him from further importunity, by calling for more coffee and replenishing our pipes. We then separated, with mutual promises of meeting again.

CHAPTER LXXVI: HAJJI BABA WRITES
THE HISTORY OF EUROPE AND WITH HIS AMBASSADOR
RETURNS TO PERSIA

I RETURNED to my ambassador full of the information I had acquired, and all-joyous at the success which had attended my first essay in diplomatic life. He was delighted at the memoir I had drawn up from the materials furnished me by the Katib, and as long as we remained at Constantinople daily sent me in search of further particulars, until we both thought ourselves sufficiently in force to be able to draw up a general History of

Europe, which the Centre of the Universe in his instructions to the ambassador had ordered him to present on his return. Most assiduously did I apply myself in composing this precious morsel of history. I made a rough draft, which was submitted to the correction of my chief, and when he had seasoned its contents to the palate of the King of Kings, softening down those parts which might appear improbable, and adding to those not sufficiently strong, he delivered it over to a clerk, who in a fair hand transcribed the whole, until a very handsome volume was produced. It was duly bound, ornamented, and inserted in a silk and muslin bag, and then the ambassador conceived it might be fit to be placed in the hands of the Shah.

Mirza Firouz having now, as he conceived, accomplished the objects of his mission, prepared to return, and announced his intention not only of taking me with him, but also of continuing me in the employ of the government, as soon as we should reach Tehran; 'for,' said he, 'a person so well acquainted with the interests of the Franks will be of great use in treating with the infidel ambassadors now in Persia.'

He could not have devised a plan better suited to my wishes; for after my cruel treatment by the Turks, I hated everything relating to them. Their city was become odious to me, and whenever I thought upon Shekerleb my heart swelled with rage. Much time had now elapsed since my affair with the chief priest of Tehran. The Mollah Nadân, so I had heard, had long ago been blown from the mouth of a mortar, and the widow, whom I left in the hands of the Cûrds, had never returned to Persia. Therefore, I concluded I might show myself in all safety, for I argued thus: should I even be recognized, still who would venture to molest me, powerfully protected as I should be by men in office? The chief executioner had recovered possession of his horse and furniture, when the unfortunate Nadân had been seized; and there was every reason to suppose that Abdul Kerim had shared the fate of his mistress, the chief priest's widow, for he had no more been heard of; so I did not fear that he would call upon me to refund the hundred tomauns. What had I then to apprehend on returning to Tehran? Nothing that I could foresee; and if once it were known that I was a servant of the Shah, even being a thousand times more criminal than I was in fact, I might put my cap on one side and walk all over the empire with impunity.

Fortified by these reflections, I made my preparations with alacrity to

Of a sudden a lattice was thrown open

accompany the ambassador. But previous to our departure, I determined upon visiting my countrymen in the caravanserai, where with a better chance of success I now might give myself those airs of importance which had succeeded so ill at my last exhibition. Having taken some trouble to make it well understood that I was attached to the embassy, I no longer dreaded their contempt; and such is the respect that one invested with that character is sure to inspire, that on this occasion I had no reason to complain of any want of attention. Every word addressed to me was now prefaced with, By your favour, By your condescension, May your kindness never be less; and compliments which never ended, interlarded all the fine discourses I heard. To hear them, nobody could have ever supposed that I was the same person whom not two months before they had laughed to scorn: on the contrary, one ignorant of the circumstance would have set me down for a personage upon whom the issues of life and death depended. But when I took my leave of the old Osman, I found him unchanged, and every word he spoke showed that his affection for the son of the barber of Ispahan was the feeling which ever actuated his conduct towards me. 'Go, my son,' said he, as he parted from me, 'whether you be a prisoner with the Turcomans, or a priest, or a seller of pipe-sticks, or a Turkish Aga, or a Persian Mirza; be you what you may, I shall always put up my prayers for your prosperity, and may Allah attend your steps wherever you go.'

Having made his visits of ceremony, and taken his leave of the Turkish authorities, the ambassador left Scutari, accompanied by a large company of his own countrymen, who conducted him about one parasang on the road to Persia, and then received their dismissal. Our journey was propitious, and nothing took place in it worthy of notice from the day of our departure until our arrival in Persia. At Erivan we heard the news of the day, though but imperfectly; but at Tabriz, the seat of Abbas Mirza's government, we were initiated into the various questions which then agitated the country and the court. The principal one was the rivalry between the French and English ambassadors; the object of the former, who had already been received by the Shah, being to keep away the latter, who had not yet reached the foot of the throne.

Various were the anecdotes related of the exertions made by them to attain their ends, and the whole of Persia was thrown into astonishment upon seeing infidels come so far from their own countries, at so much trouble and expense, to quarrel in the face of a whole nation of true believers, who were sure to despise, to deride, and to take them in.

The Frenchman, by way of enforcing his demands, constantly brought forward the power of his own sovereign, his greatness and preponderance over all the states of Europe, and did not cease to extol the immense numbers of troops he could bring into the field.

To this he was answered, 'That may be very true; but what is that to us? Whole empires intervene, and, therefore, what affinity can there be between France and Persia?'

'But,' said the Frenchman, 'we want to conquer India from the English, and we wish to have an open road through your territories.'

'What is that to us?' again said the Shah: 'you may want India, but we are in no way anxious to entertain your troops.'

'But we will conquer Georgia for you, put you in possession of Teflis, and secure you from further molestation from the Russians.'

'That is another case,' said the Shah; 'when once we see the effects of your interference, and hear that there are no more Russians on this side the Caucasus, we will treat with you: until then we can allow no passage through our territories, nor break with our old friends the English!'

On the other hand, the English said, 'The French can have no other object in coming to Persia than to molest us; we require that you send them away.'

'How!' said the Shah, 'we cannot do that; for that would be against the laws of hospitality. The gate of our palace is open to every one.'

'But,' urged the English, 'you must either retain one or the other— and must decide between us. Either agree to be our friends and expel the French, or make up your minds to receive us as enemies.'

'Why should we make ourselves enemies to please you? We want to be friends with all the world.'

'But,' continued the English, 'we will help and strengthen you, and give you money.'

'Oh! that is another case,' said the Shah; 'tell me how much, and then all may be done.'

Such was nearly the state of things when we left Tabriz, and as my ambassador was expected with impatience at Tehran, we did not tarry long with the prince royal, but prosecuted our journey with all dispatch.

On the morning of our arrival at Sultanieh, on the road from Tehran, we discovered a long train of horsemen with their baggage, whom we could make out were not Persians, and whom as they approached we saw were Franks. They were accompanied by a *mehmander*, an officer from the Shah, who informed us, that this was the French embassy on its return, who it seems had been politely requested to take its leave; and it was moreover added, that the English ambassador would very shortly take its place.

This at once explained how matters stood at court, and that between the rival bidders for his majesty's favour, the King of Kings had come to a good market. My ambassador was rather surprised how such a determination could have been taken previous to his arrival, fraught as he was with important information upon all the nations of Europe; but every difficulty is easily explained away when money is permitted to exert its eloquence, particularly if one recollects the words of the Sheikh:

Let money only appear, and every head is prostrate.

'Tis thus, the heaviest weight in the scales lowers the iron beam.

We were happy to have an opportunity of observing the manners of a nation about whom we had lately heard so much, and as we passed the day together in the same place, my chief did not fail to make himself known to the French ambassador.

We expected of course to find them much depressed in spirits, and in no good humour, having been driven as it were from the presence of the Earth's Centre; but what was our surprise to remark the contrary! Never did Persia see such a company of madmen. They were singing, dancing, and making the *lûti* all the livelong day. They all talked at once, one louder than the other, without any apparent deference to rank, for all seemed on the same footing. Without in the least respecting our carpets, they were eternally pacing them with rapid strides, and, what most shocked our feelings, spitting upon them. As I now looked upon myself in some measure identified with the Franks, considering at what pains I had lately been to acquire information concerning them, I endeavoured to discover if there was any affinity between their language and ours; but not a word could I comprehend. However, I thought to have made some progress in it, by recollecting and writing down the words in their speech which most frequently occurred, one was *sacré*, the other *Paris*, and a third *l'Empereur*.

On the whole we liked them. We thought to discern many points of similitude between them and ourselves; and were of opinion, that if as infidels they were doomed to the *douzak* of hereafter, even there, instead of moaning over and deploring their lot, they would still be found in the same happy mood we saw them at Sultanieh.

We parted on the following morning, they laughing, chattering, and screaming with joy; we, full of anxiety and apprehension about the reception with which our ambassador would meet from the King of Kings.

CHAPTER LXXVII: THE CEREMONY OF RECEIVING
A FRANK AMBASSADOR AT THE COURT IS DESCRIBED

MY chief, the Mirza Firouz, was received with great condescension by the Shah, who was pleased at the ready answers he received to his numerous questions concerning the nations of Europe. Never was man better adapted to fill the situation to which he had been appointed than the Mirza. Every question which the Shah put to him was received with a ready answer. Ignorance did not confound him, no difficulty stopped him. The words '*nemi danum*, I don't know,' ever a sin in the hearing of a king, were never known to pass his lips. He discoursed upon every matter with a confidence that made his hearers believe that whatever he said must be conclusive; and upon the subject of Europeans, to listen to him, one could not but suppose he had been born and bred among them.

As I was known to have been employed under him in 'seizing news,' as the phrase goes, concerning Europe, and also in writing its history, I in some measure enjoyed the reputation of being learned in whatever regarded its inhabitants. Although my assurance was nothing equal to my master's, yet I managed to answer the questions put to me with tolerable readiness, although, in so doing, I was obliged to be very circumspect not to commit him: therefore, I passed my days in the double fear of appearing ignorant, and of having my ears cut off in case I happened to be too wise. However, as none among our own countrymen could contradict us, we were listened to as oracles, and we exemplified what the poet Al Miei has so justly remarked: 'That in the country of the dumb the sound of one voice, be it even that of an ass, would be called harmony.'

The English Elchi (ambassador) had reached Tehran a few days before we arrived there, and his reception was as brilliant as it was possible for a dog of an unbeliever to expect from our blessed Prophet's own lieutenant. Indeed the city was almost shocked at the honours paid him, and some of the most violent of our mollahs declared, that in treating a Giaour so well, we were ourselves in some measure guilty of his infidelity, and preparing our own damnation. At different stations on the road, the throats of oxen had been cut before his horse's feet, in many places his path was strewn with sugar-candy, and on the day of his entry he was permitted to have his trumpets sounded in the procession, all of which were honours that could be exacted by none, save our own princes.

Then all the proper attentions of hospitality were shown. The house of a khan was taken from him and given to the ambassador, and whatever furniture was wanting was demanded from the neighbours and placed therein. A handsome garden was levied upon another, and added to the house. The lord high treasurer was commanded to feed the strangers at his own expense as long as they chose, and clothes and shawls were collected from the courtiers and servants of the court, for the dresses of honour which it is the custom to make on such occasions. The princes and noblemen were enjoined to send the ambassador presents, and a general command issued that he and his suite were the Shah's guests, and that, on the pain of the royal anger, nothing but what was agreeable should be said to them.

All these attentions, one might suppose, would be more than sufficient to make infidels contented with their lot; but, on the contrary, when the subject of etiquette came to be discussed, interminable difficulties seemed to arise. The Elchi was the most intractable of mortals. First, on the subject of sitting. On the day of his audience of the Shah, he would not sit on the ground, but insisted upon having a chair; then the chair was to be placed so far, and no farther, from the throne. In the second place, of shoes, he insisted upon keeping on his shoes, and not walking barefooted upon the pavement; and he would not even put on our red cloth stockings. Thirdly, with respect to hats: he announced his intention of pulling his off to make his bow to the king, although we assured him that it was an act of great indecorum to uncover the head. And then, on the article of dress, a most violent dispute arose: at first, it was intimated that proper dresses

should be sent to him and his suite, which would cover their persons (now
too indecently exposed) so effectually that they might be fit to be seen by
the king; but this proposal he rejected with derision. He said, that he
would appear before the Shah of Persia in the very same dress he wore
when before his own sovereign. Now, as there was not a Persian who had
ever been at the court of a Frank king, nobody could say what that proper
dress was; and, for aught we knew, the Elchi might put on his bed-gown
and night-cap on the occasion. This was a difficulty apparently not to be
overcome, when, turning the subject over in my own mind, I recollected that
among the paintings in the palace of Forty Pillars at Ispahan, there were
portraits of Europeans, who, in the days of the great Shah Abbas, flocked
to his court, and even established themselves in the city. In particular, I
well recollected one in the very same painting in which Shah Abbas himself is represented, whose dress was doubtless the only proper costume to
wear before a crowned head. I immediately suggested this to my master,
who mentioned it to the grand vizier, who ordered that a copy of it should,
without loss of time, be made by the best artist of Ispahan, and sent to
Tehran.

So soon as it arrived it was officially presented to the English Elchi,
with a notification that the Shah was satisfied to receive him in the same
dress he wore before his own sovereign, a model of which was now offered
to him, and to which it was expected that he and his suite would strictly
conform.

The shouts of laughter which the infidels set up, upon seeing the picture and hearing the message, are not to be described. They asked if we
thought them monkeys, that they should dress themselves as such at our
bidding, and were so obstinate in their resolution of keeping to their own
mode of attire, that at length they were permitted to do as they chose.

The audience of the Shah passed off much better than could have been
expected from such rude and uncivilized people, and we were all astonished that men, so unaccustomed to the manners and forms of the world,
should have conducted themselves on this difficult occasion without com-
mitting some act that was flagrant and improper. The king was seated on
his throne of gold, dressed with a magnificence that dazzled the eyes of
the strangers, and made even his subjects exclaim, 'Jemshîd? who was he?
or Darab? or Nûshirvan? that they should be mentioned in the same

breath?' On the right and left of the throne stood the princes, more beautiful than the gems which blazed upon their father's person. At a distance were placed the three viziers of the state, those depositaries of wisdom and good council; and, with their backs to the wall, each bearing a part of the paraphernalia of the crown, were marshalled in a row the black-eyed pages of royalty, who might be compared to angels supporting planets from the starry firmament. In the midst appeared the Franks, who, with their unhidden legs, their coats cut to the quick, their unbearded chins, and unwhiskered lips, looked like birds moulting, or diseased apes, or anything but human creatures, when contrasted with the ample and splendidly dressed persons by whom they were surrounded. And they stood their ground, not in the least abashed by the refulgent presence of the great king; but their attitude, manner, and expression of countenance, would have made us suppose they were as good and as undefiled as ourselves.

The speech made on the occasion by the Elchi was characteristic of the people he represented; that is, unadorned, unpolished, neither more nor less than the truth, such as a camel-driver might use to a muleteer; and had it not been for the ingenuity of the interpreter our Shah would neither have been addressed by his title of King of Kings, or of the Kebleh of the Universe.

It would be taking up the pen of eternity were I to attempt to describe the boundless difference that we discovered between the manners and sentiments of these people and ourselves. Some of our sages endeavoured to account for it upon philosophical principles, and attributed much to the climate of those dark, watery, and sunless regions in which they were bred and born: 'for,' said they, 'how can men living surrounded by water, and who never feel the warmth of the sun, be like those who are never a day without enjoying the full effulgence of its rays, and do not even know what the sea means?' But the men of the law settled the question in a much more satisfactory manner, by saying 'it was owing to their infidelity that they were doomed to be cursed even in this life; and that if the ambassador, his suite, and even his whole nation, would submit to become Mussulmans, and embrace the only true faith, they would immediately be like ourselves, their defilements would be washed clean, and they even might stand a chance of walking in the same story of the heavens as the genuine children of Islam would in the world to come.

CHAPTER LXXVIII: NOTICED BY THE GRAND VIZIER

HAJJI IS THE MEANS OF GRATIFYING THAT

MINISTER'S FAVOURITE PASSION

THE transactions just recorded were all propitious to my advancement. Owing to the knowledge I was supposed to have acquired respecting Europe, I was employed in most of the affairs which concerned the Franks in Persia, and this had furnished me with many opportunities of becoming known to the grand vizier, and to other ministers and men in power.

The Mirza Firouz was not rich, and the maintenance which he received in his public character ceasing as soon as he returned to Tehran, he could no longer afford to support me, and he was happy to find that I was able to work my own way into a livelihood. He did not fail to praise my good qualities, and never lost an opportunity of extolling my abilities. Nor was I backward in seconding his endeavours, for I brought everything and every person, infidels as well as true believers, to bear upon my ambitious views; and destiny (without whose aid man's endeavours are of no avail) almost as much as whispered, that the buffetings of the world had taken their departure from me.

The grand vizier was, without a doubt, the man in Persia, who from his acuteness, tact, and presence of mind, had the most influence over the Shah. He had enjoyed his high situation almost from the commencement of the present long reign, and had so interlaced his office with every transaction, public as well as private, that his councils became as necessary to the country as the rising and setting of the sun.

To secure his protection became then the first object of my endeavours. I began by daily attending his levees and standing before him, and as the affairs relating to Europe now took up his principal attention, he never saw me without asking some question referring thereto. This led to my being entrusted with messages to the English ambassador, the answers to which I always brought back, with something of my own surcharged, flattering to his abilities as a great statesman, and thus by creating goodwill between the parties, I myself became a favourite.

The leading passion of the vizier was the love of receiving presents. This was my kebleh in all transactions with the Elchi, and my ingenuity was constantly exercised in endeavouring to extract something from him which would be acceptable to the vizier, and serviceable to myself. That presents of ceremony should be received and given was a matter of course, and, therefore, I stood no chance of acquiring any credit on such occasions; but I was once or twice accessory in making the balance strongly preponderate in favour of my own countrymen, and the vizier from that time began to look upon me with a favourable aspect.

A treaty was to be negotiated between the two countries, and my patron was appointed one of the plenipotentiaries on the part of the Shah. Although this was matter in which one of my insignificance could not expect to be employed, yet I did not cease to ply about the negotiators, like a dog at an entertainment seeking for a chance bone; and every now and then I got so much of the scent as to make me almost sure of springing some game for myself.

At length, one morning, after a late sitting of the negotiators, I was summoned to attend the grand vizier in his very anderûn, a place to which none but his most confidential servants were ever admitted. I found him still in bed, bolstered up with many soft pillows, and entirely alone.

'Hajjî,' said he, in a familiar tone, 'draw near, and seat yourself close to me; I have something of importance to say.'

I was staggered by so high an honour; but as his command was law, I did not hesitate to kneel by his bedside.

Without circumlocution, he at once told me that he was placed in a situation of great difficulty, for the English ambassador had made some demands impossible to be granted, and declared that he must quit Tehran, should they not receive our acquiescence.

'Now,' said he, 'the Shah has threatened if I permit the Elchi to leave Persia dissatisfied, that my head shall answer for it; and at the same time I and my brother plenipotentiary are half persuaded that his majesty will never accede to the demands of England. What is to be done?'

'Could he not be bribed?' said I, with all humility, and looking as if I would give other meaning to my words.

'*He* be bribed?' said the vizier; 'in the first place, whence could the bribe come? and in the second, these people are such fools, that they know not what a bribe means. But give me your ear. We are no fools, whatever they may be. The Elchi is very anxious to carry his point, and you know me well enough to be aware that there is nothing I cannot accomplish if once I take it in hand. You must go and talk to him. You are his friend. You may say that you are mine—you may whisper many things to him which I cannot—do you understand?'

Upon this I kissed his hand with much fervour, and raising it to my head I exclaimed, 'By my head and by my eyes, I will go—and *Inshallah*, please God, I will not return without a white face.'

He then dismissed me, and full of happy prospects I made the best of my way to the English ambassador.

I will not relate all I said and did to induce him to come into the grand vizier's terms; but in two words, I so entirely and completely succeeded, that I returned with a heavy sack of gold, of good and solid cash, in my hand, as the forerunner of what was to follow in case all was concluded to the ambassador's satisfaction, and I also secured the promise of a large diamond ring that was forthwith to be transferred from the finger of England to that of Persia, by way of an emblem of eternal friendship between the representatives of the two states.

The vizier was so astonished when he saw me place the sack before him, that he looked at me and then at it, some time before he spoke, and then broke out into exclamations in praise of my activity and zeal.

'Hajjî,' said he, 'you are now my property. We are somebody in Persia, and you will not long remain without a cap to your head. Make an *arz*, a representation, and its accomplishment will rest with me.'

Many were the protestations I made him of fidelity and redoubled zeal. I disowned any intention of asking for any remuneration, except the favour of being permitted to stand before him; and I looked so humble, and talked in so disinterested a manner, that if he ever could have believed a Persian, I flattered myself he did me.

But he understood the value of such speeches a great deal better than I, and said, 'Do not throw away your words at random. I was once with my head turning round and round in the world for a livelihood as well as yourself, and, therefore, I know the value of the service which you have rendered. Proceed in the path which now lies before you. The Franks are proper materials for your ingenuity. I give you my sanction to work upon them. They have plenty of gold, and are in want of us. What more need be said? The people of Iran are like the earth; they require *rishweh*,[1] their interests must be highly excited, before they will bring forth fruit. The Franks talk of feelings in public life of which we are ignorant. They pretend to be actuated by no other principle than the good of their country. These are words without meaning to us; for as soon as I die, or when the Shah is no more, all that we may have done for the welfare of Persia will most likely be destroyed; and when his successor shall have well ruined the people in securing himself, the whole business of improvement and consolidation must be gone over again. Certain privileges and enjoyments are the lawful inheritance of the Shahs of Persia: let them possess them in the name of Allah! And their viziers also have their allotted portion: why should they refuse them? Certainly not for the good of the country, because not one individual throughout the whole empire even understands what that good means, much less would he work for it.'

[1] The word *rishweh*, bribery, is also used for *manure* in agriculture.

My mind was greatly enlightened by this speech, and as the curtain which hitherto had darkened my understanding drew up, I discovered new prospects, and could extend my view over a new and more diversified region of profit. The words, 'the Franks are proper materials for your ingenuity' rung in my ears, and my wits immediately began their career of invention.

CHAPTER LXXIX: OF THE MANNER
IN WHICH HE TURNED HIS INFLUENCE TO USE, AND HOW
HE WAS AGAIN NOTICED BY THE VIZIER

I GAVE myself much pains to have it well understood in the city, that I was a confidential agent of the grand vizier, and did my best endeavour to impress upon the infidels that without my interference nothing could be done. The fruits of this proceeding were soon manifest, and my services put into requisition in a manner highly conducive to mutual advantage.

One of the most remarkable features in the character of our English guests was their extreme desire to do us good against our inclination. Rather than not attempt it, they put themselves to infinite trouble, and even did not refrain from expense to secure their ends. They felt a great deal more for us than we did for ourselves; and what they could discover in us worthy of their love, we, who did not cease to revile them as unclean infidels, and as creatures doomed to eternal fires, we were quite at a loss to discover. However, I had nothing to do with their tastes; my business was to study how to turn them to account, and the subject in all conscience was rich, and repaid me well for my trouble.

My readers will perhaps recollect that, in the first volume of this my narrative, I mentioned my acquaintance with an infidel doctor, who, among other novelties in medicine, did his utmost endeavours to introduce into Persia a new mode of curing the small-pox. The practice was now totally laid aside; our faculty continued to treat the disorder as our forefathers had done, and the usual quantity of children died as heretofore. A doctor was also attached to the suite of the present Elchi, and he was impelled by more than common anxiety to do us good. His zeal to renew the practice of the cow medicine was unbounded, and the quantity of mothers whom he enticed to bring their children to him astonishing.

I, in pursuit of my own schemes, was the first to cry out, that this great influx of women of the true faith into the dwelling of an infidel, be the object what it might, was highly indecorous, and I persuaded the grand vizier to place an officer of the police as sentry at the doctor's door to prevent the women entering. This very soon stopped his practice, and he was in despair.

'But why should you grieve?' said I to him. 'You get nothing for your trouble, and the people are not obliged to you.'

'Oh,' said he (for he and his countrymen had learnt our language), 'you know not what you say. This blessing must be spread throughout the world; and if your government stops it here, it will be guilty of the blood of all those lives which might have been saved.'

'What is that to us?' answered I: 'let them die—we get nothing by their being alive.'

'If it be profit that you require,' exclaimed the doctor, 'I will willingly pay any sum you may demand, rather than lose my vaccinating matter, which must dry up and be lost if my practice ceases.'

Here we entered into a negotiation, and after much difficulty and show of apprehension concerning the risk I ran of incurring the grand vizier's displeasure, it was agreed that for certain advantages which I should enjoy, the restriction should be taken from the doctor's house; and I leave those who know me to guess the numbers of children who now flocked to the man of medicine. His gate was thronged, and nothing more was said respecting the impropriety of the women's attendance.

Another of his manias was a desire to cut up dead bodies. He did so languish after every corpse that was carried by his house for burial, that I was surprised the people did not set upon him for his impure propensities.

'But what possible good will accrue to mankind in general,' said I to him, 'if you dissect a dead Mussulman?'

'It is impossible to say what good may be lost by my not dissecting him,' said he; 'besides, if I do not keep my hand in practice, I shall lose my former skill.'

He then of his own accord proposed to give a large sum for a corpse, and avowed that he was not particular about its quality, for that of a Jew, Christian, or a true believer, would be equally acceptable.

I kept this in remembrance; and indeed I had so many opportunities afforded me of advancing the designs of the infidels, and of filling my own pockets at the same time, that I felt myself gradually growing into wealth.

The ambassador himself was not without his desires of improving (as he called it) our state; and I cannot resist relating a circumstance which took place between him and the grand vizier. He announced it as his intention to make a present to us of a certain produce of the earth, unknown in most parts of Asia, but much cultivated in Europe, which would not fail to be of incalculable benefit to the people of Persia; and he requested the vizier to assist him in his undertaking, promising shortly to send him a specimen of the intended gift. The vizier, whose nose was always carried very high whenever a present was in the wind, did not fail daily to discuss with me what this great benefit which the ambassador was about to confer might be, and his impatience to gain possession became very great. He discovered through me, that the English representative had brought with him a store of fine broadcloth, upon which he had constantly kept a steady eye. Finding that the projected public benefit was not forthcoming, he conceived in his wisdom that the Elchi would have an easy bargain, if he agreed to commute it for a private gift to himself. Therefore, one morning at his uprising he called me, and said, 'By the blessing of God, whatever we want we have: we have bread and meat—we have salt, and rice, and corn, and fruits, such as the infidels never even saw in a dream; in short, we have everything that it is possible to conceive. Then why should we become indebted to this infidel ambassador for things that we do not want? A happy thought has struck me, by which he will be a gainer, and be saved the trouble he wishes to incur: I will agree to receive cloth in lieu of the public benefit. This is so easy a transaction, that you, who, praise be to Allah! are a man of sharp wit, will easily negotiate. Go, say this to the ambassador, and without loss of time bring me the cloth.'

I forthwith presented myself, and delivered the message. Will it be believed that he and all his beardless suite, upon hearing it, set up such shouts of laughter, as might be heard from the top of Demawend? 'What affinity has cloth to potatoes?' said one. 'We wish to give a cheap and comfortable article of food to your countrymen,' said another. 'But it seems that your vizier likes to transfer the whole advantage of the gift from the bellies of the nation to his own back,' cried a third. The ambassador, however, who appeared the most reasonable of the party, without hesitation very politely ordered a piece of cloth to be delivered to me, which he requested me to present to my master with reiterated expressions of friendship; and with the assurance that it could make no alteration in the sentiments which he entertained for the Persian nation, who he hoped would still receive the potato, as a mark of his high esteem and consideration.

I returned to the vizier full of exultation at the success of my visit; and this, with the preceding and subsequent instances of my abilities, so entirely won his affections, that I soon outstripped every rival, and became his principal favourite and confidant.

CHAPTER LXXX: THE CONCLUSION.

MISFORTUNE SEEMS TO TAKE LEAVE OF HAJJI BABA
WHO RETURNS TO HIS NATIVE CITY A GREATER MAN
THAN WHEN HE FIRST LEFT IT

THE negotiations with the infidels were now about being closed; and it was agreed, in order to strengthen the bonds of friendship between the two, that an embassy on the part of the Shah should forthwith be sent to the king of England.

The experience of each succeeding day convinced me of the influence I had acquired over the mind of the grand vizier; and the event just recorded was the means of showing me to what extent he depended upon my services and zeal. The day after the treaty with England was signed, he called me into his private apartment, and spoke to me in the following manner:

'Hajjî,' said he, 'give me your ear. I have things of importance to impart, and as I look upon you as one exclusively mine, I am sure that you will listen to them with becoming attention.'

I was proceeding to make the necessary protestations of my entire devotedness, when he stopped me, and proceeded thus:

'Well or ill, our business with the English ambassador is at length concluded, and the Shah has ceded to his wishes of sending an ambassador to England in return. Now, you know the Persians as well as I, how they detest leaving their own country, and the difficulty I shall find in selecting a man to devote himself to this service. I have one in my eye, whom I wish

to send above every other; and as it is of the utmost importance to me that
he should be removed for the present from Persia, and particularly from
the presence of the Centre of the Universe, I require that you use your
best endeavours to persuade his acceptance of the appointment.'

I immediately felt assured that he could mean no other than me, although I did not see what reason he could have for removing me from the
presence of the king; and elated by so bright a prospect of sudden elevation
to rank and honours, I sprung towards him, and seizing his hand with fervour to kiss, I exclaimed, 'The least of your slaves will always prove to be
the most faithful of your servants: speak, and you will always find me
ready, even to death.'

'That is well spoken,' said he, with great composure, 'and now listen
to me. The man I allude to is Mirza Firouz' (here my countenance fell,
and I drawled out in answer a long 'belli, yes'). 'The truth is, I have lately
discovered that his influence with the Shah has been considerably upon the
increase. He possesses such great volubility of speech, and such vast command of language—he flatters so intensely, and lies so profoundly—that
the king is more amused by him than by any other man of his court. Who
knows how far he may go? Besides, I am assured that secretly he is my
most bitter enemy, whilst openly he affects to be my most devoted of servants; and although to this day I have never for a moment dreaded the hatred or the intrigues of any one, yet I cannot but own, that, in this instance, I am not without my fears. By sending him among the infidels, as
the Shah's representative, I at once cut off the source of my uneasiness;
and once let him be gone, I will so arrange matters, that even should be
return successful from his mission (which, please God, he never may!) he
shall never acquire the influence over the Shah which he is now attempting
to establish.'

I agreed to all he said with hesitation; and was losing myself in the reflection how I could possibly turn this piece of confidence to my own advantage, when the vizier accosted me again, and said:

'I have only let you into one part of my scheme: the second object is,
that you, Hajjî, should accompany the ambassador in the capacity of his
first mirza, or chief secretary. You, who are my friend and confidant, who
know all my wishes, and who have an intimate knowledge of all that has
occurred since the arrival of the infidels, you are precisely the man to fill

this situation, and you will render me the greatest of services by accepting my proposal.'

However delighted I might have been at the prospect of becoming the chief of an embassy, yet when I was offered the inferior appointment, my feelings were very different. I felt that in quitting the situation I now enjoyed, I should leave the high road to preferment, to get into one of its crooked lanes. Besides, I strongly participated in the national antipathy, the horror of leaving one's country, and particularly dreaded the idea of going to sea; and when I came to reflect that the country to which I was likely to be sent was unknown land—a land situated in eternal darkness, beyond the regions of the sun, and whose inhabitants were an unclean and unbelieving race—I drew back from the vizier's offer with the fear of one who had the gulf of perdition placed before him.

The answer I made to the prime minister was by a string of cold assents, such as constantly hang on every Persian's lips, whatever may be his real feelings. I said, 'By my eyes; I am your servant; my ear is in your hand; whatever you ordain I am bound to obey': and then remained mute as a stone.

The vizier easily discovered what passed within me, and said, 'If you dislike my offer, you are your own master, and another may easily be found to accept it. I have your advantage in view as well as my own. In the first place, you should immediately proceed to Ispahan, as the Shah's deputy, to collect a considerable portion of the presents intended to be sent by our court to the King of England, and which must be levied upon the inhabitants of that city. You would then have an opportunity of enriching yourself——'

I did not let the vizier proceed further. The temptation of returning to my native place in such a character, clothed with such powers, was too great to be withstood, and in a very altered tone I immediately exclaimed, with great earnestness:

'By the salt of your highness, by your death, and by the beard of the Shah, I am ready to go. No other word need be said—I will go wherever you command, were it even to fetch the father of all the Franks from the inmost chambers of the world below.'

'Be it so,' said the vizier; 'and as the first step towards it, go at once to Mirza Firouz, flatter and assure him that he is the only man in Persia fit to be sent upon such an embassy, and persuade him of the advantages that will accrue to him. Honour, riches, the goodwill of the Shah, and my protection all will abound; and at his return, God best knows to what heights he may not ascend. Throw out hints that some other man, some rival, whom you may discover, has been talked of for the situation, and you will see how easily he will swallow the bait. Go, and Allah be with you!'

I left his presence scarcely knowing whether I soared in the heavens, or trod on the earth. 'What,' said I to myself, 'shall I then attain the summit of all earthly happiness—shall my long past prognostics at length be fulfilled—and shall I indeed enter my native place, clothed with the *kalaat* of honour, armed with the hand of power, and mounted upon the steed of splendour? Let those who once scorned Hajjî Baba, the barber's son, now beware, for they will have to deal with the Shah's deputy. Let those crowns, which once submitted to my razor, now be prostrate, for he who can cut the head off is at hand. Ye that have deprived me of my inheritance tremble, for the power of making you restore it is mine.'

Indulging in such like feelings, I am aware that I strutted along the street with a swell and dignity of manner which must have surprised every one who saw me. I could think of nothing save my approaching honours; and my mind was riveted by the one idea of seeing myself mounted on a finely caparisoned horse, adorned by a gold chain round its neck, and a silver tassel under its throat, preceded by my led horses, and my running footmen, and greeted by a deputation from the governor of the city, to welcome my arrival in my native place.

However, I proceeded to the house of Mirza Firouz, whom I found prepared to converse on the subject of the embassy, because the English Elchi had already made proposals to him to the same effect as those which the grand vizier intended to make. Although I had attached myself almost exclusively to the service of the prime minister, yet I persevered in my friendship with the intended ambassador, who was glad to hear I was to accompany him. We talked long upon our future plans, as well as past adventures, and when, roaring with laughter, he asked whether I should now endeavour to regain possession of my faithless Shekerleb, I slipped away, not over-pleased to have that event of my life recalled to my recollection.

The next day, the Shah announced at the public audience his intention of sending Mirza Firouz to England as his representative, and the grand vizier ordered me to be in readiness to proceed to Ispahan, as soon as the proper firmans necessary to arm me with power should be prepared.

I will not tire the reader with a description of the numerous details of my preparatives for this expedition. He would sicken and I should blush at my vanity. It is sufficient to say that I travelled to Ispahan with all the parade of a man of consequence; and that I entered my native city with feelings that none but a Persian, bred and born in the cravings of ambition, can understand. I found myself at the summit of what, in my eyes, was perfect human bliss. Misfortune seemed to have taken its leave, and everything informed me that a new chapter in the book of my life was about to open. Hajjî Baba, the barber's son, entered his native place as Mirza Hajjî Baba, the Shah's deputy. Need I say more?

AND here, gentle Reader! the humble translator of the Adventures of Hajjî Baba presumes to address you, and profiting by the hint afforded him by the Persian story-tellers, stops his narrative, makes his bow, and says, 'Give me encouragement, and I will tell you more. You shall be informed how Hajjî Baba accompanied a great ambassador to England, of their adventures by sea and land, of all he saw, and all he remarked, and of what happened to him on his return to Persia.' But he begs to add, should he find, like Hajjî's friend the third Dervish, he has not yet acquired the art of leading on the attention of the curious, he will never venture to appear again before the public until he has gained the necessary experience to ensure success.

And so he very humbly takes his leave.

Tamam Shud

ABOUT THIS EDITION OF HAJJI BABA OF ISPAHAN

It was Designed and Illustrated by Cyrus Le Roy Baldridge in collaboration with the Book-of-the-Month Club, Inc. The type used is English Monotype Bell. The Composition, Printing and Binding was by The Haddon Craftsmen, Inc., in Camden, New Jersey, under the supervision of Richard Ellis, Typographer. The paper, Gladfelter Natural Wove, was supplied by Perkins & Squier Co., New York. The painting on the cover was reproduced in four-color offset, printed on Bancroft buckram by Reehl Litho Co., New York. The full-color illustrations were reproduced in offset by the Zeese-Wilkinson Co., in Long Island City.

LT. T. G. SHANAHAN, U. S. N. Ret.
7448 Sommers Rd.   Tel. WAVerly 6046